ION EXCHANGERS
IN
ANALYTICAL CHEMISTRY

ION EXCHANGERS
IN
ANALYTICAL CHEMISTRY

By

OLOF SAMUELSON

Professor of Engineering Chemistry
Chalmers Institute of Technology
Göteborg, Sweden

JOHN WILEY & SONS, INC., NEW YORK

ALMQVIST & WIKSELL, STOCKHOLM

Dedicated to

SIXTEN ULFSPARRE

who made this work possible

Preface

The latest developments concerning separations in the field of analytical chemistry are characterized mainly by the increasing use of solid adsorbents. The technique itself is by no means new. The decoloration of solutions by means of activated charcoal is an example which is known to every chemist. The principle is the removal from a solution of a substance which interferes with the determination of another substance.

Of the greatest significance in the development of modern chemistry has been the well-known work of the Russian botanist Tswett, a work which laid the foundations for chromatographic analysis. The principle of this analysis is an internal separation, in an adsorption column, of different substances with varying degrees of adsorbability.

Through the introduction of suitable ion exchangers, above all ion exchange resins, analytical chemistry now has at its disposal new valuable sorbents for the separation of ions from solutions. The application of ion exchangers for analytical separations is based upon two different principles:

1. Separation of exchangeable ions from non-exchangeable ions and non-electrolytes (ion exchange method).
2. Separation of exchangeable ions from each other due to differences in exchangeability (ion exchange chromatography).

It should be pointed out that there exist borderline cases which do not belong clearly to either group, but in general the author has found that ion exchange separation methods can be classified into these two groups.

The ion exchange method has, during the last decade, become increasingly important in various analyses in inorganic and organic chemistry. The method is simple and rapid and generally produces more reliable results than earlier separation methods. A large number of methods for the analysis of various technical products and substances of biological and medicinal interest have been evolved and have found practical applications. In Sweden this method has, for a considerable time, been included in the basic syllabus of analytical chemistry at various educational institutions, and applications of the method have also been included in official analytical methods.

A great deal of the information concerning the ion exchange method is published in periodicals with a limited distribution; this appears to be the main reason for the fact that the method is not more generally known. It is, therefore, the hope of the author that this book may contribute to a more widespread utilization of the ion exchange method. The book is intended for the guidance of those wishing to consult earlier published works dealing with the employment of this method and also for those desirous of investigating new fields of use.

Ion exchange chromatography may be considered a special example of chromatography. The method may be used even with ions of very similar properties, for example the separation of the rare earths, but the procedure is frequently so complicated as to be hardly worth using except with mixtures which are difficult or impossible to separate by other means. At the moment, the method is primarily of importance in scientific research, but, in common with the development of many other methods, it may be predicted that ion exchange chromatography will gain increasing significance in practical analyses.

Only the principles of chromatographic separations by means of ion exchange resins and some applications will be briefly mentioned in this monograph. It is not intended to be a complete reference book in this field, but rather a sketch of the possibilities revealed.

ACKNOWLEDGEMENTS

The idea of writing a book on the application of ion exchangers in analytical chemistry was conceived a number of years ago while I was associated with the Mo och Domsjö Company. For permission to devote the necessary time to several investigations upon which this book is based I am greatly indebted to the directors of this company.

In the active work on the book valuable help in several respects was provided by my assistants, Mr. Roland Andersson, Mr. Gunnar Gabrielson, Mr. Nils Hartler, and Mrs. Kerstin Schramm.

Dr. Axel Johansson (Royal Institute of Technology, Stockholm) and Dr. Folke Nydahl (University of Uppsala) read the manuscript and made many suggestions for which I am very grateful. I should also like to express appreciation to Dr. G. E. Boyd (Oak Ridge) for a critical review of the entire manuscript. To Drs. Birger Drake (Uppsala) and Waldo E. Cohn (Oak Ridge) I am indebted for the critical reading of several chapters. Others who made valuable suggestions are Drs. S. M. Partridge (Cambridge), B. Sandberg (Stockholm), E. Brunius (Stockholm), and C. O. Björling (Uppsala). The comments of all these persons have been of great value, but I am solely responsible for the statements made in this book.

For permission to make use of illustrations from publications, I wish to express my appreciation to authors of papers and to the editors of the *Journal of the American Chemical Society, Journal of Biological Chemistry, Journal of Cellular and Comparative Physiology, Acta Chemica Scandinavica, Svensk Kemisk Tidskrift, Teknisk Tidskrift,* and *IVA.*

Göteborg, Sweden
March, 1952 OLOF SAMUELSON

Table of Contents

PRACTICAL PART

APPLICATIONS

CHAPTER I

Introduction

1. HISTORICAL INTRODUCTION

A. *Inorganic Cation Exchangers*

Base exchange, or in more modern terminology cation exchange, has, since the middle of the 19th century, been the subject of a great amount of scientific investigation. In the beginning it was primarily the significance of the process in the field of agricultural chemistry which attracted scientists to research on this subject. Most investigations were carried out with clays and minerals; among the minerals the zeolites awakened great interest. These consist of aluminum silicates of a complicated composition containing water.

The technical production of material similar to the zeolites is based on work by Gans which was published about 1905 (7). The synthetic zeolites are mainly used for the softening of water. The softening proceeds, as is known, by the filtration of water which contains calcium ions through a bed of cation exchanger containing sodium ions. In this way the calcium ions in the water are exchanged for sodium ions. When the sodium ions of the bed are exhausted, the filter is regenerated by treatment with a strong solution of sodium chloride. In the regeneration step the calcium ions are displaced and the exchanger is reconverted into the sodium form.

The reaction proceeds thus:

$$\text{Ca}^{2+} + 2\,\text{Na}^+\,\text{Z} \overset{\text{sorption}}{\underset{\text{regeneration = elution}}{\rightleftharpoons}} 2\,\text{Na}^+ + \text{Ca}^{2+}\,\text{Z}_2$$

where Z = cation exchanger.

In the softening or, as generally designated, the sorption step, the reaction proceeds from left to right; in the regeneration (elution), when an excess of sodium ions is used, the reaction proceeds in the reverse direction.

It was expected that the synthetic zeolites would find many uses in various technical and scientific fields. In a lecture at the Seventh International Congress for Applied Chemistry in 1909 Siedler mentioned that synthetic zeolites might possibly find their application in analytical chemistry. However, no specific suggestions were presented.

It was not until 1917 that the first practical application of ion exchange for analytical purposes was achieved by Folin and Bell in the determination of ammonia in urine (4). This determination cannot be made directly by adding Nessler's reagent, as certain amino acids interfere. It was found that, on shaking the solution with a synthetic zeolite, ammonia was taken up whereas the interfering substances remained in solution. The ion exchanger was separated, and after treatment with sodium hydroxide the liberated ammonia was determined according to the Nessler method.

In most systems there is no quantitative uptake in batch processes, i. e. by shaking the solution with the exchanger, unless the amount of exchanger is very high. In technical practice column operation (percolation through a filter bed) was used at an early stage. This principle was introduced into analytical chemistry by Whitehorn, who used a synthetic zeolite as a reagent for amines (21).

In 1927 Bahrdt (2) published a method for the rapid estimation of sulfate in natural waters. The water to be analyzed was softened in a laboratory column containing sodium zeolite and a known amount of barium chloride was added to the effluent from the column. Excess barium chloride was back-titrated by means of potassium palmitate according to Blacher. The softening eliminated the interfering influence of calcium and magnesium upon the palmitate titration. The most remarkable fact was that calcium and magnesium were taken up so effectively that they could not be detected in the effluent water.

Bahrdt's paper received very little attention, and for a number of years the idea seemed to prevail that an enormous ion exchange column should be necessary to remove the last traces of magnesium and calcium from water.

Later a few other analytical methods, of chiefly biochemical interest, which were based on the application of synthetic zeolites were published. The utilization of inorganic ion exchangers for analytical purposes is, however, very limited, as the exchangers are stable only in a narrow range of pH: they are dissolved in acid solution and peptized in alkaline solution. Furthermore it is in most cases extremely difficult or even impossible to achieve quantitative elution.

B. *Organic Ion Exchangers*

Certain organic materials with ion exchanging properties have been known for a long time. Among cation exchangers the foremost, cellulose, has been thoroughly studied. Kullgren (11) showed that unbleached sulfite pulp contained sulfonic acid groups of a strongly acid character. Sulfonic acid groups are firmly attached to the pulp, whereas the corresponding hydrogen ions are dissociated and may be exchanged for other ions.

In connection with these investigations Kullgren found that copper was taken up by sulfite cellulose when the cellulose was washed with distilled water. Copper existed as a contaminant in the water. By extracting the pulp with acid, copper could be removed and determined approximately. The experiment showed that about 95 % of the copper which was present in the distilled water was taken up by the cellulose. This appears to have been the first time an organic ion exchanger was used for analytical purposes.

In principle an organic cation exchanger consists of an insoluble substance to which acid groups, e.g. sulfonic acid groups or carboxyl groups, are firmly attached. Exchangers of the sulfonic acid type may be used in acid as well as in alkaline solutions. Most ion exchangers containing carboxyl groups, however, may be used only in alkaline or neutral media.

Organic ion exchangers for technical use were described during the 1930's in many patents. Cation exchangers produced by the sulfonation of coal found technical applications, and cation exchange resins were later obtained. The basic patent concerning these resins was taken out in 1935 by Adams and Holmes (1).

These workers are also the originators of the anion exchange resins, which are to be recognized as insoluble resins containing basic groups, e.g. amino groups, having the ability to form salts with common acids. The anions bound to the resin may be exchanged for others. Taking the exchange between a solution of nitric acid and a resin pretreated with hydrochloric acid as an example, the formula may be written:

$$NO_3^- + Cl^- H_3 N^+ R_s \rightleftharpoons NO_3^- H_3 N^+ R_s + Cl^-.$$

The resins originally developed were satisfactory only for special purposes, but the methods for the manufacture of ion exchange resins were later improved considerably, first at the Wolfen laboratories of the I. G. Farbenindustrie. This work was summarized by Griessbach in 1939 (8).

At the same time a work by Samuelson (14) was published, showing a series of possible applications for organic ion exchangers in analytical chemistry. The experimental material was based on an investigation in which sulfonated butadiene rubber was utilized as a cation exchanger.

A series of various analytical procedures using ion exchangers has been worked out, and the ion exchange method has become a valuable complement to earlier methods in many technical and scientific laboratories. The method has greater significance for quantitative analyses, but has also simplified qualitative analyses in many cases. Since ion exchange resins have become generally available, the use of this method has increased greatly, and at the moment this group of ion exchangers is of dominating interest.

2. SCOPE OF THE ION EXCHANGE METHOD

Quite often, in qualitative as well as quantitative analysis, difficulties arise because of the fact that certain anions have an interfering effect in the determination of certain cations, and vice versa. Similarly, many determinations of non-electrolytes are complicated by the presence of electrolytes, and determinations of certain ions are complicated by the presence of non-electrolytes. Such complications may be eliminated by the use of ion exchangers, which makes possible the division of a solution into two or three (and sometimes more) fractions.

The main principle of the ion exchange method may be said to be the exchange, with the help of an ion exchanger, of all exchangeable ions of the same charge (positive or negative) for other ions of the same charge. In the elution of an ion exchanger a solution is obtained containing the ions removed from the original solution together with an excess of the regenerant. A division has thus taken place into two fractions containing (a) non-electrolytes, non-exchangeable ions, and ions of the type originally existing in the ion exchanger; (b) retained ions and ions existing in the regenerant.

Separation may be carried out with the help of either a cation exchanger (I) or an anion exchanger (II).

The principle is shown in the following diagram, where an aqueous solution of potassium phosphate and ethyl alcohol is used as an example:

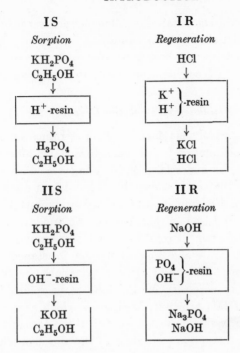

By the use of both a cation exchanger and an anion exchanger a division into three fractions is obtained, e.g. according to the following scheme:

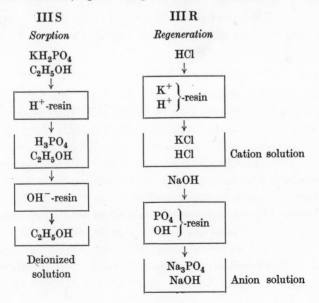

It may be convenient to designate the different fractions as (a) deionized solution, (b) cation solution, (c) anion solution.

The various fields of use are best illustrated with practical examples. The following division is schematic and does not include all possibilities.

A. *Determination of Total Salt Concentration*

One type of analysis widely employed is the determination of the total amount of ions in a salt solution by alkalimetric titration after the cations have been exchanged for hydrogen ions by using a column with cation exchanger (14). The principle is shown in Scheme I S. A number of technical analyses, e.g. the determination of sulfate in aluminum sulfate and nitrate in explosives, are based on this principle. An application of medical interest is the determination of total base in blood serum. The method, which is extremely accurate and rapid, is suitable for standardizing solutions in the laboratory. These and other applications are described in Chapter VIII. It is not necessary for the salts to be soluble in water in order to make use of this principle. With salts which are only slightly soluble a modification of this method is feasible if the corresponding acids are water-soluble. If an aqueous suspension of the almost insoluble salt is shaken with a hydrogen-saturated cation exchanger containing sulfonic acid groups, a reaction occurs between the ion exchanger and the salt, so that the cation is taken up by the ion exchanger, while an equivalent amount of hydrogen ions goes into solution. This principle has been used to determine the content of phosphoric acid in, e.g., cobalt phosphate (18).

B. *Separation of Interfering Ions of Opposite Charge*

Another important application is the separation of interfering ions of opposite charge. As an example may be mentioned the analyses of raw phosphate, including the determinations of Fe_2O_3, Al_2O_3, MgO, CaO, and P_2O_5 (16). The estimation of the metals is complicated by the presence of phosphoric acid, whereas the determination of P_2O_5 is made more difficult by the presence of the metal ions. If the sample has been dissolved in acid and is then passed through a column of cation exchanger in the hydrogen form (Scheme I S), after the column is washed with water the phosphoric acid is found to be present quantitatively in the effluent and may be determined without the interfering effect of metals, which are quantitatively retained by the exchanger. When the resin bed is treated with hydrochloric acid the metal ions are displaced quantitatively (Scheme I R). Hence the metals may be estimated in a solution free from P_2O_5. After being rinsed with water the ion exchange column can be used again; it can be employed repeatedly for hundreds of determinations. A large number of similar analytical separations have been published (Chapter VIII).

In principle the separation of ions of opposite charge might just as well be carried out by means of an anion exchanger as shown in Scheme II. Until recently, the anion exchangers which were available had definite disadvantages which explained their limited popularity. Anion exchangers of a strongly basic type are now on the market, and consequently their use has increased considerably.

In the separation of various metals from each other it may be possible to convert one or several of the metals into stable, complex anions. As an example a method for the separation of potassium and vanadium published by Samuelson (15) may be cited. The vanadium is converted into vanadate, and the solution obtained is filtered through a cation exchange column which is saturated with ammonium ions. The potassium ions are retained by the exchanger, whereas the vanadium passes on as ammonium vanadate. The potassium ions can be removed from the exchanger with hydrochloric acid and are easily and accurately determined. Even a complex binding, e.g. with cyanide or thiocyanate, may be used for a quantitative internal separation of certain metals.

Weaker complexes may be decomposed by passing them over an ion exchanger. Thus with a bed of hydrogen-saturated cation exchanger it is possible to separate cadmium and iodide quantitatively in spite of the complex ions existing in these solutions. Stronger complexes, e.g. chromium sulfate complexes, are not decomposed completely. A certain amount of chromium passes into the effluent as a negatively charged complex, while part of the sulfate remains in the ion exchanger complexly bound in the cation. Such complications limit, in certain cases, the use of the ion exchange method. On the other hand, the composition and properties of the complex may be studied by means of ion exchangers. The first investigations in this direction were published in 1922 by Günther-Schulze (9), using a synthetic zeolite. Reliable results cannot be obtained, however, with this type of ion exchanger because of its poor stability. Better results are given by investigations with organic ion exchangers. In recent years a significant number of experiments in which the complexities of various salt solutions have been studied by using ion exchange resins have been published. These investigations are referred to in Chapter XXV.

C. *Separation of Ions from Non-Electrolytes*

In certain cases a separation of ions from non-electrolytes is of interest. One example is Folin and Bell's previously mentioned method for the determination of ammonia in urine. Another is the uptake of thiamine (vitamin B_1), by means of cation exchangers, from solutions containing interfering substances present in yeast and similar products.

If it is desired to separate non-electrolytes from both cations and anions, the solution may be deionized by passage first through a cation exchanger in the hydrogen form and afterwards through a layer of anion exchanger in the free-base form (Scheme III). In the first column the cations are exchanged for hydrogen ions. The acids liberated are taken up by the anion exchange column. In certain cases a "mixed resin" deionization may be advantageous. An early example studied by Platt and Glock (12) was the removal of substances which interfere in the determination of inositol. The deionization method has been applied to various solutions, including those of proteins and carbohydrates.

D. *Isolation of Trace Constituents*

The principle used in Kullgren's determination of copper in distilled water, namely isolation of trace constituents, has been successfully adopted by several authors, such as Cranston and Thompson (3), for the determination of traces of copper in milk. Copper is retained by a cation exchange resin and subsequently eluted by means of acid. In this way the tedious evaporation of the milk and the ignition of the organic substance are avoided.

E. *Separations Based upon Ionic Size*

The possibility of separating high polymer anions from low-molecular-weight anions by anion exchange resins has been demonstrated by Samuelson (17) in investigations concerning sulfite waste liquor. This separation is based on the fact that only low-molecular-weight ions can penetrate into the narrow resin structure and be taken up. Other examples of this type of separation are the removal of interfering ions from pectic acid solution and of by-products from cellulose xanthate solutions (viscose). Possibilities of utilizing cation exchangers for separations of cations of different size also exist (13).

F. *Separations Based upon Differences in Basic or Acid Strength*

By means of exchangers containing weakly acid groups it is possible to separate more basic substances from less basic ones. For example Wieland

(22) has shown that a cation exchanger containing carboxylic groups may be used for the uptake of basic amino acids; neutral and dicarboxylic amino acids pass in the effluent. Cation exchangers containing sulfonic acid groups in the free-acid form can retain all amino acids (5).

In addition to the separation of bases by means of cation exchangers of varying acid strength, certain other separations may be effected by the use of anion exchangers containing basic groups of varying strength. This principle has been utilized for a group separation of amino acids.

The possibilities of such separations are increased by the buffering of sample solutions and ion exchange columns to a suitable pH value.

G. Separations Based upon Conversion of Non-Electrolytes to Ions by Complex Formation

An interesting application which is under development is the uptake by means of anion exchangers of non-electrolytes capable of forming anionic complexes. Examples studied thus far are aldehyde and ketone bisulfites (19, 6) and borate complexes with sugars and glycerol (10, 23).

Most of the analytical separations performed by the ion exchange method may be carried out also by other operations, e.g. precipitation, extraction, distillation, or dialysis. The advantages of the ion exchange method are that the work is simpler and less time-consuming, and in many separations higher accuracy is obtained. In many cases results are obtained more rapidly, which is of great significance, e.g. in routine analysis of factory products. In most analyses it is not the ion exchange procedure which limits accuracy but other phases of the work.

Another advantage of the ion exchange method is that it demands less skill and judgment from the analyst than many other methods. When carrying out separations by precipitation the risk of coprecipitation always exists, and through small variations in procedure considerable errors may develop. The ion exchange method is exceptionally insensitive to varying conditions since it is normally possible to work with a broad safety margin. Unskilled labor may consequently be used to advantage. Similarly, in practice it is a great advantage to be able to leave the sample, in most cases without risk of interference, and continue the analysis later at a more convenient time.

3. SCOPE OF ION EXCHANGE CHROMATOGRAPHY

Ion exchange chromatography is a method of great significance when it concerns the separation of ions of similar properties, i.e. systems which are troublesome or impossible to analyze by other methods. The separation is based on the differences in exchange potentials of different cations in a cation exchanger or different anions in an anion exchanger. The principle is the same as in the chromatographic analysis with other adsorbents. Compared with the ion exchange method, ion exchange chromatography is rather complicated. The study of chromatographic separations with physical methods, e.g. radioactive tracers, conductometric measurements, or optical methods, simplifies the work to a great extent. In general the conditions for automatic measurements are good for chromatographic methods, so that ion exchange chromatography may serve even for routine determinations.

Ion exchange chromatography has shown itself to be an excellent method for solving troublesome separation problems both in inorganic chemistry and with certain organic substances. In 1937 Taylor and Urey showed that a partial separation of the lithium isotopes was effected by percolating a solution of lithium salt through a long column filled with synthetic zeolite. The heavier isotope is preferentially held by the exchanger (20).

The availability of suitable resinous exchangers, together with improved knowledge of them and development of chromatographic working methods, has stimulated the vast expansion of ion exchange chromatography which has taken place during recent years. Of special interest in this connection are investigations, carried out under the Plutonium Project, on the separation of the fission fragments formed during fission of the heavy elements. Among the fission products are different rare earths. By means of ion exchange chromatography with the use of cation exchange resins these could be separated from each other. Several other separations of various inorganic cations have been reported.

In organic chemistry ion exchange chromatography has been used mainly for the separation of various substances of biological interest, e.g. amino acids and nucleotides. It is certain that the application of this method for the separation of organic substances will increase when ion exchange chromatography has become more generally known and further improved.

BIBLIOGRAPHY

1. Adams, B. A., and Holmes, E. L.: *J. Soc. Chem. Ind. (London)*, **54 T**, 1 (1935).
2. Bahrdt, A.: *Z. anal. Chem.*, **70**, 109 (1927).
3. Cranston, H. A., and Thompson, J. B.: *Ind. Eng. Chem.*, Anal. Ed., **18, 323** (1946).
4. Folin, O., and Bell, R.: *J. Biol. Chem.*, **29**, 329 (1917).
5. Freudenberg, K., Molter, H., and Walch, H.: *Naturwissenschaften*, **30**, 87 (1942).
6. Gabrielson, G., and Samuelson, O.: *Svensk Kem. Tid.*, **62**, 214 (1950).
7. Gans, R.: *Jahrb. preuss. geol. Landesanstalt (Berlin)*, **26**, 179 (1905); **27, 63** (1906).
8. Griessbach, R.: *Angew. Chem. Beihefte*, **No. 31** (1939).
9. Günther-Schulze, A.: *Z. Elektrochem.*, **28**, 89, 387 (1922).
10. Khym, J. X., and Zill, L. P.: *J. Am. Chem. Soc.*, **73**, 2399 (1951).
11. Kullgren, C.: *Svensk Kem. Tid.*, **43**, 99 (1931).
12. Platt, B. S., and Glock, G. E.: *Biochem. J.*, **36**, XVIII (1942); **37**, 709 (1943).
13. Rauen, H. M., and Felix, K.: *Z. physiol. Chem.*, **283**, 139 (1948).
14. Samuelson, O.: *Z. anal. Chem.*, **116**, 328 (1939).
15. Samuelson, O.: *Svensk Kem. Tid.*, **51**, 195 (1939).
16. Samuelson, O.: *Svensk Kem. Tid.*, **52**, 241 (1940).
17. Samuelson, O.: *Svensk Papperstidn.*, **46**, 583 (1943).
18. Samuelson, O.: *Svensk Kem. Tid.*, **57**, 158 (1945).
19. Samuelson, O., and Westlin, A.: *Svensk Kem. Tid.*, **59**, 244 (1947).
20. Taylor, I., and Urey, H. C.: *J. Chem. Phys.*, **6**, 429 (1938).
21. Whitehorn, J. C.: *J. Biol. Chem.*, **56**, 751 (1923).
22. Wieland, Th.: *Ber.*, **77**, 539 (1944).
23. Zager, S. E., and Doody, T. C.: *Ind. Eng. Chem.*, **43**, 1570 (1951).

CHAPTER II

Fundamental Properties of Ion Exchange Resins

1. STRUCTURE

As already mentioned, the active groups of organic cation exchangers are acid groups. The most important cation exchangers contain sulfonic acid groups which are dissociated even in an acid medium. Exchangers of the weakly acid type, particularly resins containing carboxyl groups, are also used for analytical purposes. The chemical formulae of cation exchangers in the hydrogen form can be schematically represented as:

$$\text{Sulfonic acid type} \quad R_sSO_3H$$
$$\text{Carboxylic acid type} \quad R_sCOOH$$

The exchangeable ions of the exchanger, the hydrogen ions in the above-mentioned types, are called counter ions. The cation exchangers can be regarded as polyvalent anions with attached positively charged counter ions. A cation exchanger in the hydrogen form consists of a high-molecular-weight insoluble acid.

Anion exchangers may be regarded either as polyvalent cations with negatively charged counter ions or as high-molecular-weight insoluble bases or salts of such bases, respectively. The active groups of anion exchangers are amino groups, e.g. $-NH_2$, $-NHR$, $-NR_2$, or quaternary ammonium groups, $-NR_3^+$. Anion exchange resins of strongly basic type are obtained by the introduction of quaternary ammonium groups into the resin, whereas primary, secondary, and tertiary amino groups give rise to resins of weak or medium basic strength.

The ion-active groups tend to solubilize the exchanger. Linear polymers containing sulfonic acid groups or quaternary ammonium groups are dissociated and generally soluble in water. Linear polymers which contain carboxyl groups are dissociated and soluble in alkaline media, whereas those containing primary, secondary, or tertiary amino groups are dissociated in acid media. Two very important requirements of an exchanger are insolubility and chemical stability. These can be realized only if the ion-active groups are attached to a cross-linked skeleton (18). Consequently, suitable ion exchangers have to be looked for within the group of network polymers.

The problem of solubility is closely related to the problem of swelling. The greater the number of cross-linkages of the network polymers, the lower are the flexibility and also the swelling. An example is the preparation of cation exchangers with varying degrees of swelling by sulfonating polystyrene (46, 48). Certain products swell in water to a volume of 100 ml or more calculated on 1 g of dried resin. Despite the strong swelling the chemical stability remains satisfactory. Commercial ion exchangers, with many cross-linkages, occupy in water about 2–3 ml per g dried exchanger.

The more ion exchanging groups introduced into the network skeleton, the higher is the exchange capacity calculated on unit weight basis of the exchanger. Simultaneously, however, an increase in the tendency of the exchanger to swell ensues within certain limits. This increased swelling counteracts to a certain extent the increase in exchange capacity, since, for practical analytical purposes, this is based on a certain filter volume and not on unit weight of exchanger. The exchange capacity should therefore for practical purposes be calculated on unit volume basis after swelling. A large number of ion exchanging groups are not enough to ensure an exchanger with high capacity. It is also necessary to have a relatively large number of cross-linkages in the molecular network in order that the swelling remain moderate.

Changes in the composition of the external solution are accompanied by changes in the degree of swelling of the exchanger. The swelling properties of cation exchange resins have been investigated by Griessbach (18) and in greater detail by Samuelson (46, 48) and Gregor *et al.* (17). Changes in swelling cause movements of the filter. It is commonly said that the filter "breathes," which may cause stoppages or the formation of channels in the exchange column. The more open the network structure of the exchanger, the greater is the swelling and the more pronounced the "breathing" of the filter. For general purposes an exchanger with a rather dense network structure is therefore preferable.

It is not advisable, however, to close the network structure too much by cross-linkages. Too narrow a structure of an exchanger in the swollen state may seriously decrease the rate of diffusion of the ions inside the particles. Under such conditions the exchange capacity of ions with larger radii will be less than that of ions with smaller radii. Results obtained with inorganic (51) and organic (40) cation exchangers, as well as with some anion exchange resins (47, 41), illustrate this point. In the choice of an exchanger due consideration should be given to the suitability of its characteristic properties for the particular application.

From an analytical point of view it is of utmost importance that ordinary exchangers do not retain high-molecular-weight ions (47) and colloids (42, 49). The pore spaces of the network structure are smaller than the dimensions of the high-molecular-weight ions of the solution. Obviously these ions cannot penetrate and be retained by the exchanger. The resin structure thus acts as a sieve, which separates the larger and smaller ions. It is therefore possible to effect a separation for analytical purposes of high-molecular-weight and low-molecular-weight ions of the same charge type, since only the smaller ions can penetrate the exchanger. This principle has formed the basis for the separation of low- and high-molecular-weight acids by the use of anion exchange resins. Examples of this type of anion exchange separation have been mentioned. By varying the number of cross-linkages of the exchanger, the sizes of pore spaces can be varied so as to allow the separation of ions by differences in their dimensions (47, 29, 26). In this way it is possible to produce a series of sieves with varying sizes of pore spaces. This field is as yet little explored, but would seem to hold great possibilities for future investigations.

Types of network polymer in which the network structure can be altered continuously are copolymerizates of styrene and divinylbenzene, which have been investigated systematically by Staudinger and Heuer (53). The divinylbenzene forms cross-linkages between the chains of polymerized styrene (cf. Fig. 1). The more divinylbenzene, the denser is the network and the less the swelling. Cation exchangers with varying swelling properties can be produced by sulfonating such copolymers. Dowex 50 is an ion exchanger obtained by sulfonation of a copolymer consisting of 92% styrene and 8% divinylbenzene (1). A detailed study of the preparation of sulfonated polystyrene-divinylbenzene resins has been published by Pepper (37).

If instead basic groups are introduced into network polymers with increasing numbers of cross-linkages, anion exchangers with decreasing degrees of swelling are obtained (26, 59).

Wheaton and Bauman (59) report that the strongly basic anion exchangers Dowex 1 and Dowex 2 are produced from polystyrene-divinylbenzene copolymerizates containing 7.5% divinylbenzene. The formulae may be written:

$$R_sN^+ \begin{array}{l} \diagup CH_3 \\ -CH_3 \\ \diagdown CH_3 \end{array} \qquad\qquad R_sN^+ \begin{array}{l} \diagup CH_3 \\ -C_2H_4OH \\ \diagdown CH_3 \end{array}$$

Dowex 1   Dowex 2

Fɪɢ. 1.   Chemical structure of a styrene-divinylbenzene resin.

The ion-active groups attached to the resin matrix and corresponding counter ions are obviously bound to remain inside the ion exchange particles or near the surface. The volume within which these ions are present will be called the inside solution, or the resin phase.

An ion exchanger may be compared to a solution of a high-molecular-weight electrolyte inside a semipermeable membrane of a pore size which will allow small ions to diffuse while preventing the colloidal ions from passing through. A solution of Congo red (the sodium salt of a complex sulfonic acid) inside a semipermeable membrane may serve as a model of a sodium saturated ion exchanger of the sulfonic acid type. In contact with an external solution containing sodium chloride, chloride ions will diffuse through the membrane. To maintain electrical neutrality the same number of sodium ions as chloride ions must diffuse from the external solution through the membrane to the inside solution. When equilibrium is attained, the concentration of chloride ions will be greater in the solution free from Congo red than in the inside solution. The total concentration of sodium ions, on the other hand, will be greater in the inside solution. If a_{Na_w} and a_{Cl_w} represent the activities of the ions of the external solution and a_{Na_r} and a_{Cl_r} the activities of the ions of the inside solution, the equilibrium condition will be:

$$a_{Na_w} \cdot a_{Cl_w} = a_{Na_r} \cdot a_{Cl_r}.$$

This and similar membrane equilibria were first studied by Donnan and are called Donnan equilibria. They are of great importance for exchange material of various kinds and have been investigated, e.g. by Procter (39) in his studies with gelatin and by Du Rietz (9) for sulfite cellulose.

If, for instance, a dried cation exchanger in the sodium form is introduced into a sodium chloride solution, the sodium chloride solution will penetrate into the resin. According to the Donnan theory, the concentration of sodium chloride in the inside solution, after equilibrium has been reached, must be lower than that in the external solution. The sodium chloride concentration in the inside solution may be difficult to determine, but from the difference between the concentration of the solution in equilibrium with the ion exchanger and the original solution it should be possible to make a theoretical calculation of the volume of the inside solution, provided this could be regarded as homogeneous and the activity coefficients were known.

Unfortunately much information about the activity coefficients of the resin phase is lacking, and the results of studies with certain exchange resins indicate that the inside solution is not homogeneous (48). The results of experiments with sulfonated resins by Samuelson (48) and Bauman and Eichhorn (1) agree qualitatively, however, with the Donnan theory.

For certain purposes it may be of interest to calculate an apparent water adsorption ("salzfreie Wasserhaut") from the increase in anion concentration obtained when a dried cation exchanger is introduced into an electrolyte solution. For such a calculation the assumption is made that the chloride ions do not enter the inside solution.

Samuelson (43, 46, 48) has made such estimations with sulfonated phenolic resins and highly swollen sulfonated polystyrene at different concentrations and with various anions and cations (cf. Chapter XXV). By extrapolating the values of the apparent water adsorption to zero concentration, the true water adsorption is obtained, namely the volume of the inside solution, when the external solution is pure water.

The experiments showed that the volume of the inside solution of the exchanger varied with the degree of swelling, which is closely dependent on the amount of cross-linkages and on the counter ions existing in the inside solution. The swelling is further decreased by increasing the electrolyte concentration of the external solution. In the case of polystyrene sulfonic acid the volume of the inside solution was found to be equal to the volume of the swollen resin. Bauman and Eichhorn (1) later obtained the same results with commercial exchangers. It would therefore seem justifiable to designate the inside solution as the resin phase and to calculate with ion concentrations and ion activities of the resin phase in the same way as is customary for ordinary electrolyte solutions.

The concentration of the inside solution, namely the exchange capacity per unit volume, thus increases with decreasing swelling of the ion exchanger. Table 1 gives the values of the concentrations of the inside solutions of exchangers of the commercial type [sulfonated phenol-formaldehyde resin, Dowex 50, and synthetic zeolite (Natrolit)] as well as of a strongly swollen polystyrene sulfonic acid. It must be emphasized that the values should be regarded as average values, since the inside solutions probably were not homogeneous.

TABLE 1

The concentration of the inside solution of different cation exchangers

	Outer Solution	Counter Ion	Concentration of Inside Solution, equiv/1000 g H_2O
Sulfonated phenol-formaldehyde resin	H_2O	H^+	2.7
Sulfonated phenol-formaldehyde resin	H_2O	Ca^{2+}	3.9
Sulfonated phenol-formaldehyde resin	H_2O	Ba^{2+}	4.9
Sulfonated polystyrene	H_2O	H^+	0.027
Sulfonated polystyrene	0.005 N HCl	H^+	0.041
Sulfonated polystyrene	H_2O	Ba^{2+}	0.10
Natrolit (synthetic zeolite)	H_2O	Na^+	~ 3
Dowex 50 (commercial grade)	H_2O	Na^+	6.2
Dowex 50 (1% cross-linking)	H_2O	Na^+	2.0

From this table it is obvious that ion exchangers of the commercial type possess high concentrations of the inside solutions. The sulfonated polystyrene, on the other hand, had an extremely low ion concentration in the resin phase. For lightly cross-linked resins the values are very much influenced by the counter ions and by the concentrations of the external solutions.

To produce ion exchangers which are capable of retaining high-molecular-weight ions, it would be necessary to work with exchangers with strong swelling and consequently with a low exchange capacity per unit volume. This type of work can be successful only in very dilute solutions.

2. CATION EXCHANGE RESINS OF SULFONIC ACID TYPE

A. *Ion Exchange Properties*

Most investigations with organic cation exchangers have been made with materials containing sulfonic acid groups. This type of exchanger is the most important in analytical work; and, since the conditions with other types of exchangers are analogous in many respects, it seems justifiable to present a more detailed review of the results obtained with exchangers of the sulfonic acid type.

As already mentioned Kullgren (23) has shown that unbleached sulfite pulp could be utilized as exchanger in acid solutions because of the presence of sulfonic acid groups. Later investigations made with Du Rietz (24) proved that the sulfonic acid was completely dissociated.

Hägglund (22) showed that polymerized insoluble ligninsulfonic acid precipitated from sulfite waste liquor was capable of inverting a sucrose solution. This and similar catalytic reactions can be demonstrated using commercial cation exchangers of the sulfonic acid type (45, 54, 30). These experiments confirm the view that the sulfonic acid is dissociated and exists in a concentrated inside solution. Ion exchangers acting as catalysts are of some technical importance. As examples of reactions which can be performed in the presence of cation exchangers in the hydrogen form, esterification, acetal synthesis, alcoholysis, and ester hydrolysis may be mentioned. It is evident further that ion exchangers can also be used as catalysts in certain analyses. Of great interest in this connection is the fact that only reactions between low-molecular-weight substances which can penetrate into the resin phase may be catalyzed by the ion exchanger (7).

Samuelson (45) found that cation exchangers in the hydrogen form reacted with zinc powder, calcium carbonate, and zinc sulfide, evolving hydrogen, carbon dioxide, and hydrogen sulfide gas, respectively. The reaction between exchangers and difficultly soluble compounds can also be utilized in special analytical work.

Potentiometric alkali titration curves for exchangers containing sulfonic acid groups were published by Du Rietz (9), using sulfite pulp, and by Griessbach (18), using the phenolic resin Wofatit [cf. also (13)]. Both types of products contained sulfonic acid groups with additional weakly acid groups. Obvious similarities existed between the titration curves of these materials and those of low-molecular-weight sulfonic acids despite the additional weakly acid groups of the exchangers. In the absence of other

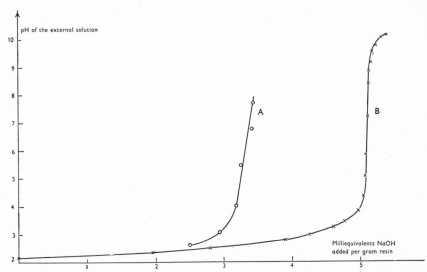

FIG. 2.   Potentiometric neutralization curves of cation exchange resins. *A*. Sulfonated
phenolic resin. *B*. Sulfonated polystyrene [from (46)].

acid groups Samuelson (46), using a sulfonated polystyrene, was able to
demonstrate complete similarity. Certain commercial products, e.g. Dowex
50, also show similar curves (1). The neutralization curve of a pure sulfonic
acid resin and that of an exchange resin with additional weakly acid groups
are shown in Fig. 2.

In the case of simple ions the exchange capacity of an ion exchanger
containing only sulfonic acid groups is independent of the pH of the solution
as well as of the nature of the counter ions, provided the network structure
is not so dense as to obstruct penetration. Samuelson (48) measured the
exchange capacity of sulfonated polystyrene and of a sulfonated phenol-
formaldehyde resin by treating the H^+ exchangers with different chloride
solutions until no more acid was liberated. The liberated acid was determined
by titration. With the sulfonated polystyrene practically the same values
were obtained for Na^+, K^+, NH_4^+, Ca^{2+}, and Ba^{2+}. With the phenol-formaldehyde resin the deviations were only small, the divalent ions giving
somewhat higher values, a result which can be ascribed to the presence
of weakly acid groups. This type of exchanger was also used to estimate
the exchange capacity for Zn^{2+}, Ni^{2+}, Co^{2+}, and Cu^{2+} by a different method
(50). The H^+ exchanger was treated with different chloride solutions until
no more uptake of ions occurred. After washing with water the cations were
eluted with hydrochloric acid and determined after the acid was dispelled.

The deviations from previous results were within the limits of experimental errors [cf. (16)].

The exchange capacity rises when the pH value of the solution increases because of additional weakly acid groups in the exchanger, e.g. carboxylic or phenolic groups beside the sulfonic acid groups. This has been demonstrated in experiments by, among others, Griessbach (18) and Piret and Carlson (38). Working with exchangers produced by sulfuric acid treatment of coal, Nelson and Walton (35) found that the uptake of K^+ ions in 0.1 N solution rose from 1.0 meq per g at pH 3 to 4.1 meq per g at pH 13.

An interesting observation made by Miller and Kline (33) is that in strongly alkaline medium a sulfonated phenolic resin has a great selective adsorptive capacity for cesium ions, which is ascribed to the presence of phenolic groups.

Conditions are more complicated with ions possessing a tendency to form basic salts, even when pure sulfonic acid resins are used. When treating various cation exchangers with basic bismuth perchlorate solutions, Samuelson (48) found that the amount of bismuth retained was much greater than corresponded to the formation of Bi^{3+} exchanger, and for some exchangers greater than corresponded to the formation of BiO^+ exchangers. The experiments demonstrated the capacity of the ion exchanger to form basic salts.

According to investigations by Djurfeldt and Samuelson (8) with Wofatit KS, the uptake from Fe^{3+} solutions is greater than can be calculated from the exchange capacity, using mono- or divalent ions. Ferric ions are probably taken up in a hydrolyzed form.

Cations in a complex form can also be retained by cation exchangers, e.g. $[Cu(NH_3)_2]^{2+}$, $[Ni(NH_3)_2]^{2+}$, $[Co(NH_3)_6]^{3+}$, and $[Co(NH_3)_5 Cl]^{2+}$ (46, 35). Cations containing anions held in coordinative positions show a pronounced tendency to decompose (46). These conditions will be discussed in greater detail in Chapter XXV.

The formation of a coordinate bond between the sulfonic acid groups of the resin and basic chromium ions has been reported by Gustavson (19).

Various workers have shown that organic cations can be retained by synthetic zeolites and cation exchange resins. A detailed investigation was published in 1923 by Whitehorn (60).

The uptake of amino acids by ion exchangers is of particularly great analytical interest (4, 11). Since the charge of amino acids depends greatly on the pH value of the solution, it follows that their retention by cation exchangers varies greatly at different pH values. A resin of the sulfonic acid type can retain even dicarboxylic amino acids, such as aspartic and glutamic acids, provided the inside solution of the resin is sufficiently acid (Chapter XX).

B. *Adsorption of Acids by Cation Exchange Resins*

A prerequisite for the utilization of ion exchangers for quantitative separation of cations and anions is that the anions are not adsorbed by the cation exchanger, at least not so strongly that they cannot be desorbed in the subsequent washing.

Samuelson (43, 46, 48, 50) studied the adsorption of anions from hydrochloric and sulfuric acid solutions, as well as from various chloride solutions. "Negative adsorption" was obtained in all cases, which shows that water is adsorbed more strongly than the anions. Some of these experiments were made with resins of the sulfonated phenol-formaldehyde type and others with strongly swollen polystyrene sulfonic acid. In solutions containing weak acids such as phosphoric acid (44) and organic acids (48) a considerable uptake of the acid was observed with resins of the sulfonated phenol-formaldehyde type. The following sequence of adsorption of the acids under investigation was obtained: formic acid < lactic acid < acetic acid < succinic acid < propionic acid < butyric acid. With the aliphatic monocarboxylic acids the adsorption increases with increasing length of the carbon chain.

The adsorbed acids could be removed quantitatively by washing with water. The more strongly the acids were adsorbed the greater was the amount of water necessary for complete removal. The adsorption is not due to the presence of sulfonic acid groups, but to adsorption forces (van der Waals') arising from the resin skeleton, and is consequently dependent on the type of resin. The strongly swelled sulfonated polystyrene did not adsorb any detectable amounts of acetic or butyric acid.

According to Erler (10), the particle size of a resin greatly affects the adsorption of weak acids, the adsorption increasing with increased particle size.

However, cation exchangers with a tendency to adsorb various acids, e.g. phosphoric and acetic acids, can be employed for a quantitative separation of cations from these acids, provided the washing process is slow and a sufficiency of water is used (44, 48).

Erler (10) published the results of an investigation on the removal of adsorbed acid by washing with water, using a cation exchange resin, Wofatit F. The amount of water necessary for complete removal of acid increased according to the series: nitric acid < oxalic acid < acetic acid < adipic acid < butyric acid.

Tolliday, Thompson, and Forman (57) found that the adsorption of a number of organic acids varied for different commercial resins. Aromatic acids, such as benzoic and gallic acids, were more strongly adsorbed than aliphatic acids, such as formic, acetic, and tartaric acids.

3. CATION EXCHANGE RESINS OF CARBOXYLIC ACID TYPE

Among ion exchangers of the weakly acid type, resins containing carboxyl groups are of great interest. Resins whose active groups consist exclusively of phenolic groups have been prepared but have not as yet been utilized for analytical purposes. Carboxylic acid resins may be prepared by addition polymerization of methacrylic acid and divinylbenzene (20). Griessbach (18) studied potentiometrically the neutralization of an ion exchanger with carboxyl groups (Wofatit C). The neutralization curves resembled those of low-molecular-weight acids containing carboxyl groups, a result confirmed later by Kunin and Barry (27), as well as by Honda (21), working with a similar product: Amberlite IRC–50. The results indicate that the dissociation of this type of exchanger is incomplete, analogous to that of the low-molecular-weight acids. The number of dissociated carboxyl groups in the inside solution is determined by the pH value, which is governed by the concentration of ions in general and H^+ ions in particular, of the external solution (9). Consequently the exchange capacity is small in acid solution but increases at increased pH of the solution.

Amberlite IRC-50 swells approximately 50% on transformation from the hydrogen to the sodium form; the swelling is reversible (15). It has been stated that any apparent damage to the bed structure is not caused by the swelling.

Resins of this type can be employed successfully in the removal of NaOH from solutions or in retaining Ca^{2+} ions from bicarbonate solutions, whereas they are unsuitable for a quantitative uptake of cations, e.g. from NaCl solution. An important feature of this type of exchanger is the small amount of acid necessary for its regeneration (27).

Exchange columns of this type have sometimes had a large-scale use as buffers for controlling pH values of solutions. This buffering capacity may have special analytical applications also.

The possibility of using this type of exchanger in the separation of bases of varying strength is of great analytical interest. Strong bases may be retained quantitatively by the acid form of the resin, whereas weak bases are not taken up. Wieland (61) has described the separation of various amino acids with Wofatit C (cf. Chapter XX). A series of separations using Amberlite IRC-50, which are based on this principle, have been suggested by Winters and Kunin (63).

According to Gustavson (19), the carboxyl groups of the resin have a marked tendency to penetrate into polynuclear chromium complexes under the formation of a coordinate linkage.

4. OTHER TYPES OF CATION EXCHANGE RESINS

Skogseid (52) has synthesized a number of polystyrene derivatives and studied their cation exchanging properties. Most interesting is a resin of the formula:

This resin was shown to have an extremely high affinity for potassium ions. The structure of the resin is similar to that of highly nitrated aromatic amines, which form potassium salts with low solubility in water. It seems probable that this type of resin could be of interest for separating potassium in ion exchange chromatography.

Attempts to prepare selective ion exchangers have been reported by Gregor and Citarel (14), who investigated resins with chelating properties. Promising results have been cited [cf. Boyd (5)].

5. ANION EXCHANGE RESINS OF WEAKLY BASIC TYPE

Anion exchange resins are conveniently characterized by means of potentiometric neutralization curves (62, 25, 28, 58, 21). An outstanding characteristic of resins of the weakly basic type is that the number of ionized groups and hence the exchange capacity depend to a marked degree on the pH value of the solution. Resins containing only weakly basic groups, e.g. condensation products of meta-phenylene diamine and formaldehyde, will be highly ionized and may be used for the uptake of acids and for anion exchange in acid medium. At higher pH values the resins will be mostly un-ionized and inert (18). Wofatit M and Amberlite IR-4 with medium basic strength may also be used for anion exchange in neutral solution. Reportedly Wofatit M is a condensation product of m-phenylene diamine, polyethylene imine, and formaldehyde. Anion exchangers of weakly basic type may also be made from cross-linked polystyrene resins (Dowex 3 and Amberlite IR-45).

Extremely weak acids, such as silicic acid, are not retained by the weakly basic groups (34). Anion exchangers of this type can therefore be utilized for separating acids of different strength. Several complex anions, e.g. tin oxalate, may be retained quantitatively even from extremely acid solution such as 1 N hydrochloric acid (32).

Wiklander (62) showed that Wofatit M was able to neutralize bases in alkaline solutions and must therefore be characterized as an ampholytoid. Similar observations have been made for Amberlite IR-4 and De-Acidite B (36). These results explain the difficulty of freeing anion exchangers of this type from alkali.

Another inconvenience is the slowness in reaction. Experiments lasting over a period of two months showed that the uptake of various acids on Wofatit M had not attained equilibrium (47). The exchange capacity was greater for acids with low than with high molecular weight. Similar results were obtained by Bhatnagar, Kapur, and Bhatnagar (3), who worked with a material produced by condensation of m-phenylene diamine and formaldehyde. A possible explanation is that the network structure is very narrow.

The exchange capacity is further affected by the valence of the anions, as shown by several authors (2, 34, 25). The acid-binding capacity expressed as equivalents is greater towards sulfuric than towards hydrochloric acid. Wiklander (62) propounded the following equation for the uptake of sulfuric acid:

$$R_sNH_2 + 2\,H^+ + SO_4^{2-} \rightleftharpoons R_sNH_3^+ \, SO_4^{2-} H^+$$

Despite the difficulties in analytical work with the anion exchangers of the above-mentioned types a series of significant analytical investigations has been made. Of great interest are, among others, the various separations of high- and low-molecular-weight acids. The employment of anion exchangers containing varying numbers of cross-linkages opens up new possibilities for further analytical separations.

Anion exchangers possess the property of binding coordinatively certain cations with a strong tendency for forming amine complexes. When an aqueous solution, containing copper as the simple cupric ion or as cuprammonium complex, was filtered through a bed of alkali-regenerated anion exchanger, copper was removed from the solution (55). The copper-exchange capacity of the resin was about 20% of its capacity for the uptake of acids. Sussman (55) explained the low capacity by assuming that steric effects prevented part of the amino groups of the resin from entering into complex formation.

A penetration of the amino groups of the exchanger into basic chromium complexes has also been reported (19).

6. ANION EXCHANGE RESINS OF STRONGLY BASIC TYPE

A considerable increase in the utilization of anion exchangers in analytical chemistry was made possible by the recent availability of resins containing quaternary ammonium ions. As already mentioned the strongly basic anion exchangers Dowex 1 and Dowex 2 are produced from polystyrene-divinyl-benzene resins. Other commercial resins are probably built up in a similar manner. The exchange capacity is independent of the pH of the solution. A hydroxyl-ion-saturated resin of this type behaves as a strong base, and the exchanger must be considered completely dissociated (28). The anion exchanger can thus be used in alkaline solutions, e.g. for liberating bases from neutral salts. The resins hitherto available seem to contain slight amounts of weakly basic groups in addition to the quaternary ammonium groups (59).

Davies and Nancollas (6) demonstrated that carbonate ions could be quantitatively exchanged for hydroxyl ions when a sodium hydroxide solution, containing carbonate, passed through a column of such an exchanger. These resins can further be used for the uptake of weakly acid compounds, e.g. amino acids (63), silicic acid (28, 31), and hexoses (64). The uptake of complex anions, e.g. complex citrates and oxalates, is of particularly great analytical interest (Chapter IX: 2 B). A most important observation is that certain metal ions [e.g. iron (III), cobalt (II)] may be taken up quantitatively from strong hydrochloric acid (e.g. 9 N) (Chapter

XIII: 2). The inside solution possesses a high concentration of hydroxyl ions which enables exchangers of this type to be used as catalysts in reactions catalyzed by OH ions (12, 7).

BIBLIOGRAPHY

1. Bauman, W. C., and Eichhorn, J.: *J. Am. Chem. Soc.*, **69**, 2830 (1947).
2. Bhatnagar, S. S., Kapur, A. N., and Puri, M. L.: *J. Indian Chem. Soc.*, **13**, 679 (1936).
3. Bhatnagar, S. S., Kapur, A. N., and Bhatnagar, M. S.: *J. Indian Chem. Soc.*, **16**, 249, 261 (1939).
4. Block, R. J.: *Proc. Soc. Exptl. Biol. Med.*, **51**, 252 (1942).
5. Boyd, G. E.: *Annual Review of Phys. Chem.*, **2**, 309 (1951).
6. Davies, C. W., and Nancollas, G. H.: *Nature*, **165**, 237 (1950).
7. Deuel, H., Solms, J., Anyas-Weisz, L., and Huber, G.: *Helv. Chim. Acta*, **34**, 1849 (1951).
8. Djurfeldt, R., and Samuelson, O.: *Acta Chem. Scand.*, **4**, 165 (1950).
9. Du Rietz, C.: Diss., Tekn. Högskolan, Stockholm, 1938.
10. Erler, K.: *Z. anal. Chem.*, **131**, 106 (1950).
11. Freudenberg, K., Molter, H., and Walch, H.: *Naturwissenschaften*, **30**, 87 (1942).
12. Galat, A.: *J. Am. Chem. Soc.*, **70**, 3945 (1948).
13. Gregor, H. P., and Bregman, J. I.: *J. Am. Chem. Soc.*, **70**, 2370 (1948).
14. Gregor, H. P., and Citarel, L.: Abstr. of Papers, Am. Chem. Soc. 118th Meeting, 1950.
15. Gregor, H. P.: *J. Am. Chem. Soc.*, **73**, 642 (1951).
16. Gregor, H. P., Bregman, J. I., Gutoff, F., Broadley, R. D., Baldwin, D. E., and Overberger, C. G.: *J. Colloid Sci.*, **6**, 20 (1951).
17. Gregor, H. P., Gutoff, F., and Bregman, J. I.: *J. Colloid Sci.*, **6**, 245 (1951).
18. Griessbach, R.: *Angew. Chem. Beihefte*, **No. 31** (1939).
19. Gustavson, K. H.: *J. Soc. Leather Trades' Chemists*, **35**, 160 (1951).
20. Hale, D. K., and Reichenberg, D.: *Disc. Faraday Soc.*, **1949**, No. 7, 79.
21. Honda, M.: *J. Chem. Soc. Japan*, **71**, 183, 440 (1950).
22. Hägglund, E.: *Svensk Kem. Tid.*, **44**, 163 (1932).
23. Kullgren, C.: *Svensk Kem. Tid.*, **42**, 179 (1930).
24. Kullgren, C., and Du Rietz, C.: *Svensk Papperstidn.*, **34**, 433 (1931).
25. Kunin, R., and Myers, R. J.: *J. Am. Chem. Soc.*, **69**, 2874 (1947).
26. Kunin, R., and Myers, R. J.: *Disc. Faraday Soc.*, **1949**, No. 7, 114.
27. Kunin, R., and Barry, R. E.: *Ind. Eng. Chem.*, **41**, 1269 (1949).
28. Kunin, R., and McGarvey, F. X.: *Ind. Eng. Chem.*, **41**, 1265 (1949).
29. Lautsch, W.: *Die Chemie*, **57**, 149 (1944).
30. Levesque, C. L., and Craig, A. M.: *Ind. Eng. Chem.*, **40**, 96 (1948).
31. Lindsay, F. K., and D'Amico, J. S.: *Ind. Eng. Chem.*, **43**, 1085 (1951).
32. Lur'e, Yu. Yu., and Filippova, N. A.: *Zavodskaya Lab.*, **14**, 159 (1948).
33. Miller, H. S., and Kline, G. E.: *J. Am. Chem. Soc.*, **73**, 2741 (1951).
34. Myers, R. J., Eastes, J. W., and Urquhart, D.: *Ind. Eng. Chem.*, **33**, 1270 (1941).
35. Nelson, R., and Walton, H. F.: *J. Phys. Chem.*, **48**, 406 (1944).
36. Partridge, S. M., and Brimley, R. C.: *Biochem. J.*, **44**, 513 (1949).

37. Pepper, K. W.: *J. Applied Chem.*, **1**, 124 (1951).
38. Piret, E. L., and Carlson, R. W.: *Proc. Minn. Acad. Sci.*, **9**, 70 (1941).
39. Procter, H. R.: *J. Chem. Soc.*, **105 T**, 313 (1914).
40. Rauen, H. M., and Felix, K.: *Z. physiol. Chem.*, **283**, 139 (1948).
41. Richardson, R. W.: *Nature*, **164**, 916 (1949).
42. Ryznar, J. W.: *Ind. Eng. Chem.*, **36**, 821 (1944).
43. Samuelson, O.: *Svensk Kem. Tid.*, **51**, 195 (1939).
44. Samuelson, O.: *Svensk Kem. Tid.*, **52**, 158 (1940).
45. Samuelson, O.: *Svensk Kem. Tid.*, **53**, 60 (1941).
46. Samuelson, O.: *Svensk Kem. Tid.*, **54**, 170 (1942).
47. Samuelson, O.: *Svensk Papperstidn.*, **46**, 583 (1943).
48. Samuelson, O.: Diss., Tekn. Högskolan, Stockholm, 1944.
49. Samuelson, O.: *Svensk Kem. Tid.*, **57**, 158 (1945).
50. Samuelson, O.: *Iva*, **17**, 17 (1946).
51. Schachtschabel, P.: *Kolloid-Beihefte*, **51**, 199 (1940).
52. Skogseid, A.: Diss., Oslo, 1948.
53. Staudinger, H., and Heuer, W.: *Ber.*, **67**, 1164 (1934).
54. Sussman, S.: *Ind. Eng. Chem.*, **38**, 1228 (1946).
55. Sussman, S.: in Nachod's *Ion Exchange*, New York, 1949.
56. Thomas, G. G., and Davies, C. W.: *Nature*, **159**, 372 (1947).
57. Tolliday, J. D., Thompson, G. W. H., and Forman, G.: *J. Soc. Leather Trades' Chemists*, **32**, 291 (1948); **34**, 221 (1950).
58. Topp, N. E., and Pepper, K. W.: *J. Chem. Soc.*, **1949**, 3299.
59. Wheaton, R. M., and Bauman, W. C.: *Ind. Eng. Chem.*, **43**, 1088 (1951).
60. Whitehorn, J. C.: *J. Biol. Chem.*, **56**, 751 (1923).
61. Wieland, Th.: *Ber.*, **77**, 539 (1944).
62. Wiklander, L.: Diss., Uppsala, 1946.
63. Winters, J. C., and Kunin, R.: *Ind. Eng. Chem.*, **41**, 460 (1949).
64. Yorston, F. H.: *Pulp & Paper Mag. Can.*, **50**, 108 (1949).

CHAPTER III

Ion Exchange Equilibria

1. GENERAL CONSIDERATIONS

When an ion exchanger is brought into contact with an electrolyte solution by shaking a given quantity of exchanger with the solution, exchange of ions will take place until equilibrium is attained. At equilibrium the solution contains generally the same ionic species as it originally did, although the concentrations of these species have changed, together with additional ions previously attached to the exchanger. The same ionic species as in the solution are found in the ion exchanger, but the concentrations differ from those in the solution. Only in exceptional cases will a quantitative uptake of ions be obtained when a moderate amount of ion exchanger is shaken with a solution. As a rule, percolation of the solution through an ion exchange column is necessary to ensure a quantitative uptake. The principles of column operation will be discussed in Chapter V; this chapter will deal exclusively with ion exchange reactions in batch systems.

A comprehensive knowledge of the laws governing the distribution of ions between the solution and the ion exchanger would facilitate considerably the selection of the most suitable conditions in which to employ different exchangers for various analytical and technical purposes. As mentioned in Chapter II, the resin phase of ordinary ion exchangers consists of a concentrated electrolyte solution. The theory of reactions in concentrated solutions of common electrolytes is as yet but little developed, and our knowledge of conditions in the resin phase is still very imperfect.

Because of their great practical importance, ion exchange equilibria have been the object of numerous investigations with both inorganic and organic ion exchangers. The theories as well as the experimental results have often been contradictory, which is not surprising in view of the very complicated nature of some ion exchangers used in these studies.

Samuelson (35) approached the problem by synthesizing ion exchange resins having the simplest possible constitution and possessing a low ion concentration in the resin phase. The prepared "model exchangers" consisted of sulfonated polystyrene, which did not contain any exchanging groups except the completely dissociated sulfonic acid groups. As mentioned in Chapter II, the ion concentration in the resin phase varied with the various preparations. Of greatest interest from a theoretical point of view were materials with extremely low ion concentration ($<0.1\ N$) in the resin phase. The ion exchange equilibria with these idealized systems will form the starting point in the subsequent discussion. The results obtained with more complicated resins will be dealt with chiefly in an empirical manner, since the present theories, which may be satisfactory from a hypothetical point of view, are too complicated for practical application.

2. CATION EXCHANGERS OF SULFONIC ACID TYPE

A. *Exchange of Cations of Equal Valence*

a. THE DONNAN THEORY

The simple case will be considered in which a sulfonic acid resin in the hydrogen form is immersed in a solution containing sodium chloride. An ion exchange will result; i.e. sodium ions together with a certain amount of chloride ions will diffuse into the resin phase, while the amount of hydrogen ions necessary to maintain electrical neutrality will leave the ion exchanger. If the ion exchange is regarded as a Donnan equilibrium, the following relationship holds between the ion activities in the resin phase (r) and those in the external solution (w):

$$a_{H_r} \cdot a_{Cl_r} = a_{H_w} \cdot a_{Cl_w} \tag{1}$$

$$a_{Na_r} \cdot a_{Cl_r} = a_{Na_w} \cdot a_{Cl_w} \tag{2}$$

or by division:

$$\frac{a_{H_r}}{a_{Na_r}} = \frac{a_{H_w}}{a_{Na_w}}. \tag{3}$$

If the amounts of cations in the resin phase are to be calculated, it is necessary to consider not only the cations equivalent to the fixed sulfonic acid groups but also the cations equivalent to the movable anion (e.g. Cl^-), which have entered the resin phase. For resins with low concentration in the resin phase this fact has a considerable influence even if the concentration in the external solution is low, whereas for commercial resins the penetration of anions into the resin phase may often be neglected provided the external electrolyte concentration is low.

Experimental data on ion exchange equilibria between hydrogen ions and other monovalent cations — Na^+, K^+, NH_4^+, $[N(CH_3)_4]^+$ — showed good accordance with the Donnan theory when a polystyrene sulfonic acid with a low ion concentration in the resin phase was used. In this particular case the activity coefficients in the resin phase could be neglected. It should be mentioned that no changes in the swelling occurred with this type of ion exchanger when hydrogen ions were exchanged against the monovalent cations mentioned above (35).

When divalent instead of monovalent ions were used, however, the experimental data did not agree with values derived from the above equations (without considering the activity coefficients in the resin phase), one reason being that these ions possess different activity coefficients in the resin phase. The divalent ions show individual differences also in their effects on the swelling of the ion exchanger. The ions with highest replacing ability show the least swelling (35).

For ion exchangers of the common highly cross-linked type, where the ion concentration in the resin phase is 3–7 N, it is obvious that the Donnan equation cannot be applied without giving due consideration to the activity coefficients in the resin phase. A great number of experimental results have confirmed this statement (35). Different ions of equal valence are retained differently, a fact which can be ascribed to differences in their respective activity coefficients. The larger the differences in the exchange potential of the ions, the greater are the deviations from the values derived from the Donnan equation. The present lack of reliable data concerning activity coefficients is one of several reasons why the Donnan equation generally is not applicable for quantitative calculations when resins of the highly cross-linked type are used. By a reverse process it is possible to estimate the ratio between activity factors in the resin phase by comparing experimental data with the theoretically calculated values (10, 35). This method cannot claim complete accuracy, however, since the Donnan equation in its above simplified form is valid in dilute solutions only.

The swelling of these ion exchangers varies with the individual ion, thus reducing further the value of the Donnan equation in quantitative calculations (35, 13). When ions of equal valence are compared, the above rule holds that the least swelling of the ion exchanger is caused by the most strongly retained ions (35).

In one important respect, namely the effect of dilution, satisfactory agreement between experimental data and the Donnan equation has been obtained for highly cross-linked ion exchangers of the sulfonic acid type. Diluting the external solution does not cause any discernible alteration of the exchange equilibrium when ions of the same valence are used (19, 35).

Similar results have been obtained with inorganic ion exchangers (40). A necessary supposition for obtaining such agreement is that no hydrolysis occurs either in the external solution or in the resin phase.

Because of the discrepancies between experimental results and calculations according to the Donnan theory (without considering the activity coefficients in the resin phase) and because of the questionable applicability on theoretical grounds of the simplified Donnan concept, it is only natural that investigators have attempted to use different methods for calculations and other theories of exchange reactions.

An extended Donnan theory of great interest from a theoretical point of view has been proposed by Gregor (12, 13). In this approach account is given to changes in free energy caused by variations in swelling. As yet, lack of data prevents the application of this theory for quantitative calculations. Experimental studies have been published by Gregor and Bregman (14).

b. THE MASS ACTION LAW

Several authors have applied the mass action law to describe the ion exchange equilibrium. The thermodynamic equilibrium constant K of an exchange reaction

$$B^+ + A^+ R_s \rightleftarrows B^+ R_s + A^+$$

may be defined by

$$\frac{a_{B_r}}{a_{A_r}} \cdot \frac{a_{A_w}}{a_{B_w}} = K. \qquad (4\,a)$$

This expression may be rewritten

$$\frac{X_{B_r}}{X_{A_r}} \cdot \frac{C_{A_w}}{C_{B_w}} \cdot \frac{\gamma_{A_w}}{\gamma_{B_w}} = K \cdot \frac{\gamma_{A_r}}{\gamma_{B_r}} \qquad (4\,b)$$

where X_{A_r} and X_{B_r} are the equivalent fractions in the resin phase, C_{A_w} and C_{B_w} the ion concentrations in the external solution, and γ the activity coefficients. All quantities on the left side in eq. 4 b can be experimentally determined, and for practical purposes it may be appropriate to introduce an "apparent equilibrium constant" K_a, defined by

$$\frac{X_{B_r}}{X_{A_r}} \cdot \frac{C_{A_w}}{C_{B_w}} \cdot \frac{\gamma_{A_w}}{\gamma_{B_w}} = K_a \left[= K \frac{\gamma_{A_r}}{\gamma_{B_r}} \right]. \qquad (4\,c)$$

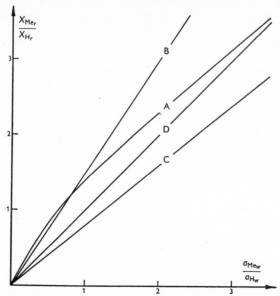

FIG. 3. Cation exchange equilibria.
A. Experimental curve for the exchange between ammonium and hydrogen ions [from (35)]. Straight lines calculated from eq. 4 c. B. $K_a = 1.5$. C. $K_a = 0.80$. D. $K_a = 1$ (Donnan equation valid, without regarding activity coefficients in the resin phase).

The analogous expression with concentrations instead of activities is

$$\frac{X_{B_r}}{X_{A_r}} \cdot \frac{C_{A_w}}{C_{B_w}} = Q. \tag{4 d}$$

At low concentration in the external solution the activity coefficients will approach unity and $Q = K_a$. Experimental data collected by a great number of authors show that K_a does not generally remain constant when the ratio X_{B_r}/X_{A_r} is varied. This means that the resin phase cannot be considered an ideal solution. In certain cases, particularly in exchange reactions of ions with similar properties, e.g. K^+ and NH_4^+, nearly constant values have been obtained with different types of ion exchangers, including zeolites (42, 32), sulfite cellulose (10), and cation exchange resins (6). When K_a remains constant in exchange reactions between ions of the same valence, the K_a values, in general, are nearly equal to 1.*

---

* According to the Donnan theory (eq. 3) the constant K should be equal to 1, and K_a equal to the ratio between the activity coefficients in the resin phase.

In general K_a is dependent on the ratio X_{B_r}/X_{A_r} (35, 8, 30) and may be regarded as a constant only within a certain range (5, 23) (cf. Fig. 3). In exchange reactions between ions of dissimilar properties e.g. H^+ and Ag^+, the variations in K_a values become very large (17).

Attempts have been made to calculate the activity coefficients in the resin phase and the equilibrium constant K thermodynamically from ion exchange data. Ekedahl, Högfeldt, and Sillén (11), as well as Argersinger, Davidson, and Bonner (1), have based their calculations on the Gibbs-Duhem equation. Other approaches to this problem have been reported by Kielland (22) and Skogseid (37). Readers interested in the theory of ion exchange equilibria may also be referred to papers by Jenny (20) and Davis (24, 7).

c. EMPIRICAL EQUATIONS

Where it is desired to collate ion exchange data, simple mathematical equations with one or two empirical parameters may be applied to express the relationship between ion concentrations in the external solution and in the ion exchanger. Sometimes it may be convenient to use eq. 4d; but when K_a or Q varies considerably as the relative amounts of the exchangeable ions are varied, other formulae, e.g. the Freundlich or the Langmuir adsorption isotherm for two competing adsorbates, may be more useful. As far as cation exchangers containing a constant amount of exchangeable ions (e.g. sulfonic acid resins) are concerned, the best agreement seems to exist between the experimental data and the Rothmund and Kornfeld formula (34):

$$\frac{X_{B_r}}{X_{A_r}} \cdot \left(\frac{C_{A_w}}{C_{B_w}}\right)^p = k \tag{5}$$

where k and p are empirical parameters.

If eq. 5 is valid, a straight line should be obtained when $\log (X_{B_r}/X_{A_r})$ is plotted against $\log (C_{B_w}/C_{A_w})$. According to Walton (39), almost all data in the literature on distribution in ion exchange resins fit Rothmund and Kornfeld's equation.

d. ION EXCHANGE AFFINITY

The exchange affinity of different ions is of utmost importance from an analytical point of view. As shown by Samuelson (35) and later confirmed by several other authors (3, 13, 33), the relative affinity is dependent on the total ion concentration in the resin phase (the degree of cross-linking), the differences in affinity increasing with increased concentration in the resin phase. On the other hand the sequence of affinity seems to be largely independent of this factor. The differences in the exchange potentials can, in the main, be attributed to differences in the activity coefficients in the resin phase. It should be noted that the replacing ability is related to the radii of the ions. Ions with larger radii (non-hydrated) are held more strongly by the ion exchanger than are ions with smaller radii. This relationship was demonstrated for inorganic ion exchangers by Wiegner (43). It supports the view that differences in affinity can be associated with activity coefficients in the resin phase, since a relationship between ionic radii and activity coefficients also holds in common electrolyte solutions. Several investigators have found that the relative affinity is largely independent of the temperature (5, 8, 23). According to Gregor and Bregman the differences in exchange potentials between two ions is determined not only by the ratio of the activity coefficients in the resin phase but also by differences in ionic volumes and by the thermodynamic osmotic pressure (14).

The K_a value (e.g. at $X_{B_r}/X_{A_r} = 1$) may be regarded as a practical measure of the relative affinity of the ions for the ion exchanger. Two ions possess the same exchange affinity if K_a equals 1. Boyd, Schubert, and Adamson (5) found a correlation between K_a values and the parameter a^0 in the Debye-Hückel approximation for the activity coefficients in dilute solutions:

$$\log \gamma = \frac{- A \cdot \sqrt{\mu}}{1 + B\, a^0 \sqrt{\mu}}$$

where μ signifies ionic strength and A and B are constants. Plotting $\log K_a$ against $1/a^0$ when various cations were exchanged against hydrogen ions, Boyd et al. (5) obtained a straight line with alkali metals. Therefore $1/a^0$ may be regarded as an expression of the relative affinity coefficient. Kressman and Kitchener (23), applying the Debye-Hückel approximation as formulated by Stokes and Robinson, obtained similar results.

To collate the affinity of different ions under conditions where other ions are present in large excess, it is convenient to use the distribution coefficient K_d as a measure of the affinity (cf. p. 37).

The following sequences of affinity have been observed for mono-, di-, and trivalent cations with ion exchangers of the common highly cross-linked type:

$(CH_3)_4N < Li < H < Na < NH_4 < K < Rb < Cs < Tl < Ag$ (35, 2, 23).

$Mg < Ca < Sr < Ba$ (45).

$Al < Sc < Y < Eu < Sm < Nd < Pr < Ce < La$ (5).

$Lu < Yb < Tm < Er < Ho < Y < Dy < Tb < Gd < Eu < Sm < Pm < Nd < Pr < < Ce < La$ (21).

An observation which may be worth mentioning is that the basic beryllium ion $[Be_2O]^{2+}$ is held more strongly by the resin than Be^{2+} (16).

B. Exchange of Cations of Different Valence

As an illustration of ion exchange reactions between ions of different valence, the reaction between a solution containing calcium ions and an H^+-ion-saturated exchanger will be considered.

At equilibrium the Donnan concept would be expressed by

$$\frac{a_{H_r}}{\sqrt{a_{Ca_r}}} = \frac{a_{H_w}}{\sqrt{a_{Ca_w}}}.$$ (6)

Because of the differences in powers of the activities of the two ions the calculations become more complicated than when ions of equal valence exchange. It follows from eq. 6 that the volume of the external solution, as well as the total ion concentration in the resin phase, asserts an effect even in the purely theoretical instance when activity coefficients can be neglected. The experimental results obtained with a polystyrene sulfonic acid of high swelling deviated considerably from the values calculated by the Donnan equation, disregarding the activity coefficients in the resin phase (35).

Various workers have shown that dilution of the external solution (19, 44, 45), as well as the swelling of the ion exchanger (35), influences ion exchange equilibria. The results obtained with various types of resinous ion exchangers showed that with increasing dilution the position of equilibrium was displaced in favor of an increased uptake of ions with higher valence. This fact had been observed in exchange reactions with inorganic ion exchangers and had been propounded by Mattson (31) as supporting evidence for regarding ion exchange equilibria in principle as Donnan equilibria.

Some results from work by Wiklander (44) will serve to demonstrate the large dilution effects in exchange reactions between ions of different valence. A resin of the sulfonic acid type (Wofatit K) was treated until equilibrium was attained with a solution 1 N in respect to NH_4Cl and $CaCl_2$. After washing, the ratio of equivalents of NH_4^+ and Ca^{2+} in the ion exchanger was determined. The value of the ratio was 0.54. In similar experiments with the solution diluted to 0.0001 N in respect to NH_4Cl and $CaCl_2$, the ratio NH_4^+/Ca^{2+} in the exchanger was 0.01.

According to the Donnan theory, the ion concentration in the resin phase affects the ion exchange equilibrium when ions of different valence are used. The uptake of ions with higher valence will be greater the higher the ion concentration in the resin phase, i.e. the lower the swelling property of the ion exchanger. Results of experiments with sulfonated polystyrene resins of varying swelling properties are qualitatively in agreement with the Donnan theory (35). Also for systems in which exchange reactions include more than two exchangeable ions the Donnan theory will yield some conclusion (45, 46). It is evident from the facts just discussed that in general the Donnan equation can only predict the change of direction of ion exchange equilibria caused by changes in the composition of the system.

Other approaches besides the Donnan theory have often been applied in studies of ion exchange equilibria between monovalent (A) and divalent (D) ions.

Analogously to eq. 4c, ion exchange equilibrium can be expressed:

$$\frac{X_{A_r}^2}{X_{D_r}} \cdot \frac{a_{D_w}}{a_{A_w}^2} = K_b. \tag{7}$$

Conditions in the resin phase are better described by using the equivalent (X) rather than the molar fraction.

Applying the Donnan theory, K_b may be expressed as:

$$K_b = \frac{\gamma_{D_r}}{2 \cdot C_r \cdot \gamma_{A_r}^2} \tag{8}$$

where C_r is the total equivalent concentration in the resin phase expressed as equivalents per unit volume of the resin phase [cf. (9, 35)].

If the concentration of the external solution is low in comparison with that of the resin phase, the penetration of anions (e.g. Cl^- ions) into the resin phase may be ignored. In this particular case C_r thus signifies the concentration of exchangeable groups per unit volume of the resin phase, i.e. the normality of the resin phase.

Several authors (45, 5) have found that the quantity K_b may be regarded as constant when the ratio X_{A_r}/X_{D_r} varies within certain limits. In certain cases the variations in K_b values remain insignificant, even when this ratio varies over a wide range. Where eq. 7 does not fit experimental data satisfactorily, Rothmund and Kornfeld's equation or the Freundlich or Langmuir adsorption isotherm may be useful for practical purposes.

C. *Equilibrium at Tracer Concentration*

In special cases certain approximate equations derived from the Donnan equation may be useful. The problem of distribution of ionic species present at low concentration between the external solution and the ion exchanger, when another ionic species is present in large excess, is of special interest in ion exchange chromatography (38).

The Donnan equation may be given as:

$$\left(\frac{a_{A_w}}{a_{A_r}}\right)^{1/p} = \left(\frac{a_{B_w}}{a_{B_r}}\right)^{1/q} \tag{9}$$

where p and q values denote the valence of the ions A and B. The following symbols will also be introduced:

v = volume (milliliters) of the resin phase per gram ion exchanger.
g = amount of ion exchanger in gram.
b_r = millimoles of ion B in the resin phase.
b_w = millimoles of ion B in the external solution.
w = volume (milliliters) of the external solution.

With these designations the equation becomes:

$$\frac{b_r}{b_w} \cdot \frac{w}{g} = v \left(\frac{a_{A_r}}{a_{A_w}}\right)^{q/p} \cdot \frac{\gamma_{B_w}}{\gamma_{B_r}}. \tag{10}$$

If A is present in large excess, then A will determine both the swelling and the activity coefficients in the resin phase. This would imply that a_{A_r} and γ_{B_r} and the volume (v) of the resin phase can be regarded as constant. If the calculations further are restricted to the specific case when a_{A_w} is kept constant, it follows that γ_{B_w} must also be constant, since A is present in a large excess. The right-hand side of eq. 10 thus becomes a constant represented by K_q. Rewriting eq. 10, one obtains

$$\frac{b_r}{b_w} \cdot \frac{w}{g} = K_d. \qquad (11)$$

K_d is called the distribution coefficient of B. It is evident from eq. 11 that under these special assumptions the concentration of B expressed on a weight basis of ion exchanger is directly proportional to the concentration of B in the external solution. It is further apparent from the derivation that eq. 11 is valid independently of the valence of the ions. The range of validity of eq. 11 has been studied by Tompkins and Mayer (38), who investigated the uptake of rare earths in ammonium citrate solution by an ammonium-saturated ion exchanger of the sulfonic acid type. The analyses were facilitated by using radioisotopes of the ions. Distinct differences in K_d values of different rare earths were obtained.

By determining K_d values under varying experimental conditions it is possible to select the most effective conditions for separating small amounts of various ions by ion exchange chromatography. The ratio of the distribution coefficients of two different solutes at low concentrations is called the separation factor and may be used to evaluate the ease of separating the two ions.

3. CATION EXCHANGERS OF WEAKLY ACID TYPE

The discussions above have been confined to cation exchangers of the sulfonic acid type. For cation exchangers containing weakly acid groups, e.g. carboxyl groups, consideration has to be given to the fact that the degree of dissociation of the acid groups will change when the composition of the outside solution varies. The pH of the external solution has a marked effect on the number of dissociated groups in the resin phase. It may be assumed that with certain qualifications the dissociation of the carboxyl groups can be expressed by the dissociation equilibrium of weak electrolytes, e.g.

$$RCOOH \rightleftharpoons RCOO^- + H^+.$$

The theory of reactions of weak electrolytes may also be applied to the effect of common ions on the equilibrium of reactions with this type of ion exchanger. It is obvious, however, that H^+ ions possess a higher affinity than other cations for the cation exchanger and that divalent ions are taken up more readily than, for instance, Na^+ and K^+ (29). If due consideration is given to the varying numbers of dissociated groups in the resin phase, the conditions with this type of exchanger can reasonably be regarded as analogous to those prevailing with cation exchangers of sulfonic acid type. The systems, however, become more complicated. The equations which in these cases would have theoretical validity are at present not satisfactory for practical calculations. It is, therefore, frequently more convenient to apply empirical expressions such as Freundlich's adsorption isotherm. The validity of this equation should not be interpreted as proof that the reaction mechanism is a "physical adsorption."

4. ANION EXCHANGERS OF STRONGLY BASIC TYPE

The complete dissociation in the resin phase of anion exchangers which, like Amberlite IRA-400, Dowex 1, or Dowex 2, contain quaternary ammonium groups makes the ion exchange reactions with these exchangers comparable in all respects to cation exchange reactions with sulfonic acid resins.

The Donnan theory may also be applied to anion exchange equilibria. In exchange reactions of ions of equal valence, e.g. $[R_s \ NR_3^+] A^- + B^- \rightleftharpoons [R_s \ NR_3^+] B^- + A^-$, the following equation holds:

$$\frac{X_{B_r}}{X_{A_r}} \cdot \frac{C_{A_w}}{C_{B_w}} = \frac{\gamma_{A_r}}{\gamma_{B_r}} \cdot \frac{\gamma_{B_w}}{\gamma_{A_w}} [= Q]. \tag{12}$$

The number of exchanging groups in the resin phase of ion exchangers of this type may be regarded as constant when the composition of the solution changes. Because of imperfect knowledge of activity coefficients in the resin phase the equation can in general be used only for qualitative predictions. Decreases in the degree of cross-linking have been found to affect the exchange equilibria by decreasing ion selectivity. This is in agreement with the results already reported for cation exchangers of the sulfonic acid type (27, 41). For exchangers of the commercial type with a normal degree of cross-linking the variations in Q are very large when the relative amounts of the ions are altered.

The affinity of an anion depends on its structure, size, and valence. According to Kunin and McGarvey (28), the affinity increases in dilute solutions according to the following sequence:

acetate < fluoride < hydroxyl < formate < chloride < thiocyanate < bromide < < chromate < nitrate < iodide < oxalate < sulfate < citrate [cf. also (41)].

In certain cases the order of affinity changes when the concentration of the solution is altered.

5. ANION EXCHANGERS OF WEAKLY BASIC TYPE

Anion exchangers of weakly basic type, such as Amberlite IR-4B or Wofatit M, are to a large extent undissociated in an alkaline or neutral medium. The dissociation equilibrium may be written thus:

$$R_sNH_2 + H_2O \rightleftharpoons [R_sNH_3^+] + OH^-.$$

The fact that these ion exchangers are inert in alkaline medium led to the concept of regarding the reaction as an adsorption of the whole acid molecule (36). The ion exchange in acid medium is an equilibrium reaction of the type:

$$[R_sNH_3^+]A^- + B^- \rightleftharpoons [R_sNH_3^+]B^- + A^-.$$

With this type of resin the calculations are more complicated than with strongly basic resins, as variations in the dissociation of the resin phase must be considered. Qualitative accordance between experimental data and values derived from the Donnan equation is found in regard to the effect of dilution. Thus Wiklander (45) found that multivalent anions accumulated in the ion exchanger when equilibrium mixtures of anions of different valences were diluted [cf. Honda (15)].

From the foregoing theoretical considerations it is obvious that the hydroxyl ion has an extremely high affinity for the resin, i.e. that other anions are easily displaced by hydroxyl ions. In other respects the affinity series remains by and large the same as with anion exchangers of strongly basic type. Kunin and Myers (26) report the following sequence:

fluoride < chloride < bromide = iodide = acetate < molybdate < phosphate <
< arsenate < nitrate < tartrate < citrate < chromate < sulfate < hydroxyl.

Changes may occur in concentrated solution. Wiklander (45) found that in concentrated solutions chloride ions possessed a stronger affinity than sulfate ions for a resin of the weakly basic type.

In collating experimental data from ion exchange equilibria determinations, empirical relationships between the concentrations in the external solutions and in the resin phase, respectively, have been used. Thus Kunin and Myers (26) obtained good agreement between values derived from Freundlich's adsorption isotherm and experimental data of exchange equilibria in dilute solutions ($< 0.05\ N$), using a weakly basic anion exchanger, whereas results from similar experiments with more concentrated solutions did not fit either the Freundlich or the Langmuir adsorption isotherm (25) [cf. (4)].

BIBLIOGRAPHY

1. Argersinger, W. J., Davidson, A. W., and Bonner, O. D.: *Trans. Kansas Acad. Sci.*, **53**, 404 (1950); *J. Am. Chem. Soc.*, **74**, 1044, 1047 (1952).
2. Bauman, W. C., and Eichhorn, J.: *J. Am. Chem. Soc.*, **69**, 2830 (1947).
3. Bauman, W. C.: 23rd National Colloid Symposium, Minneapolis, Minn., June 6—8 (1949).
4. Bhatnagar, S. S., Kapur, A. N., and Puri, M. L.: *J. Indian Chem. Soc.*, **13**, 679 (1936).
5. Boyd, G. E., Schubert, J., and Adamson, A. W.: *J. Am. Chem. Soc.*, **69**, 2816 (1947).
6. Cosgrove, D. J., and Strickland, J. D. H.: *J. Chem. Soc.*, **1950**, 1845.
7. Davis, L. E.: *J. Colloid Sci.*, **5**, 71 (1950).
8. Duncan, J. F., and Lister, B. A. J.: *Disc. Faraday Soc.*, **1949**, No. 7, 104.
9. Du Rietz, C.: *Svensk Kem. Tid.*, **49**, 52 (1937).
10. Du Rietz, C.: Diss., Tekn. Högskolan, Stockholm, 1938.
11. Ekedahl, E., Högfeldt, E., and Sillén, L.-G.: *Acta Chem. Scand.*, **4**, 556, 828 (1950).
12. Gregor, H. P.: *J. Am. Chem. Soc.*, **70**, 1293 (1948).
13. Gregor, H. P.: *J. Am. Chem. Soc.*, **73**, 642 (1951).
14. Gregor, H. P., and Bregman, J. I.: *J. Colloid Sci.*, **6**, 323 (1951).
15. Honda, M.: *J. Chem. Soc. Japan*, **71**, 405 (1950); *J. Japan. Chem.*, **2**, 386 (1948).
16. Honda, M.: *J. Chem. Soc. Japan*, **72**, No. 4 (1951).
17. Högfeldt, E., Ekedahl, E., and Sillén, L.-G.: *Acta Chem. Scand.*, **4**, 1471 (1950).
18. Högfeldt, E.: *Acta Chem. Scand.*, **5**, 1400 (1951).
19. Ivanov, A. N., and Gapon, E. N.: *J. Phys. Chem. (U.S.S.R.)*, **15**, 659 (1941).
20. Jenny, H.: *J. Phys. Chem.*, **40**, 501 (1936).
21. Ketelle, B. H., and Boyd, G. E.: *J. Am. Chem. Soc.*, **69**, 2800 (1947).
22. Kielland, J.: *J. Soc. Chem. Ind.*, **54**, 232T (1935).
23. Kressman, T. R. E., and Kitchener, J. A.: *J. Chem. Soc.*, **1949**, 1190, 1201, 1208, 1211.
24. Krishnamoorthy, C., Davis, L. E., and Overstreet, R.: *Science*, **108**, 439 (1948).
25. Kunin, R., and Myers, R. J.: *J. Phys. & Colloid Chem.*, **51**, 1111 (1947).
26. Kunin, R., and Myers, R. J.: *J. Am. Chem. Soc.*, **69**, 2874 (1947).
27. Kunin, R., and Myers, R. J.: *Disc. Faraday Soc.*, **1949**, No. 7, 114.
28. Kunin, R., and McGarvey, F. X.: *Ind. Eng. Chem.*, **41**, 1265 (1949).
29. Kunin, R., and Barry, R. E.: *Ind. Eng. Chem.*, **41**, 1269 (1949).
30. Lowen, W. K., Stoenner, R. W., Argersinger, Jr., W. J., Davidson, A. W., and Hume, D. N.: *J. Am. Chem. Soc.*, **73**, 2666 (1951).
31. Mattson, S.: *Soil Sci.*, **28**, 179 (1928).
32. Möller, J.: *Kolloid-Beihefte*, **46**, 1 (1937).
33. Reichenberg, D., Pepper, K. W., and McCauleu, D. J.: *J. Chem. Soc.*, **1951**, 493.
34. Rothmund, V., and Kornfeld, G.: *Z. anorg. u. allgem. Chem.*, **103**, 129 (1918); **108**, 215 (1919).
35. Samuelson, O.: Diss., Tekn. Högskolan, Stockholm, 1944.
36. Schwartz, M. C., Edwards, Jr., W. R., and Boudreaux, G.: *Ind. Eng. Chem.*, **32**, 1462 (1940).
37. Skogseid, A.: Diss., Oslo, 1948.

38. Tompkins, E. R., and Mayer, S. W.: *J. Am. Chem. Soc.*, **69**, 2859 (1947).
39. Walton, H. F.: *J. Franklin Inst.*, **232**, 305 (1941); *Trans. Illinois State Acad. Sci.*, **34**, No. 2, 124 (1941).
40. Weisz, L.: Diss., Zürich, 1932.
41. Wheaton, R. M., and Bauman, W. C.: *Ind. Eng. Chem.*, **43**, 1088 (1951).
42. Whitehorn, J. C.: *J. Biol. Chem.*, **56**, 751 (1923).
43. Wiegner, G.: *Kolloid-Z.*, **36**, 341 (1925).
44. Wiklander, L.: *Svensk Kem. Tid.*, **57**, 54 (1945).
45. Wiklander, L.: *Ann. Roy. Agr. Coll. Sweden*, **14**, 1 (1946).
46. Wiklander, L., and Gieseking, J. E.: *Soil. Sci.*, **66**, 377 (1948).

CHAPTER IV

Ion Exchange Kinetics

The ion exchange process may be quite rapid, and equilibrium may under certain conditions be reached almost instantaneously. On the other hand, ion exchangers having the ion-active groups accessible only through very small pores exhibit a low speed of exchange. For example, for a strongly swollen polystyrene sulfonic acid equilibrium was attained within 1 min, whereas for a sulfonated phenolic resin the corresponding value was 90 min (11). For tightly cross-linked resins the rate of reaction is slower than for resins with a low degree of cross-linking (3).

It may be concluded that the ion exchange occurs instantaneously, and that in most cases the diffusion of the ions through the resin particle is the rate-determining factor (11).

Other facts which are of importance from an analytical point of view are that the rates of exchange increase considerably with decreasing particle size (2, 8, 4) and increasing temperature (2, 6). If dried resins are used, the reaction is slower than for resins which have been kept in water for some time (11). The rate of uptake decreases with increasing charge and volume of the ions (2, 6, 3). With cation exchange resins of carboxylic acid type the rate of exchange is considerably lower in the free-acid form than in the salt form (7). For certain types of anion exchangers the rate of acid sorption is extremely low, several days being required to attain equilibrium (10, 9).

Theoretical studies of ion exchange kinetics have been published by several authors (2, 5, 4, 6, 1). Boyd *et al.* (2) have considered not only the diffusion through the resin particle and the exchange reaction but also the diffusion through the solution to the surface of the resin (diffusion through a Nernst liquid film surrounding the particles). The conditions under which the film diffusion has an influence or eventually is the rate-determining factor have also been discussed by Hale and Reichenberg (4), as well as by Kressman and Kitchener (6).

The rates of ion exchange have a great influence upon the efficiency of ion exchange separations by column operation. Thus, the rate determines the steepness of the break-through curves, the sharpness of elution peaks, and the degree of overlap in chromatographic separations (cf. Chapters V, VI, and VII).

BIBLIOGRAPHY

1. Adamson, A. W., and Grossman, J. J.: *J. Chem. Phys.*, **16**, 1002 (1949).
2. Boyd, G. E., Adamson, A. W., and Myers, Jr., L. S.: *J. Am. Chem. Soc.*, **69**, 2836 (1947); **72**, 4807 (1950).
3. Gregor, H. P., Bregman, J. I., Gutoff, F., Broadley, R. D., Baldwin, D. E., and Overberger, C. G.: *J. Colloid Sci.*, **6**, 20 (1951).
4. Hale, D. K., and Reichenberg, D.: *Disc. Faraday Soc.*, **1949**, No. 7, 79.
5. Juda, W., and Carron, M.: *J. Am. Chem. Soc.*, **70**, 3295 (1948).
6. Kressman, T. R. E., and Kitchener, J. A.: *Disc. Faraday Soc.*, **1949**, No. 7, 90.
7. Kunin, R., and Barry, R. E.: *Ind. Eng. Chem.*, **41**, 1269 (1949).
8. Kunin, R., and Myers, R. J.: *J. Phys. & Colloid Chem.*, **51**, 1111 (1947).
9. Nachod, F. C., and Wood, W.: *J. Am. Chem. Soc.*, **66**, 1380 (1944).
10. Samuelson, O.: *Svensk Papperstidn.*, **46**, 583 (1943).
11. Samuelson, O.: Diss., Tekn. Högskolan, Stockholm, 1944.

CHAPTER V

Ion Exchange in Column Operation

1. GENERAL CONSIDERATIONS AND TERMINOLOGY

When ion exchangers are utilized for analytical purposes, the solution is percolated through a fixed bed of ion exchanger packed in a column. Ordinarily the column is operated downflow by running the solution through the exchanger from top to bottom. The solution which enters the column is called the influent, and the filtrate from the column the effluent.

The first operation in an exchange cycle is the sorption step. At the beginning of this step the exchanger contains normally only one kind of exchangeable ions. The influent, which may contain one or several exchangeable ions, is passed through the column. After the column is rinsed with water the exchanger contains the exchangeable ions from the solution as well as a certain amount of the ions originally present in the exchanger. The next step is the regeneration or elution. The latter term is used especially in chromatographic procedures. The retained ions are removed by passing an excess of electrolyte solution (elutriant or regenerant) through the column. Ordinarily the elution is performed with a solution containing one exchangeable ion. After the column is washed with water the cycle is finished and the exchanger is ready for a new exchange cycle.

The total number of exchanging groups in the column, conveniently expressed as milliequivalents, is called the total capacity of the column. In column operation another expression is used for the filter capacity, namely the break-through capacity, which is defined as the amount of ions which can be taken up quantitatively by the column under the conditions in question, i.e. the number of milliequivalents which can be retained without any leakage being observed.

The break-through capacity is of course always lower than the total capacity of the column and is dependent upon a number of different variables, such as particle size, filtration rate, and composition of the solution. Published results from experiments on the capacity of technical ion exchange filters cannot be applied when ion exchange columns are used for analytical purposes. The reason is partly that for technical purposes a considerable leakage of ions is tolerated, and partly and principally that regeneration for economic reasons is not continued until the filter is 100% regenerated. These experiments will not, therefore, be discussed in this book.

Certain abbreviations are convenient in describing an ion exchange column. This is best illustrated with an example: column: 12×200 mm; Dowex 50 [H^+; 0.2–0.4 mm], which means a column of inner diameter 12 mm and a resin bed with a height of 200 mm. The ion exchanger consists of Dowex 50 with particle size 0.2–0.4 mm and is used in the hydrogen form. *

Where an anion exchanger in the free-base form is concerned, it is correct to describe it as, e.g., Amberlite IRA-400 [OH^-] only when the anion exchanger is of the strongly basic type. For the sake of simplicity this type of description will be used also for anion exchangers of the weakly basic type.

2. THE SORPTION STEP

Let us, as a simple example, consider the exchange between a solution of sodium chloride and a bed of an H^+-exchange resin of the sulfonic acid type. The principle is demonstrated in Fig. 4.

A solution of sodium chloride is introduced into the top of the column. When the first part of the influent comes into contact with the top layer of the ion exchanger, an exchange takes place so that sodium ions are taken up by the ion exchanger and an equivalent amount of hydrogen ions is transferred to the external solution. In ideal cases this reaction can continue until equilibrium has been attained. As the solution moves downwards the first part comes into contact with a new layer of hydrogen-saturated ion exchanger. The uptake of sodium ions continues: the reaction attempts to attain a new state of equilibrium in which the amount of sodium ions in the solution is less than in the original. Simultaneously, a new part of the sodium chloride solution comes into contact with the top layer of the ion exchanger, which in this way takes up a further amount of sodium ions. When the first part of the solution comes into contact with the third layer of the ion exchanger simultaneously a third portion of the solution comes into contact with the top layer of the ion exchanger, etc.

After a certain amount of solution has been introduced into the column, the upper part of the resin bed is saturated with sodium ions whereas the lower parts are still in the hydrogen form. The concentration of sodium ions (C) in the solution is, in the upper part of the column, the same as in the influent (C_0), whereas in the lower parts C is equal to zero. In an intermediate zone of the column both sodium and hydrogen ions are present

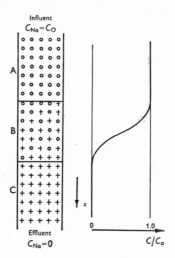

FIG. 4.   Principle of column operation (completed with an exchange isochrone).
A. Na$^+$-saturated resin.
B. Boundary zone.
C. H$^+$-saturated resin.

in the solution as well as in the resin. In this boundary zone the concentration is different in different points, the composition of the solution being a function of the distance (x) from the top of the resin bed. The ratio C/C_0 as a function of x at a given time is indicated schematically in Fig. 4 (exchange isochrone). The effluent from the column will be free from sodium ions and will contain an equivalent amount of hydrogen ions until such an amount of solution has been run through the column that the boundary zone has reached the end of the resin bed.

When a certain amount of the solution has passed through the filter, the so-called break-through point is reached, which means that sodium ions are detected in the filtrate. When an ion exchanger is used for analysis, the amount of ion exchanger must be adjusted to the amount of solution to be passed through it, so that the break-through point is not reached during the sorption step.

In studying the most suitable conditions for various analyses, it is sometimes desirable to continue filtration until the break-through point is passed. The amount of sodium ions in the effluent usually increases quickly, and the concentration of hydrogen ions decreases to a corresponding extent. After a certain time the filter is saturated with sodium ions, and the sodium chloride solution passes unchanged through the filter bed. The procedure

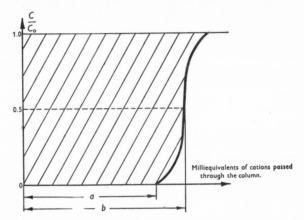

FIG. 5.   Exchange isoplane (break-through curve) with one exchangeable ion in the influent.

may be shown with curves of the ratio C/C_0 between the effluent and influent concentrations as a function of time or effluent volume. The curves are called exchange isoplanes or break-through curves. In certain cases it is practical to use as abscissa the total amount of ions passed through the filter (in this example $H^+ + Na^+$).

A comparison between the total exchange capacity and the break-through capacity is conveniently made from the break-through curves. An example is given in Fig. 5.

The shaded area represents the total capacity of the column. For symmetric break-through curves this is the same as the abscissa (b) corresponding to the point $C/C_0 = 0.5$. Ordinarily the experimental curves deviate from the symmetrical shape, but in most cases the distance b may be used as an approximative measure for the total capacity. The distance a represents the break-through capacity of the filter under the conditions in question.

It should be pointed out that the break-through capacity is not an exactly defined value but depends on the sensitivity of the method used to determine the point where leakage of ions begins. When comparing the break-through capacity under varying conditions a suitable value must be chosen for C/C_0, e.g. $C/C_0 = 0.001$. This defines the break-through capacity as the amount of ions taken up by the filter when this value is obtained. If the experiment is terminated when the value C/C_0 has attained 0.001, this means an uptake in the last fraction of the filtrate of 99.9%. In earlier parts of the filtrate C/C_0 lies below the value 0.001. In the accumulated filtrate the average take-up value lies thus considerably over 99.9%,

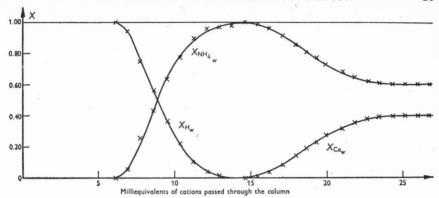

Fig. 6. Exchange isoplanes (break-through curves) with two ions of different ex-
changeability in the influent.
Column: 24 × 103 mm; sulfonated phenolic resin [H⁺; 0.3–0.8 mm]
Flow rate: 3.5 ml sqcm⁻¹ min⁻¹.   [from (27)]

and therefore from an analytical viewpoint the uptake may be considered
to be quantitative.

   If the influent contains more than one exchangeable ion, a certain separation of these ions will be obtained, since the various ions differ in their
affinities for the resin. Because the solution is continually passing new
parts of the ion exchanger and new solution is continually passing through
the column, the partial separation which is obtained by a single shaking
of the ion exchanger with the solution is "multiplied," so that, under
certain conditions, a quantitative separation of different exchangeable ions
from each other may occur. An example is the filtration of a solution containing calcium chloride and ammonium chloride through a column of
hydrogen-saturated cation exchanger. The composition of the effluent
expressed in equivalent fractions, X, as a function of the total number
of milliequivalents passed through the column is given in Fig. 6. As the
figure shows, a quantitative uptake of ammonium ions as well as calcium
ions is obtained at the beginning. After a certain time the break-through
point for ammonium ions is attained. Later the amount of ammonium ions
in the effluent increases; and for a certain period the effluent contains no
other cations than ammonium ions. Still later the break-through point
for calcium ions is reached, and the composition of the effluent changes
successively so that an increasing content of calcium ions is obtained at
the same time that the amount of ammonium ions decreases, until the composition of the original solution is obtained (i.e. the solution passes through
the filter unchanged).

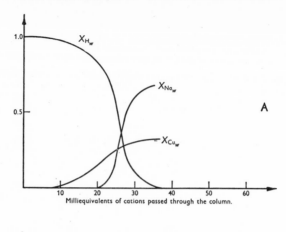

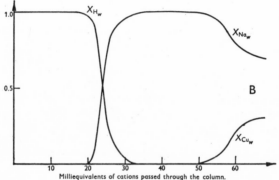

FIG. 7.   Influence of a complexing agent on the exchange isoplanes.
   A. Complex systém: copper sulfate (0.012 N) + sodium polymetaphosphate
   (0.024 N).
   B. "Complex free" system: copper sulfate (0.012 N) + sodium sulfate (0.024 N).
   Column: 9.8 × 140 mm; Amberlite IR-120 [H^+; < 0.43 mm]
   Flow rate: 2.7 ml sqcm^{-1} min^{-1}.   [from (30)]

The principle of this separation is the same as that of chromatography according to the frontal analysis principle, introduced by Tiselius (37) and thoroughly studied by Claesson (6). In a pure condition the only component obtained is the one with the least adsorbability.

Of utmost interest from an analytical point of view is the influence of an addition of a complexing agent, which gives a complex of medium strength, retarding the uptake of a certain ion but not preventing this uptake completely. An example is demonstrated in Fig. 7 A, which shows the break-through curves for a solution containing copper sulfate and sodium metaphosphate. For comparison the results with a complex free system, copper sulfate and sodium sulfate, have been reproduced in Fig. 7 B. As seen from the figure, the copper ions appear in the effluent considerably later than the sodium ions when a sulfate solution is passed through a sulfonic acid resin in the hydrogen form. In the presence of metaphosphate which forms complexes with copper ions the sequence is the opposite. It must be observed that the break-through capacity for the copper ions in the polymetaphosphate solution is considerably lower than that for sodium ions in the complex free solution.

3. THE THEORY FOR BREAK-THROUGH CURVES

It is apparent that the behavior of an ion exchange resin bed resembles in many respects the adsorption of gases by active charcoal or chromato- graphic analysis by different adsorbents. The adsorption of gases on active charcoal was thoroughly treated by Wicke (44) in 1939. Soon afterwards a similar theory for chromatographic analysis was published by Wilson (45). This theory, which is derived using continuous variables, was applied to ion exchange columns by Samuelson (27) and later extended by Sillén (31, 32, 9, 33), Boyd, Myers, and Adamson (3), Glueckauf (10, 11, 12, 13, 14, 15, 16, 17, 18), and several other authors (1, 8, 35, 41, 36).

It seems unnecessary to discuss the calculations in this book, and there- fore only a short summary of the results will be given.

A. *The Theory Based on Continuous Variables*

According to this theory, the shape of the break-through curves is largely dependent upon the type of exchange isotherm governing the static equilibria. The exchange isotherm can be illustrated, as seen from Fig. 8, by plotting the equivalent fraction in the resin phase as a function of the same fraction in the external solution. Three different types may be considered, namely linear, convex, and concave isotherms. It must be pointed out that this figure depicts behavior for idealized conditions only. Actually, exchange isotherms may have inflection points owing to variations in selectivity with resin composition.

The simplest type is the linear isotherm, which, however, is valid only in some special cases, e.g. at the exchange of ions of the same valence under the assumption that the Donnan theory is valid and in some instances when a second ion is present in a great excess in the external solution. The usual type is the convex isotherm, which represents the case that

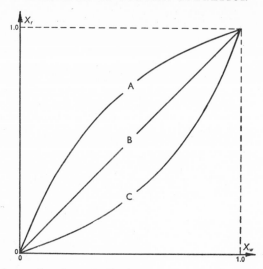

FIG. 8.   Different types of exchange isotherms.
    A. Convex isotherm.
    B. Linear isotherm.
    C. Concave isotherm.

the ion to be taken up has a higher affinity for the resin than the ion originally present in the column. If the ion to be taken up is bound less strongly than the original ion, the third type, the concave isotherm, is represented.

In the idealized case that equilibrium is reached in all parts of the column — the so-called equilibrium case — the theory predicts that the boundary zone will approach a sharp front provided the static equilibria may be represented by a linear or a convex isotherm (3, 4, 5). The boundary is displaced at constant rate through the resin bed, and a sudden change will occur in effluent concentration, as illustrated by Fig. 9 *A*. With a concave isotherm the boundary zone is progressively broadened on prolonged passage through the column. The theoretical shape of the exchange isochrone is demonstrated in Fig. 9 *B*.

The assumptions on which the theory is based are not strictly correct. However, they may all be approached under certain experimental conditions. In practice, differences between the theoretical and experimental isochrones and isoplanes are obtained for various reasons, the foremost being that equilibrium is not attained in the various parts of the layer and that deviations exist from the ideal condition concerning the liquid flow. These factors will cause the break-through curves to be less sharp than the theoretical curves. With a slower rate of filtering the curves

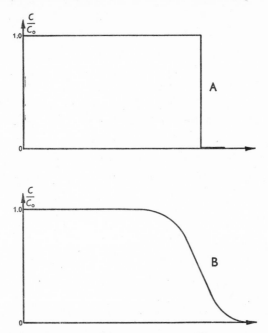

FIG. 9.   Theoretical exchange isochrones for the equilibrium case.
(C/C₀ versus distance from the top of the bed.)
A. Linear or convex isotherm.
B. Concave isotherm.   [from (5)]

are naturally sharper than with a faster rate. Only if the flow rate is extremely low must the diffusion in the void space between the resin particles
be taken into account. This factor will cause a broadening of the S curve.
Any factor which contributes to an increased speed of reaction, e.g. a
diminished particle size or an increased temperature, will involve a sharpening
of the curves. No theory has yet been advanced to explain deviations from
the ideal conditions concerning the liquid flow, but many interesting
investigations have been carried out on the lack of equilibrium in the resin
bed (non-equilibrium case).

A calculation of the theoretical curves (isochrones and isoplanes) in
the non-equilibrium case must be based on assumptions about the kinetics
of the ion exchange reaction. From a practical point of view it is interesting
to note that in the non-equilibrium case a self-sharpening of the isochrones
is predicted for convex isotherms. The isochrone will, on prolonged passage
through the column, approach a final form (33). This final front will move
at constant velocity through the column. On the other hand, a broadening

of the boundary zone will occur in the case of linear or concave isotherms (6, 4, 5, 33). These conclusions are arrived at independently of the type of kinetics used for the calculation.

B. *The Plate Theory*

A different approach to this problem was made by Martin and Synge (21), who developed a theory for chromatographic columns similar to the plate theory for solvent extraction and distillation. For purposes of calculating separations, a column may be considered as being made up of a number of plates with adsorbent, each successively equilibrating with portions of the solution. A modification of this theory was used by Mayer and Tompkins (22, 40) in their investigations concerning separation of rare earths by elution from an ion exchange column.

4. BREAK-THROUGH CURVES FROM CATION EXCHANGE COLUMNS

A. *Influence of the Particle Size*

Samuelson (28) showed that the particle size of the exchanger had a very great influence upon the break-through curves. Solutions of potassium nitrate

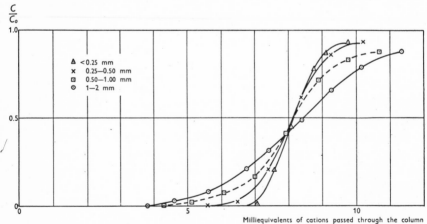

FIG. 10. Exchange isoplanes (break-through curves) at different particle size for a KNO$_3$ solution (0.037 N).
Column: 10 × 135 mm; Wofatit K[H$^+$].
Flow rate: 12.5 ml sqcm^{-1} min^{-1}.   [from (28)]
Particle size: O 2.0–1.0 mm   × 0.5–0.25 mm
                  □ 1.0–0.5 mm   △ < 0.25 mm

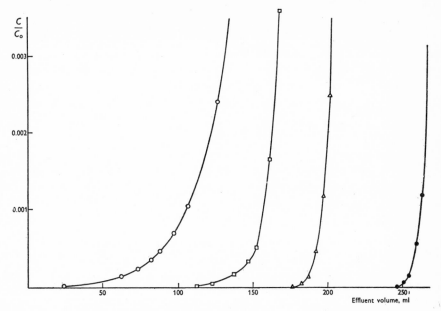

FIG. 11.   Exchange isoplanes (break-through curves) at different particle size for a
FeCl$_3$ solution (0.03 mol/l).
Column: 12 × 95 mm; Wofatit KS [H$^+$].
Flow rate: 4.0 ml sqcm^{-1} min^{-1}.   [from (7)]
Particle size: ○ 0.6–1.0 mm
                 □ 0.4–0.6 mm
                 △ 0.2–0.4 mm
                 ● 0.1–0.2 mm

were passed through columns containing a sulfonic acid resin in the hydrogen
form. The effluent was collected in small fractions in which the amount of
nitric acid was determined by titration. Figure 10 shows some of the results.

For analytical purposes the lower parts of the curves are of the greatest
interest. Djurfeldt and Samuelson (7) made a study of these lower parts
for Wofatit KS with iron (III) chloride solutions. The results are presented
in Fig. 11.

As may be seen from these figures, the break-through capacity of the
column is greatly increased as the size of the particles is diminished. Where
a quantitative uptake is desired, it is obviously of great importance to
use relatively fine particles of the ion exchanger in the column. Kunin
and Barry (20) have published some break-through curves for a carboxylic
acid resin, Amberlite IRC-50. For this exchanger, also, the break-through
capacity increases when the particle size is diminished.

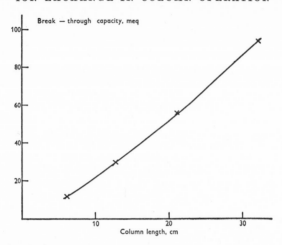

FIG. 12.   The break-through capacity at different column lengths for a solution of
NaCl (0.02 N).
Column: diameter 26 mm; sulfonated phenolic resin [H$^+$; 0.3–0.8 mm].
Flow rate: 4 ml sqcm^{-1} min^{-1}.   [from (27)]

B. *Influence of the Shape of the Column*

Break-through curves from experiments with columns of constant diameter
and varying length were studied by Samuelson (27), as well as by Boyd,
Myers, and Adamson (3). In all cases S-shaped curves were obtained.

In Samuelson's experiments a solution of sodium chloride was passed
at constant rate through columns containing a sulfonated phenol-formaldehyde resin saturated with hydrogen ions. The results are summarized in
Fig. 12, which shows the break-through capacity as a function of the total
capacity of the resin (or column length). From this diagram it is possible
to read off directly the minimum amount of ion exchanger which is necessary
to achieve a quantitative uptake at varying influent volumes. The excess
of resin necessary for quantitative conversion, i.e. the difference between
the total capacity and the break-through capacity in percentage of the total
capacity, decreases when the column length increases.

The influence of the diameter of the column at constant volume of the
resin bed has also been studied by Samuelson (28). These experiments
were performed with a commercial exchange resin (Wofatit K) in the
hydrogen form. A solution of potassium nitrate was passed through the
columns under such conditions that the time of contact was the same in
all experiments. The results are presented in Fig. 13.

As seen from the figure, the break-through curves are sharper for long

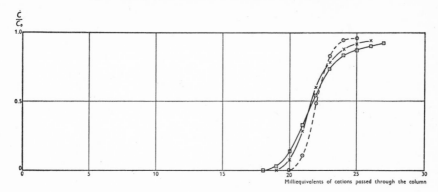

FIG. 13.   Exchange isoplanes (break-through curves) at varying diameters of the
column, but constant resin volume (= 30 ml) for a KNO_3 solution (0.037 N).
Column: Wofatit K [H^+].
Flow rate: 12.5 ml sqcm^{-1} min^{-1}.   [from (28)]
Diameter:
☐ 25 mm
× 19.5 mm
○ 13 mm

columns than for wide columns. The break-through capacity becomes
greater for increasing length of the column. With long and narrow columns
a somewhat smaller amount of resin may be used than with short layers of
large diameter.

C. *Influence of the Flow Rate*

The effect of the flow rate on the break-through curves for sodium
chloride solutions was studied by Samuelson (27) in experiments with a
sulfonated phenol-formaldehyde resin in the hydrogen form. It was shown
that the curves were sharper and the break-through capacity higher at a
low flow rate than at a high.

Similar results — but more marked differences — were obtained in
experiments with cadmium iodide solutions and columns containing Wofatit
KS in the hydrogen form. Fig. 14 shows the break-through capacity for
the cadmium ions as a function of the flow rate, all other factors being
constant (29).

The effect of the flow rate is greatly dependent upon the constitution
of the exchanger and the particle size (28). For exchangers with an open
network structure the flow rate has a rather small influence, whereas for
strongly cross-linked resins this factor is very significant, especially if

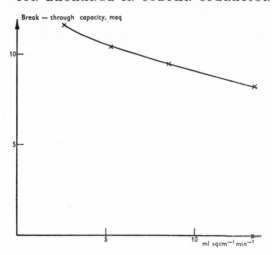

FIG. 14. The break-through capacity at varying flow rates for a CdI_2 solution (0.0405 N).
Column: 11 × 160 mm; Wofatit KS [H^+; 0.2–0.4 mm].   [from (29)]

the particles are coarse. This is easy to understand, as the network structure and the particle size are of utmost importance for the exchange velocity.

The column behavior of the carboxylic acid type of resin is similar, as was shown in investigations by Kunin and Barry (20).

D. *Influence of the Temperature*

As a variable which contributes to an increase in the rate of ion exchange, an increase in temperature causes a sharpening of the break-through curves and an increased break-through capacity. The great importance of this factor has been demonstrated by Ketelle and Boyd (19) in connection with the chromatographic elution of rare earths by means of citrate buffers, but it is evident from their results that this factor may also have a great influence on the break-through curves.

E. *Influence of the Acidity of the Solution*

Systematic investigations concerning the influence of the acidity of the solution on the break-through curves have been published by Partridge (24) and Wickbold (43), as well as by Djurfeldt and Samuelson (7). The last-mentioned authors made experiments with solutions of KCl, $CuCl_2$, and $FeCl_3$ containing varying amounts of HCl. The cation exchange resin, which was used in the hydrogen form, was of the sulfonic acid type (Wofatit

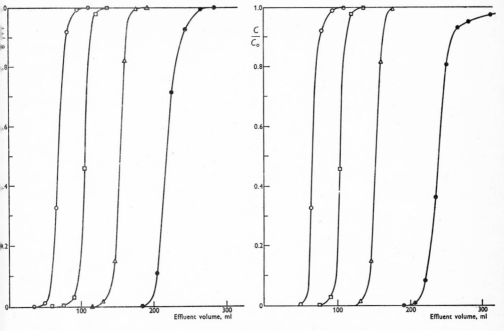

Fig. 15. Exchange isoplanes (break-through curves) for solutions of KCl (0.05 M), and $CuCl_2$ (0.0025 M) at varying acidities.

Column: 12×95 mm; Wofatit KS [H^+; 0.2–0.4 mm].

Flow rate: 4 ml sqcm^{-1} min^{-1}.   [from (7)]

O $C_{HCl} = 0.35$ mol/l
□   0.15 mol/l
△   0.05 mol/l
●   0   mol/l.

KS). Some break-through curves are shown in Fig. 15. In Table 2 the break-through capacities are tabulated for different acidities of the salt solutions. The break-through capacity is arbitrarily chosen as the point

TABLE 2

Break-through capacities for different acidities.

Solution	Concentration of HCl, mol per liter			
	0	0.05	0.15	0.35
KCl [0.05 M]	8.8	5.4	2.9	1.6
$CuCl_2$ [0.025 M]	9.5	5.3	3.3	1.8
$FeCl_3$ [0.0167 M]	12.1	9.1	7.6	4.8

where C/C_0 reaches 0.001. From the diagrams and the table it is seen that a quantitative separation can be performed by filtering even very acid solutions through H^+-saturated filters. However, the break-through capacity of the filter is diminished when the acidity of the solution is raised.

Furthermore, the experiments demonstrate that the effect of an addition of acid upon the break-through capacity is much greater for ions with low affinity for the resin, e.g. potassium, than for ions which are more strongly retained, e.g. copper and particularly iron.

F. Influence of the Composition of the Solution

Prokhorov and Yankovskiĭ (25) studied the influence of different cations on the shape of the break-through curves and the break-through capacity. Experiments were performed with a column containing a cation exchanger of sulfonic acid type in the hydrogen form. The results are summarized in Table 3. The break-through capacities are recalculated into milliequivalents per square centimeter column area for a column of 50-cm length.

TABLE 3

Break-through capacities for different chloride or nitrate solutions (0.0037 N).
Linear flow rate 17 cm min^{-1}.

Solution	Break-through Capacity, meq	Solution	Break-through Capacity, meq
LiCl	6.65	CuCl$_2$	20.10
NaCl	9.35	SrCl$_2$	18.90
KCl	16.80	CdCl$_2$	17.65
NH$_4$Cl	13.35	BaCl$_2$	20.80
CsCl	14.40	Pb(NO$_3$)$_2$	23.65
AgNO$_3$	18.85	MnCl$_2$	16.90
BeSO$_4$	15.85	NiCl$_2$	18.90
MgCl$_2$	18.90	CoCl$_2$	18.30
CaCl$_2$	20.10		

It must be pointed out that the particle size of the resin was 0.60–0.75 mm, i.e. of ordinary size for technical use, but too large for most analytical purposes. Even if the effects are less obvious under the conditions ordinarily employed for analyses, the results are of interest also from an analytical point of view.

5. THE ELUTION (REGENERATION) STEP

In ordinary separations of exchangeable ions from non-exchangeable components in a solution, e.g. separations of cations from anions by means of cation exchange columns, the elution is usually made with a solution containing one exchangeable ion.

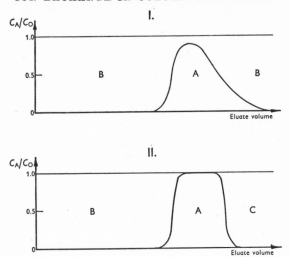

FIG. 16. Elution curves from a cation exchanger:

C_A = eluate conc.

C_O = elutriant conc.

  I. Elution of the cation A^+ from a resin in the B^+-form by means of an elutriant containing B^+-ions.

      Replacing ability: $A^+ > B^+$.

  II. Elution ("displacement") of the cation A^+ from a resin in the B^+-form by means of an elutriant containing C^+-ions.

      Replacing ability: $C^+ > A^+ > B^+$.

For ordinary analytical purposes hydrochloric acid is generally chosen as elutriant when cation exchangers are used. A systematic investigation concerning the elution of cation exchange columns (sulfonic acid type) with hydrochloric acid has been published (7), whereas very few data are available concerning the elution of anion exchange columns.

The course of the elution is illustrated either by integral elution (regeneration) curves, i.e. plots of the percentage elution versus time or eluate volume (cf. Fig. 20), or by differential elution curves (Fig. 16), in which the effluent concentration is plotted against time (or eluate volume).

In the elution step a separation of different exchangeable ions from each other may be obtained because of differences in exchange potentials. The most important applications of ion exchange chromatography are based on separations during the displacement (elution) of retained ions. Common elutriants are acids, salts, and complexing agents. The principle of chromatographic separation by means of elution may be illustrated by the following example.

Let us consider the separation of sodium and potassium (2, 43). The solution to be analyzed is introduced into a column containing a considerable excess of resin in the hydrogen form. Sodium and potassium are retained in a band at the top of the column, and the liberated acid may conveniently be removed by washing with water.

After this step the ions are eluted by passing dilute hydrochloric acid (e.g. 0.1 N) through the column. When the first part of the acid enters the column, sodium and potassium ions are partially replaced and carried downwards. As a new portion of acid is brought into contact with the upper resin layer, the replacement proceeds. At the same time the first part of the solution comes into contact with a second portion of the resin, causing a new shift in the composition of the solution and the resin phase. As mentioned in Chapter III: 2, the potassium ions have a higher replacing ability than sodium ions. Therefore the composition of the solution will be shifted successively so that the ratio Na^+/K^+ in solution will increase as the solution moves downwards. Under proper conditions this shift in composition will proceed so far that a complete separation of sodium ions and potassium ions in different bands will be obtained. These bands move downwards at different rates. In the effluent (eluate) the sodium ions will appear in a certain interval and the potassium ions in a subsequent interval. It must be pointed out that in this case, where the exchangeable ion in the elutriant (H^+) has a lower replacing ability than the ions to be separated (Na^+ and K^+), the effluent contains, during the whole course of elution, also the exchangeable ion present in the elutriant (H^+). The eluate is divided into small fractions which are analyzed. If the concentrations of the fractions are plotted against effluent volume (or time), an elution curve is obtained. A typical elution curve is reproduced in Fig. 17. In the curve each exchangeable ion is represented by a peak. The area A under a peak gives the amount of substance according to the equation:

$$A = \int_{V_1}^{V_2} C \, dv.$$

Compared to the frontal analysis, the elution analysis has the great advantage that all ions to be separated come out in separate fractions. A disadvantage is that in certain cases the peaks have a considerable width ("tailing"), which may render the separation difficult and make the determination of the area A inaccurate. The choice of elutriant has the greatest influence upon the shape of the peaks. The peaks representing the ions which are held most strongly by the resin show the most marked broadening of

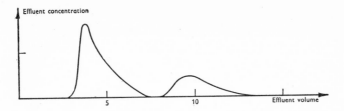

FIG. 17. Elution of different retained ions.

the trailing edge. In order to facilitate the separation it is in many analyses advisable to carry out a stepwise elution, i.e. first to elute one or several ions with one elutriant and then to complete the elution with a second elutriant which is more effective in displacing the ions still left in the column.

A limiting case of elution analysis is the displacement development proposed by Tiselius (38) and studied at length by Claesson (6). Here the elutriant contains an ion, "developer," with higher replacing ability than any of the ions to be separated. The components of the mixture are forced by the developer to move forward through the column in front of the developer without being mixed with it. The ions will displace one another, so that they are separated into bands in an order of increasing replacing ability, the one with the lowest replacing ability appearing first in the effluent. After a stationary state has been reached, the bands move forward at constant rate. The width of each band, measured as the volume it occupies in the effluent, is proportional to the amount of the substance in question. It may be pointed out that after a steady state has been reached (i.e. bands fully developed) increased column length gives no added improvement in separation.

The chief advantage of the displacement analysis is that "tailing" is avoided. On the other hand, the bands are in close contact, and consequently it may be difficult to cut the fractions properly in the effluent. This means a serious disadvantage as far as analytical separations are concerned, particularly when only small quantities are investigated. In carrier displacement chromatography proposed by Tiselius and Hagdahl (39), this difficulty is overcome by the addition of "carriers," i.e. substances of intermediate adsorption affinities, which form separate bands during the displacement and can be removed afterwards, e.g. by evaporation or extraction. No applications of this principle in ion exchange chromatography seem to have been published.

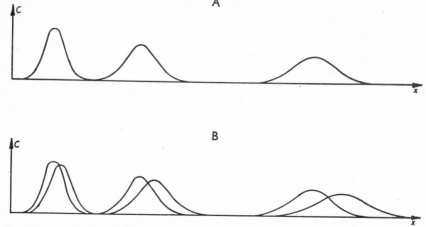

FIG. 18.   *A*. Elution isochrones for single species with linear isotherm and finite exchange reaction rate.

B. Elution isochrones for the separation of two species with linear isotherms.

The theoretical treatment of the elution is similar to the theory of the sorption step, i.e. may be performed by using continuous variables (Wilson's theory) or the plate theory (Martin and Synge). The former theory has been applied to ion exchange chromatography by several authors already cited. Data of actual interest from an analytical point of view have been presented in papers by Boyd (5), Sillén (33), and Vermeulen and Hiester (42).

Mayer and Tompkins (22), Boyd and Matheson (4, 5), Beukenkamp and Rieman (2), and others have demonstrated the applicability of the plate theory to ion exchange chromatography (linear isotherm). By determining the equilibrium distribution coefficients of any two solutes in the elutriant solution and their separate elution curves from a short column, it is possible to calculate how much elutriant must be forced through a column of any other size before the solutes appear in the eluate. This theory may also be applied for analyzing elution curves and for predicting the degree of separation of ions with overlapping elution curves. The theoretical elution curves have been shown to approach the form of the normal curve of error as the number of theoretical plates becomes large. The calculation may be further simplified by approximating the elution curves to triangles. Some theoretical elution curves are presented in Fig. 18 *A* and 18 *B*.

Of considerable interest from an analytical point of view are the following results which have been arrived at by the plate theory and also by an extended Wilson theory [linear isotherm and finite exchange reaction rate] (4, 5).

1. Peak moves down the bed at a constant velocity.
2. Height of peak diminishes inversely as the square root of the distance travelled.
3. Width of peak (at an ordinate value of $1/e$ of the maximum, where e is the base of the natural logarithm) increases directly as the square root of the distance travelled.

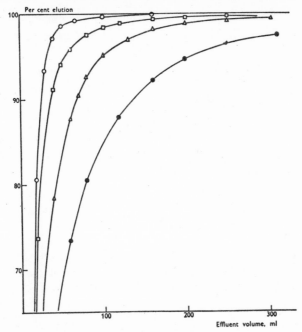

Fɪɢ. 19. Integral elution curves at varying particle sizes.
Elutriant: 5 N HCl.
Column: 12 × 95 mm; Wofatit KS [Fe^{3+}].
Flow rate: 4.0 ml sqcm^{-1} min^{-1}. [from (7)]
Particle size:

○ 0.1–0.2 mm   △ 0.4–0.6 mm
□ 0.2–0.4 mm   ● 0.6–1.0 mm.

In certain cases good agreement has been observed between theory and practical results, but it must be pointed out that in other cases (e.g. with non-linear equilibria) the deviations may be considerable (cf. Fig. 16). Furthermore it must be observed that the number of plates in any one column varies for the different components, although frequently the variations may be small.

6. ELUTION (REGENERATION) CURVES FROM CATION EXCHANGE COLUMNS

A. *Influence of the Particle Size*

The particle size has been shown to be of greatest importance for the shape of the elution curves and the efficiency of the separation in chromatographic elution (8, 19, 7, 43).

The effect of this factor is demonstrated by the experiments presented in Fig. 19, where the percentage elution is plotted against the effluent volume. The resin (Wofatit KS) was partially transformed into the Fe^{3+} form and afterwards regenerated by passing 5 N hydrochloric acid through the column at constant flow rate. The effluent was collected in small fractions which were analyzed.

The experiments show that the volume of acid necessary for the elution of the column increases greatly when the particle size of the ion exchanger is increased. Using a smaller particle size means a saving of elution acid as well as of time.

B. *Influence of the Concentration of the Acid*

The effect of the acid concentration has been studied by Djurfeldt and Samuelson (7) using cation exchange columns containing K^+, Cu^{2+}, Al^{3+}, and Fe^{3+}. It was observed that for the cations studied the elution can be performed with a minimum volume of the elutriant if a certain optimum concentration of the hydrochloric acid is chosen. This optimum concentration is about 3–4 N HCl and is approximately the same for all the ions examined. The optimum is most decided at a high flow rate. The most obvious effects were observed for Fe^{3+}. When too strong a solution of hydrochloric acid is used, it is practically impossible to elute Fe^{3+} quantitatively. Fig. 20 illustrates the effect of the acid concentration on the elution curves.

Increased acid concentration increases the elution rate because of a displacement of the ion exchange equilibrium. On the other hand, the resin shrinks at higher acid concentration, causing a diminished diffusion velocity of the ions in the network structure of the resin, and consequently a lowered rate of elution. The increasing viscosity of the more concentrated acid has an influence in the same direction. The interaction between these effects explains the occurrence of an optimum acid concentration for K^+, Cu^{2+}, and Al^{3+}.

As far as iron (III) is concerned, it has been shown (7) that also in batch experiments (equilibrium) a maximum displacement of iron is obtained at medium acid concentration, e.g. 5 N HCl. This explains why the optimum in the elution curves is extremely pronounced in this case.

The amount of acid which is necessary to obtain a complete elution is greatly dependent upon the nature of the cations and increases generally for increasing valence of the cation.

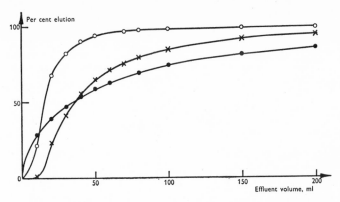

FIG. 20. Integral elution curves at varying acidities of the elutriant (hydrochloric acid).
Column: 12 × 95 mm; Wofatit KS [Fe^{3+}; 0.2–0.4 mm].
Flow rate: 4.0 ml sqcm^{-1} min^{-1}. [from (7)]

× C_{HCl} = 1.09 mol/l
○   2.17 mol/l
●   12.3 mol/l.

C. *Influence of the Flow Rate*

A study of the effect of flow rate was also made by Djurfeldt and Samuelson (7). Ion exchange columns containing Wofatit KS partially transformed into the Cu^{2+} and Fe^{3+} forms were eluted with 3.3 N HCl at different flow rates.

The experiments show that the integral elution curves (% elution against effluent volume) are sharpened considerably for decreased flow rates. If instead % elution is plotted against time the curves will, within wide limits, be almost independent of the flow rate. It is the "contact time" of the elution process that determines the efficiency, not the flow rate or the volume of acid used. The elution of the Cu^{2+} column is complete in less than 10 min, whereas the elution of the Fe^{3+}-charged filter takes about 30 min, independently of the flow rate (except for very low flow rates, of course). It is useless to try to hasten the elution by increasing the flow rate over a certain value. For example, it was shown that, if the flow rate of the elutriant is raised from 2 to 10 ml sqcm^{-1} min^{-1}, the only effect will be that the amount required for complete elution will increase from 70 to 350 ml. The efficiency of the elution will not be increased, nor will the result be achieved in a shorter time (except for a difference in the time required for displacing the water in the column at the beginning).

7. BREAK-THROUGH CURVES FROM ANION EXCHANGE COLUMNS

The experimental material concerning break-through curves from anion exchangers which has hitherto been published is rather meager. Investigations by Sussman, Nachod, and Wood (34) showed that the shapes of the curves are in principle the same as those of curves from cation exchange resins. Curves are reproduced for the uptake of chromate, vanadate, molybdate, ferrocyanide, and chloroplatinate by weakly basic resins in the chloride form. All curves are rather broad, which may be explained by the low reaction rate with this type of resin, especially as the particles were coarse. In the case of chromate solutions it was demonstrated that the break-through capacity of a sulfate-saturated resin is only about 50 % of that of the chloride resin.

The influence of the particle size has been studied by Regestad and Samuelson (26), using anion exchangers of strongly basic type. The results are in principle the same as those with cation exchange resins, an increased break-through capacity and slope of the curves being obtained when the particle size is diminished. An increased flow rate causes a lowered break-through capacity.

The column behavior of solutions containing two exchangeable anions is the same as in the case of cation exchange resins with two exchangeable cations. Early experiments by Myers, Eastes, and Urquhart (23) demonstrated a rather complete separation between sulfate and chloride, the sulfate being held more strongly by the resin.

8. ELUTION (REGENERATION) CURVES FROM ANION EXCHANGE COLUMNS

The influence of the particle size and elutriant concentration may be illustrated by means of some curves obtained in experiments with a resin of strongly basic type (26). A constant amount of thiosulfate was taken up by the resin in the chloride form and subsequently eluted by means of sodium chloride solutions at different concentrations.

As seen from Fig. 21 the elutriant volume required for a complete displacement of the thiosulfate decreased when the concentration of sodium chloride was increased from $0.5\ N$ to $3\ N$. It may be added that in separate experiments with $0.1\ N$ solution thiosulfate could not be detected in the first 120 ml of effluent.

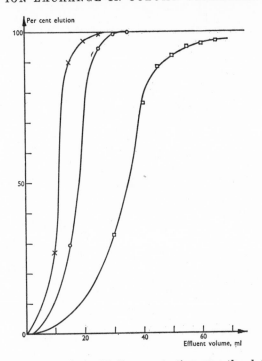

FIG. 21.   Influence of the elutriant NaCl concentration upon the elution curve.
Column: 9×150 mm; Amberlite IRA-400 [$S_2O_3^{2-}$; 0.12–0.385 mm].
Flow rate: 3 ml sqcm^{-1} min^{-1}.   [from (26)]

× 3 N NaCl
○ 1 N NaCl
☐ 0.5 N NaCl

The particle size has also a marked influence; the lower the particle size the more rapid is the elution. With resins of the particle size which is common in technical operation the elution is much more difficult than with the fraction used in these experiments.

Experiments with resins of weakly basic type show that the elution is much easier to perform with sodium hydroxide than with sodium chloride (30). This is explained by the fact that in alkaline solution the weakly basic groups become undissociated and therefore incapable of retaining anions. A comparison between these two elutriants for the displacement of thiosulfate from a resin (which also contains chloride) is presented in Fig. 22. The influence of the flow rate is also demonstrated by this figure. When the particle size is increased, the influence of the flow rate is more marked than is indicated by these experiments.

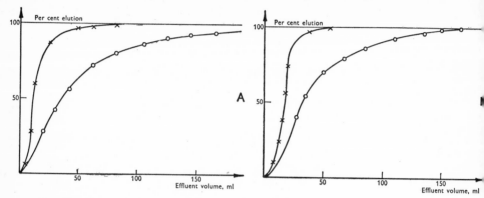

FIG. 22.   Integral elution curves for two different elutriants.
Column: 9.8×140 mm; Amberlite IR–4B [$S_2O_3^{2-}$; 0.12–0.30 mm].
Flow rate: A. 4.0 ml sqcm^{-1} min^{-1}.
          B. 1.3 ml sqcm^{-1} min^{-1}.   [from (30)]
○ 1 N NaCl
× 1 N NaOH.

BIBLIOGRAPHY

1. Beaton, R. H., and Furnas, C. C.: *Ind. Eng. Chem.*, **33**, 1501 (1941).
2. Beukenkamp, J., and Rieman III, W.: *Anal. Chem.*, **22**, 582 (1950).
3. Boyd, G. E., Myers, Jr., L. S., and Adamson, A. W.: *J. Am. Chem. Soc.*, **69**, 2849 (1947).
4. Boyd, G. E., and Matheson, L. A.: *Abstracts Am. Chem. Soc.* 113th Meeting (Chicago 1948).
5. Boyd, G. E.: Paper presented at the Gordon Research Conference 1950.
6. Claesson, S.: *Arkiv Kemi, Mineral. Geol.*, **23 A**, No. 1 (1946).
7. Djurfeldt, R., and Samuelson, O.: *Acta Chem. Scand.*, **4**, 165 (1950).
8. Du Domaine, J., Swain, R. L., and Hougen, O. A.: *Ind. Eng. Chem.*, **35**, 546 (1943).
9. Ekedahl, E., and Sillén, L.-G.: *Arkiv Kemi, Mineral. Geol.*, **25 A**, No. 4 (1947).
10. Glueckauf, E.: *Nature*, **156**, 205, 748 (1945).
11. Glueckauf, E.: *Proc. Roy. Soc. (London)*, [A] **186**, 35 (1946).
12. Glueckauf, E.: *Nature*, **160**, 301 (1947).
13. Glueckauf, E., and Coates, J. I.: *J. Chem. Soc.*, **1947**, 1308, 1315.
14. Glueckauf, E.: *J. Chem. Soc.*, **1947**, 1302, 1321.
15. Glueckauf, E.: *J. Chem. Soc.*, **1949**, 3280.
16. Glueckauf, E.: *Disc. Faraday Soc.*, **1949**, No. 7, 12.
17. Glueckauf, E., Baker, K. H., and Kitt, G. P.: *Disc. Faraday Soc.*, **1949**, No. 7, 199.
18. Glueckauf, E.: *Nature*, **166**, 775 (1950).
19. Ketelle, B. H., and Boyd, G. E.: *J. Am. Chem. Soc.*, **69**, 2800 (1947).
20. Kunin, R., and Barry, R. E.: *Ind. Eng. Chem.*, **41**, 1269 (1949).
21. Martin, A. J. P., and Synge, R. L. M.: *Biochem. J.*, **35**, 1358 (1941).
22. Mayer, S. W., and Tompkins, E. R.: *J. Am. Chem. Soc.*, **69**, 2866 (1947).

23. Myers, R. J., Eastes, J. W., and Urquhart, D.: *Ind. Eng. Chem.*, **33**, 1270 (1941).
24. Partridge, S. M.: *Disc. Faraday Soc.*, **1949**, No. 7, 296.
25. Prokhorov, F. G., and Yankovskiĭ, K. A.: *Zavodskaya Lab.*, **13**, 656 (1947).
26. Regestad, S. O., and Samuelson, O.: unpublished.
27. Samuelson, O.: *Svensk Kem. Tid.*, **53**, 422 (1941).
28. Samuelson, O.: *Tek. Tid.*, **76**, 561 (1946).
29. Samuelson, O.: *Svensk Kem. Tid.*, **58**, 247 (1946).
30. Samuelson, O.: unpublished.
31. Sillén, L.-G.: *Arkiv Kemi, Mineral. Geol.*, **22 A**, No. 15 (1946).
32. Sillén, L.-G., and Ekedahl, E.: *Arkiv Kemi, Mineral. Geol.*, **22 A**, No. 16 (1946).
33. Sillén, L.-G.: *Arkiv Kemi*, Nos. 34 and 35 (1950); *Nature*, **166**, 722 (1950).
34. Sussman, S., Nachod, F. C., and Wood, W.: *Ind. Eng. Chem.*, **37**, 618 (1945).
35. Thomas, H. C.: *J. Am. Chem. Soc.*, **66**, 1664 (1944).
36. Thomas, H. C.: *Ann. N. Y. Acad. Sci.*, **49**, 161 (1948).
37. Tiselius, A.: *Arkiv Kemi, Mineral. Geol.*, **14 B**, No. 22 (1940).
38. Tiselius, A.: *Arkiv Kemi, Mineral. Geol.*, **16 A**, No. 18 (1943).
39. Tiselius, A., and Hagdahl, L.: *Acta Chem. Scand.*, **4**, 394 (1950).
40. Tompkins, E. R.: *J. Chem. Education*, **26**, 32, 92 (1949).
41. Walter, J. E.: *J. Chem. Phys.*, **13**, 229, 332 (1945).
42. Vermeulen, T., and Hiester, N. K.: *Ind. Eng. Chem.*, **44**, 636 (1952).
43. Wickbold, R.: *Z. anal. Chem.*, **132**, 401 (1951).
44. Wicke, E.: *Kolloid-Z.*, **86**, 167, 295 (1939).
45. Wilson, J. N.: *J. Am. Chem. Soc.*, **62**, 1583 (1940).

CHAPTER VI

Technique of Ion Exchange Separations for Analytical Purposes

1. GENERAL CONSIDERATIONS

The aim of this chapter is to give general guidance to those readers desiring to apply published analytical methods and also to those who intend to investigate new fields of use. The problems which will be dealt with are the choice of ion exchangers and the technical performance of separations of exchangeable ions from ions which are not retained by the exchanger and from non-electrolytes. The technique of separations based on different exchange potentials of exchangeable ions, i.e. ion exchange chromatography, will be briefly discussed in Chapter VII.

Any generally valid rules for obtaining an accurate result in the shortest possible time cannot be given, one reason being that the properties of the ion exchange resins may differ considerably and that no standard grades suitable for analytical purposes are generally available as yet. In recent years the capacity and stability of the resins have been improved considerably. Certain preparations used in previously published investigations are no longer of actual interest. On the other hand, it is possible to obtain some general indications and, by comparison with, e.g., capacity data for various ion exchangers, to calculate such values as the height required for the column.

One significant advantage derived from ion exchange separations of the type discussed in this chapter is that the accuracy of analyses is not affected by working within a considerable latitude of safety in respect to ion exchanger, washing water, or regenerant. When an ion exchange method is introduced for routine analysis, a suitable margin of safety with respect to the variables concerned should be determined by direct experiments.

2. COLUMN OPERATION AND BATCH OPERATION

Column operation is by far the most important method of ion exchange separation. As already mentioned, a quantitative uptake can be achieved in batch operation only in special cases. Examples are the uptake by cation exchangers in the free-acid form of cations from solutions containing free alkali or carbonate but free from anions which are stable in acid solution. Similarly a complete uptake of free acids can be achieved by means of anion exchangers in the free-base (or carbonate) form.

In a limited number of column operations complications occur, and in those cases it is advisable first to shake the solution with the resin. In a second step the solution and the resin are transferred to a column containing a small amount of resin to complete the reaction. This combined operation is recommended in analyses where an evolution of gas occurs which would cause channeling and eventually stoppage in the resin bed. Important examples are solutions containing carbonate, sulfite, and sulfide when the hydrogen cycle is used (17). Nor is it advisable to employ anion exchangers containing these ions in a column process when acid solutions are investigated.

Combined operation is also expedient when operating systems contain solid substances (Chapter VIII: 1 E and X: 1 B) or when there is risk of precipitation (37).

When strongly alkaline solutions are used in the hydrogen cycle, it may in certain cases be advisable to resort to combined operation. This may be desirable when the resin is attacked by the alkaline solution. When, instead, an excess of the hydrogen-saturated resin is introduced into the solution, it becomes acid so quickly that no considerable attack will occur. However, the recent availability of extremely alkali-resistant resins has made it possible to use common column operation also with alkaline solutions.

3. SEPARATIONS BY MEANS OF CATION EXCHANGERS

A. *The Choice of Resin*

a. SULFONIC ACID TYPE

The choice of cation exchanger is dependent upon the field of application. Most important are resins of the sulfonic acid type, which may be used for cation exchange in acid, neutral, or alkaline solution. Simple and complex inorganic as well as organic cations may be taken up quantitatively. Positively charged colloids and high-molecular-weight cations are unadsorbed or adsorbed to only a slight extent. The resins have also been widely used for the uptake of ampholytic substances, e.g. amino acids.

The durability of the ion exchanger is not of prime importance for analytical purposes. A cation exchanger may under certain conditions last a year or even longer without becoming damaged. In some cases, on the other hand, where attacking solutions are used, the exchanger may have to be discarded after a short period of service. If any uncertainty exists as to the reliability of an ion exchanger, a check of the exchange capacity is helpful.

The absence of interfering reactions affecting the analytical results is more important than the durability of the exchanger. Interfering reactions can be caused by interaction between certain solutions and the solid exchangers, either directly or by splitting soluble compounds from the exchanger.

Cation exchangers of the phenol sulfonic acid type, which at present are commercially available, are usually of satisfactory chemical stability, provided they are used in neutral or acid solutions, free from strong oxidizing agents. Caution in the choice of an exchanger is further advisable when alkaline solutions are used, since their dissolving action on the exchanger may affect the analytical results. The attack on the ion exchanger increases considerably at higher temperatures, 80–100° C, and in these regions only certain types of exchangers can be utilized.

The sulfonated hydrocarbon resins, e.g. sulfonated styrene-divinylbenzene resins, are more stable than the sulfonated phenol-formaldehyde resins and are therefore preferable under severe conditions. A comparison between the chemical stability of a phenolic resin and a resin of the sulfonated hydrocarbon type has been published by Bauman, Skidmore, and Osman (5). Laboratory tests showed that the elimination of the phenolic group from the resin structure enhanced the chemical stability and permitted the use of the exchanger even in alkaline media and in water solutions up to 100° C. The stability in the presence of such oxidizing agents as dissolved oxygen and chlorine was also higher for the sulfonated hydrocarbon resin. Solutions of bromate and iodate were reduced on passing through a column of a sulfonated coal type of exchanger (14) or of a sulfonated phenolic resin (40), whereas no reduction was observed when a resin of the sulfonated hydrocarbon type was used (43).

A vigorous attack on cation exchangers containing phenol sulfonic acid groups is effected by treatment with strong nitric acid, when the decomposition of the exchanger is accompanied by evolution of gas. If nitric acid is desirable for regenerating an exchanger containing, e.g., silver ions, the concentration of nitric acid should be kept low, about 1 N. Dilute aqueous solutions of permanganate, chromate, and molybdate (30) attack ion exchangers.

The ion exchangers are almost insoluble in various organic solvents, e.g. ethyl alcohol, mixtures of ethyl alcohol and water, butanol, ethyl acetate, xylene, toluene, and benzene.

The requirements for stability are higher for some uses than for others. When resins in the hydrogen form are utilized for conversion of salts into corresponding acids and the concentration of the solution is afterwards determined by alkali titration, it is very important that the exchanger does not release any acidic substances. If the column has been left for some time, for instance over night, this factor may have an influence. However, with most commercial exchangers no traceable amounts of acid are obtained if the column is washed with water shortly before the salt solution is percolated through it. Certain statements in the literature on acid release from the resin may be explained by the presence of small amounts of impurities in the distilled water.

Cation exchangers manufactured by sulfonating coal have been tried for analytical purposes (14), but according to the author's experience this type of exchanger has great disadvantages compared to the ion exchange resins.

The first commercially available cation exchange resins were produced at the Wolfen plant (Germany) belonging to I. G. Farbenindustrie. The trade name of these resins is Wofatit (A, K, KS, P). These products have been utilized successfully for analytical purposes. Later the manufacture of similar products was taken up in several other countries. Certain resins which are manufactured in the United States by Rohm and Haas under the trade name Amberlite (IR-1, IR-100, etc.) have also found wide application in the analytical field. These products are phenolic resins containing sulfonic acid groups. Besides sulfonic groups these resins contain weakly acid groups, chiefly phenolic. Therefore the exchange capacity increases for increasing pH of the solution. A reduction of mercuric salts to mercuro salts and silver ions to metallic silver has also been observed with this type of resin (8).

The resins of the sulfonated hydrocarbon type have recently become commercially available. This type of exchanger has the same exchange capacity in acid and in alkaline media. The products have high capacity, and the chemical stability is, as already mentioned, superior to that of the phenolic types, especially at high temperature and high pH. Products of this type, which have found application in analytical chemistry, are Dowex 50, which is produced by the Dow Chemical Company, and Amberlite IR-120 (Rohm and Haas). These resins are spherical beads. The Dowex resins are available also with different particle size. Better volume capacity is observed in beds of spherical than of irregular particles.

The Dow Chemical Company has made available sulfonic acid resins with different degrees of cross-linking. These resins may be used to effect separations of ions of different sizes, as a lesser number of cross-linkages permits exchange with larger ions (Chapter II: 1).

Most strongly cross-linked sulfonic acid resins are dark in color (red or black), which in certain cases is a disadvantage, since it is difficult to study visually the course of adsorption and desorption. However, cross-linked polystyrene sulfonic acids are now available in light yellow or amber colors so that some degree of visual chromatography is now possible.

Before the sorption step the resin is usually saturated with monovalent ions, as the presence of divalent ions will decrease the break-through capacity considerably. In most applications the ion exchanger is used in the hydrogen form. In the presence of ions which are easily hydrolyzed and precipitated, e.g. ferric and aluminum salts, it is necessary to use this form of the resin to eliminate the risk of precipitation during the washing step. When the hydrogen cycle is operated, the regeneration can be made quantitatively by means of hydrochloric acid, which may be obtained in high purity at a low price.

In certain cases when hydrogen ions interfere in the analysis of the effluent, it is possible to substitute other, preferably monovalent, ions. In determining chloride argentometrically by Mohr's method in a solution containing salts of heavy metals, these may be exchanged for, e.g., sodium ions and the chloride determined in the sodium chloride solution obtained. In such analyses it is well to use an ion exchanger in the hydrogen form and later neutralize the effluent with alkali.

There are, however, important analyses which cannot be carried out with a hydrogen-saturated ion exchanger: those in which the acids corresponding to the anions are almost insoluble or unstable. Certain anions which have oxidizing properties react with the ion exchanger in an acid medium but not in a neutral or alkaline medium. In such cases the ammonium form may be used. Examples of this type are the separations of Na^+ and K^+ from vanadate (32), chromate, molybdate, tungstate, and phosphomolybdate (30). In separations of weakly basic substances, resins in the ammonium form may also be used (cf. Chapter XX: 3 A).

One essential condition for a cation exchanger, when it is to be used for analytical purposes, is that it be free from anion exchanging groups, lest anion exchange occur simultaneously. The technical preparations investigated by the author have, in general, satisfied this condition. There exists, however, in many cation exchangers, an adsorption tendency for weak acids. This adsorption tendency, appearing in various degrees in several materials, means that larger quantities of water are required in order to wash out these weak acids (cf. Chapter II: 2 B).

b. CARBOXYLIC ACID TYPE

Cation exchangers of the carboxylic acid type have been used as tools for special analytical purposes. Of greatest interest is the application of this type of resin for the separation of basic amino acids and the separation of strong organic bases from weak ones. The separation may be facilitated by buffering the filters at different pH's by pretreatment with different buffer solutions.

This type of resin may also be used for the uptake of organic bases of considerable molecular weight, e.g. streptomycin (cf. Chapter XXIII). Another important feature of this type of exchanger is the great affinity for hydrogen ions. Only a small amount of dilute hydrochloric acid is required to effect complete removal of bases from the resin.

As examples of ion exchange resins of the carboxylic acid type Wofatit C (I. G. Farbenindustrie) and Amberlite IRC-50 (Rohm and Haas) may be mentioned. These ion exchangers possess good chemical stability in acid, neutral, and alkaline aqueous solutions and are stable also in the presence of aliphatic and aromatic solvents (22). When first used these exchangers may shed considerable amounts of polyelectrolytes. It is recommended the resin be conditioned, e.g. by treatment with 2 N NaOH followed by water, 2 N HCl, and finally washing with distilled water. The resins are white or light yellow.

B. *Grinding and Purification*

Ion exchange resins are manufactured chiefly for the purposes of water softening and deionization and are usually delivered in a moist condition. Most of the exchangers are not available in the desired particle size and purity. The particle size may vary within wide limits.

The exchangers may be air-dried without altering their properties. Oven drying should be avoided, since most exchangers may be partly decomposed as a result. For most purposes, however, it is not necessary to dry the resin, as grinding, screening, and purification can also be carried out in the moist or air-dry condition.

As shown in Chapter V, the particle size of the resin has a very great influence upon the sorption step as well as upon the regeneration. It is of great importance that finely divided exchangers be used. The break-through capacity of a column is greatly increased as the particle size is diminished. Furthermore coarse particles should be avoided because of their detrimental effect, even in small quantities, on the regeneration of the column.

Very fine particles should also be removed as they diminish the flow rate too much. When cation exchangers are used for analytical purposes, a particle size of 0.2–0.4-mm diameter (40/70 mesh US series) is usually suitable. For certain purposes, where the time of operation does not matter, it may be convenient to reduce the particle size; in other cases, where a high filtering velocity is desirable, the particle size may be increased.

When columns are operated at elevated temperature, the particle size may be further diminished without decreasing the flow rate too much (20). For work on a microscale the particles should ordinarily not be greater than 0.3 mm (38). In ion exchange chromatography extremely low particle size is recommended.

Commercial exchange resins are hard and brittle. Crushing or grinding the particles always causes a considerable loss of material. For most purposes only small quantities of resin are needed, and crushing may be done in a mortar. It is advisable first to screen the resin to take out the particles which from the beginning have the desired mesh size. Then the resin is crushed in wet or air-dry condition for a short period and afterwards screened again. The fraction which is still too large is crushed for another period, etc.

The resin which has passed through the screen corresponding to the upper limit (e.g. 0.4-mm mesh size) is then freed from fines by screening or by repeatedly washing the exchanger with water, allowing the larger particles to settle, and decanting off the fines. Even when the fines are removed by screening, it is advisable to wash with water and decant several times.

When large quantities of resin are needed, grinding in a ball mill is recommended. Details are given in a paper by Tompkins (46).

Before utilization for analytical purposes the resin is soaked in strong (e.g. 5 N) hydrochloric acid several times in order to remove impurities such as rust flakes. The treatment may be performed at room temperature or more rapidly on a steam bath until no further dissolution of iron occurs.

In recent years analytical grade ion exchange resins have been placed on the market. Those resins, which have been tested by the author, have too large particles for ordinary purposes. If the resins do not have the desired particle size, there is no need for this special grade, as grinding and screening are the most laborious procedures in the preparation of a suitable product from industrial cation exchangers. It is probable that in the near future resins will be available in a form which is suitable in all respects.

C. *Apparatus in Column Operation*

The apparatus and technique for column operation are very simple. The column may be made from any kind of glass tube. A plug of glass wool or a sintered glass disc at the bottom supports the resin bed but allows solution to pass through the column. The resin must be placed in the tube wet, as the dry material swells considerably when water is taken up. It is very important that air never enter the exchanger bed, since this would cause channeling, which would decrease the efficiency considerably. The resin should preferably be slurried in a beaker and then washed into the column, allowing the particles to settle to form the bed. The bed should be kept covered with water, so that air is prevented from entering it. Air bubbles in the glass wool plug (or glass filter) should also be avoided. If air has entered the bed, the easiest way is to empty the column and fill it again.

Usually the precaution is taken of keeping the outlet from the column above the top of the resin bed. The washing step is facilitated if the outlet tube consists of a capillary (1–2-mm diameter) or in any case is much narrower than the column. In wide outlet tubes it may be difficult to displace the solution by water. A typical column of this type is shown in Fig. 23. The apparatus is a standard type suitable for most purposes.

The solution to be analyzed is introduced into the funnel. The stopcock is opened, so as to obtain a proper flow rate. In analyses for which it is desirable to have as small a volume as possible, the first part of the filtrate, which contains only water displaced from the resin bed, may be discarded. After the liquid surface has passed the funnel, the residual solution on the walls of the funnel is rinsed with water. Afterwards a proper amount of water is supplied into the funnel, so that the solution is displaced continuously from the resin bed.

In the regeneration step the solution is also passed downwards through the filter.

If the ion exchange method is required only now and then and apparatus is not available, a burette may be used with a rubber or plastic tube and pinch clamp serving as outlet tube.

Other types and arrangements of the apparatus have been designed for

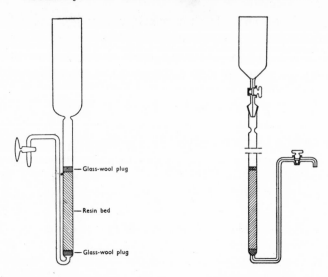

FIG. 23. Apparatus of
standard type. [from (11)]

FIG. 24. Apparatus used
particularly for routine
analyses.   [from (35)]

special purposes. In addition to the column shown in Fig. 23 a similar type
was developed for routine analyses (Fig. 24). This type is useful when only
solutions of nearly constant volumes are analyzed. The contraction of the
column shown in the figure at its upper end is not essential but simplifies
work on series analyses.

The free volume in the tube above the resin bed should be slightly larger
than the volume of the solution to be analyzed. If, for instance, the latter
volume is 25 ml and the solution is transferred into the column with pipette,
the free volume should be about 30 ml. After addition of the solution,
water is introduced on top of the tube carefully so that excessive mixing
does not occur. Afterwards the funnel is put in its place and filled with
water, and the stopcock is opened.

Another construction of the ion exchange column is shown in Fig. 25 (41).
The upper glass wool plug must be well packed, so that by means of the
capillary forces of the liquid the air is prevented from entering the filter.
The resistance of the plug to the streaming liquid is not great compared
to the resistance of the rest of the column. However, this construction is
possible only for rather short columns. The exit opening must not be more
than about 15 cm below the upper glass wool plug. This type of column
is very useful in microanalytical work.

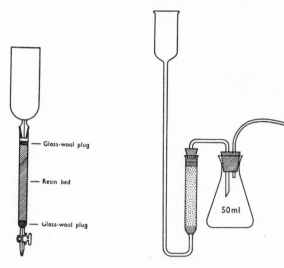

FIG. 25.   Apparatus for   FIG. 26.   Apparatus for microanalytical
microanalytical work.   work using upflow operation.
        [from (41)]   [from (38)]

In the apparatus hitherto discussed, downflow operation has been used. Especially for the regeneration step, this procedure is less desirable than upflow operation. For regeneration, solutions are used which have a decidedly greater specific weight than the water which is in the bed. With downflow operation, therefore, convection currents occur, which means that a larger volume of solution is required than with upflow operation. In certain work with solutions of a high specific weight, upflow operation is advantageous even in the sorption step. Fig. 26 shows an apparatus for microscale work using upflow operation (38). Filling is carried out with a funnel which is connected through a capillary tube to the bottom of the column. To remove the air pocket formed in the capillary one blows through the rubber tube so that the liquid rises through the capillary.

To avoid transporting the ions through the whole column in the elution step the directions of flow at sorption and elution may be reversed. A semimicrocolumn designed for downflow operation in the sorption step but upflow regeneration has been described by Applezweig (1). The regeneration may be facilitated by the countercurrent principle, as also observed by Wickbold (50) and Nydahl (25). Wickbold suggested a tip column, which was shown to facilitate the regeneration considerably under the conditions used.

FIG. 27.   Apparatus of standard type with applied pressure.   [from (42)]

In those cases where a large excess of resin is needed in the sorption step and, simultaneously, it is desirable to use the minimum amount of regenerant, the tip column may be of great value (see Chapter XI: 2). However, when working with proper particle size of the resin and under suitable conditions in other respects, the advantages are less pronounced (11); and, in the experience of the present author, too complicated column constructions are not generally worth while.

Columns have also been designed for operation at elevated temperatures. In this case jacketed columns can be used, so that the temperature in the columns may be controlled either by the passage of steam or the circulation of liquid from a thermostat. Columns of this type have proved most useful in ion exchange chromatography (20).

When a resin of very small particle size is utilized, it may be necessary to increase the flow rate by applying pressure. An example is showed in Fig. 27. Such columns may also be convenient when extremely high columns are required or when the solution has a high viscosity.

A special apparatus which involves the re-use of the hydrochloric acid used as regenerant may be of value when it is desired to keep the volume of regenerant at a minimum (14). The effluent obtained in the regeneration step is distilled, and the distillate is passed continuously through the column. However, when proper conditions are chosen (e.g. resin, particle size, acid concentration, and flow rate), the exchange cycle can in most cases be performed much more simply in ordinary columns.

a. The Shape of the Resin Bed

For a given solution the volume of the resin bed may be lower if the column is narrower. However, within certain limits the shape of the column has only a comparatively small influence upon the break-through capacity (Chapter V: 4 B). Long and narrow resin beds exhibit extremely low filtration rates. In practice a compromise is made with the result that the length of the column is usually 10–20 times the diameter, but these proportions are by no means fixed. If, for instance, it is necessary to operate quickly, the proportion may be lowered.

For most analytical purposes columns varying in diameter from 8 to 15 mm are employed. For microchemical work the diameter may be decreased. In this case it is suitable to decrease the particle size also. Samuelson used microcolumns with a diameter of 6 mm. The particle size was less than 0.3 mm (38). Columns used by Riches (29) had a diameter of only 2.5 mm. As pointed out by Boyd, Myers, and Adamson (7), extremely narrow columns may cause channeling and wall effects.

D. *The Sorption Step*

a. Regulation of the Filtration Rate

The time required to carry out filtration through an ion exchange bed depends on the cross-section area of the bed and the rate of filtration per unit surface area. The latter is determined not only by the length of the resin bed and the height of the liquid column (with possible external pressure or vacuum) but also primarily by the particle size and form and also the viscosity of the solution. The particle size has the greatest effect; the form of the particles is also significant, but to a lesser extent. Spherical grains produce greater resistance to filtering than irregular grains. This is due to the fact that the void space is lower with spherical grains, which may be considered an advantage from other viewpoints. A considerable decrease in the viscosity of aqueous solutions is obtained, as is known, with increased temperature. Working at elevated temperature may therefore be an advantage, especially when the particle size is low.

If a fast rate of filtration is desired, coarse particles must be chosen, but it must then be remembered that the break-through capacity of the filter is considerably lowered and therefore a large excess is required to obtain quantitative uptake in the sorption step. Another disadvantage is that regeneration becomes more difficult (Chapter V).

The rate of filtration may be regulated, if desired, either by altering the variables just mentioned or by partly closing the stopcock in the outlet tube. Since a decrease in the particle size is advantageous, as discussed above, it is better to use smaller resin particles than to decrease the rate of filtration by throttling the outlet.

It must be borne in mind, however, that an increase in the rate of filtration, even with a constant particle size, means that a larger filter bed is required, since, as mentioned in Chapter V: 4 C, the break-through capacity decreases with increasing rate of filtration. The greater the rate of filtration, the smaller the amount of the total active groups in the ion exchanger which are utilized.

Where there is a risk of the decomposition of the solution during its passage through the ion exchanger, an exceptionally high rate of filtration may be expedient. In routine analysis of factory products also it is often desirable to obtain results as quickly as possible, and therefore a high rate of filtration is used. Also, when a very dilute solution is to be analyzed, much time may be saved by working at high flow rate.

Samuelson (35) carried out sulfate determinations in zinc sulfate solutions in which the rate of filtration was varied. At varying rates, 25 ml of the sample solution and 75 ml of washing water were passed through a resin bed of cation exchanger in the hydrogen form. The sulfuric acid formed was determined by titration with alkali. The height of the filter was 160 mm and the diameter 12 mm. The total exchanging capacity was 12 milliequivalents, which is about 7 times greater than the amount of cations in the sample solution. The results, given in Table 4, show that quantitative exchange and washing could be carried out in 4 min. This corresponds to a rate of filtration of 22 ml sqcm^{-1} min^{-1}.

TABLE 4

Analyses of zinc sulfate solutions at varying filtration rates.

Time for Filtration and Washing	NaOH Consumption, meq	
min	Calculated	Found
45	1.626	1.627
20	1.626	1.626
10	1.626	1.628
5	1.626	1.627
4	1.626	1.626

Normally a lower rate of filtration is used, e.g. with cation exchange columns 3–10 ml sqcm^{-1} min^{-1} or, in certain cases, even lower. Under these circumstances the amount of ion exchanger and the volume of washing water may, naturally, be decreased.

Sometimes the rate of filtration of a filter decreases after it has been in use for some time. The ion exchanger is then taken out, agitated in water, and decanted so that the finest particles are removed.

With certain types of ion exchanger considerable changes in swelling may occur (cf. Chapter II:1) and the filter becomes clogged. In such cases it is advisable to work with short, wide filters and to introduce the ion exchanger into the tube in the form which shows the greatest swelling.

b. Concentration of Solution to be Analyzed

Ion exchange is principally applied to solutions of relatively low ion concentration. This rule is applicable not only in analytical chemistry but also for preparative and technical purposes. The chief reason is that the exchange capacity per unit volume is limited.

In certain cases it is not necessary to calculate the dimensions of the resin bed from the total amount of ions in the solution. From a solution containing, e.g., Ca^{2+} and Na^+, Ca^{2+} can be quantitatively taken up, in spite of the fact that the exchanging capacity of the filter bed is considerably lower than the total quantity of cations in the solution. This is shown in Fig. 28 (cf. Chapter V:2).

As discussed in Chapter III:2 B, an increased uptake of divalent ions in batch operation takes place by dilution of the sample solution. This also occurs in column operation. The more dilute the solution is, the better the separation. As an example, Fig. 28 shows the result of a series of experiments with sample solutions containing 50 milliequivalents of sodium chloride and 1.5 of calcium chloride. The total exchange capacity of the filter was 12 milliequivalents, i.e. considerably lower than the amount of sodium chloride. Nevertheless a quantitative retention of the calcium ions is obtained if the solution is extremely dilute.

With extremely low concentrations difficulties may occur in certain cases. Samuelson (37) found that, when dilute solutions of ferric salts (nitrate and perchlorate) were percolated through a layer of sulfonic acid resin in the hydrogen form, only part of the iron content was retained by the resin. In fresh solutions quantitative uptake was observed at a lower concentration than in aged solutions. The explanation is that in dilute solution the ferric ions are hydrolyzed irreversibly (formation of colloidal basic salts). Some results from similar experiments by Djurfeldt, Hansen, and Samuelson (10) with ferric chloride solutions are reproduced in

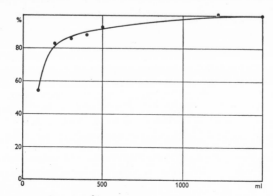

FIG. 28.   Per cent uptake of Ca^{2+} ions from a solution containing an excess of Na^+ ions as function of the volume of the solution.
Influent: 50 meq NaCl and 1.5 meq $CaCl_2$.
Column: 12 × 100 mm; Wofatit K [H^+; 0.1–0.3 mm].   [from (38)]

Table 5. In experiments with solutions containing aluminum chloride and beryllium sulfate performed under the same conditions, the uptake was quantitative in the dilute solutions even after aging.

TABLE 5

Uptake of ferric ions from dilute solutions of different age.

Age of Solution	Concentration, meq per liter	Uptake %
Freshly prepared	100	100.0
Freshly prepared	2	100.0
Freshly prepared	1	93.9
Freshly prepared	0.5	72.6
2 days	100	100.0
2 days	2	71.6
2 days	1	33.6
2 days	0.5	21.1
18 days	100	100.0
18 days	2	37.9
18 days	1	20.4
18 days	0.5	11.8

In extremely dilute solutions or at normal concentration, where risks of complications due to hydrolysis of the solution prevail, the difficulties may, in most cases, be avoided by the addition of a proper amount of acid to the solution to be analyzed. For example, a solution containing ferric ions and for instance phosphate or sulfate must be acid in order to be analyzed

(35, 37, 25). It may also be mentioned that in dilute solutions of ferric salts the uptake is to a large extent dependent upon flow rate. If at normal flow rate a certain leakage is obtained, the uptake may be quantitative when the flow rate is lowered considerably (38).

Of utmost interest is the application of the ion exchange method to concentrate dilute solutions, e.g. biological and technical solutions containing trace elements or radioelements. In most cases the possibility of obtaining a quantitative uptake seems to exist even at extremely low concentrations, e.g. with $10^{-5}-10^{-6}$ M solutions. No general statements can be made as to a lower concentration limit which should not be passed, as different ions behave differently and, furthermore, the limit for a certain ion is dependent upon the concentration of other ions present in the solution, e.g. hydrogen ions.

At extremely low concentrations ordinary chemical and physicochemical means are inadequate to determine accurately the amount of ions leaching through the column, but this determination can easily be made if radioactive tracers are available.

An investigation of the uptake of tracer amounts of barium (Ba[140]) and lanthanum (La[140]) from solutions containing varying amounts of inactive barium chloride was published by Ayres (4). It was shown that the percentile leakage increased as the influent concentration decreased. For a solution 0.00041 M in Ba^{2+} and 5×10^{-13} M in La^{3+} the leakage was 7.5 $\times$ $\times 10^{-4}\%$ Ba[140] and 0.03% La[140], whereas for a solution with 10 times lower concentration with respect to Ba the corresponding figures were 3.3×10^{-3} and 0.14.

For most analytical purposes the concentration of the solution has been about 0.05–0.1 N. If a solution of higher concentration is at hand, it is usually advisable to dilute it with water. In exceptional cases it may be inconvenient to analyze the filtrate from the exchange column if the concentration of the solution is lowered by dilution. Under such circumstances it may be practical to use solutions of higher concentration, e.g. 0.5 N.

c. ACIDITY OF SOLUTION TO BE ANALYZED

Many solutions to be analyzed contain hydrogen ions besides the ions to be removed by the exchanger. As an example may be mentioned phosphate analysis, where a low pH is necessary in order to prevent precipitation. As discussed in Chapter V:4 E, the hydrogen ions decrease the break-through capacity for the other cations. Therefore, the higher the acidity, the greater the filter capacity needed for the quantitative retention of a certain amount of cations. The influence of the hydrogen-ion concentration is dependent upon the composition of the solution. The affinity of the cations for the exchanger is of great importance, and the higher the affinity the greater is the amount of cations which at a certain acidity may be taken up by a column without any leakage.

For every type of routine analysis it is advisable to find out the amount of ion exchanger necessary to obtain quantitative conversion at the acidities concerned. The data given in Chapter V:4 E may provide some guidance. From these data the following very crude rule can be formulated: The separation will be quantitative if the amount of metal cations and hydrogen ions together does not exceed the break-through capacity of the filter for a pure salt solution. This rule may be of interest for the analyst not familiar with the ion exchange technique. It may fail (Li$^+$), but for the most part it leads to overdimensioned filters [cf. (24, 26, 49)].

As the dimensions of the resin bed have to be increased for increased acidity, it is of course desirable not to add too large amounts of acid when preparing the solution for analysis. Higher acidity than 0.05 N is not recommended when monovalent and divalent ions are to be taken up. When only trivalent ions are present, the acidity may be increased to 0.1 N without affecting the capacity too much. If a sample is to be dissolved in, e.g., hydrochloric acid and afterwards passed through an ion exchange column, it is advisable to remove as much of the acid as possible by evaporation before the sorption step. There is no reason to neutralize the free acid by means of alkali or ammonia before the sorption step, as the ions introduced into the solution have in general the same effect as the hydrogen ions.

As mentioned above, the amount of ion exchanger necessary for complete removal of polyvalent cations in the presence of monovalent ions is lowered on diluting the solution with water. Therefore, in the case of acid solutions from which only polyvalent cations are to be retained, the uptake may be facilitated considerably by diluting the solution with water.

It may be pointed out, however, that in solutions containing certain complexing agents, such as citrate, the uptake of cations may be facilitated on addition of acid. This is explained by the decomposition of the complex when the pH of the solution is lowered (44) [see also Chapter VII:2 A].

Even with cation exchangers containing weak acid groups multivalent ions are taken up more easily than monovalent. Here hydrogen ions hold a unique position, and these ions have the greatest affinity for ion exchangers of this type. A decrease in the pH value of the solution means a considerable decrease in the uptake of various cations, and the addition of even a small amount of acid means that uptake may cease entirely (cf. Chapter III: 3).

d. TEMPERATURE

In the utilization of an ion exchanger for analytical purposes the ion exchange cycle is in most cases performed at room temperature. Ion exchangers of the sulfonated hydrocarbon type, e.g. Dowex 50, which have become available, may, however, be operated at elevated temperatures without any appreciable decomposition. At higher temperature the diffusion velocity is more rapid than at room temperature, and therefore all steps — the sorption and the washing as well as the regeneration — may be performed more easily and more rapidly. When an elevated temperature is employed, the resistance to flow is lowered. Consequently it is possible to decrease the particle size, which in some cases is a great advantage (cf. Chapter VII: 2 B).

However, as the operations in most analyses can be performed easily at room temperature, it is often questionable whether it is worth while to operate the column at elevated temperature. For solutions which tend to hydrolyze irreversibly, e.g. solutions containing ferric iron, increase of temperature is not recommended.

When solutions are investigated which are easily decomposed at room temperature the column may in certain cases be operated at lowered temperature without any detectable decomposition. An example studied by Samuelson is the exchange of sodium ions for hydrogen ions in polymetaphosphate solutions (36).

E. *The Washing Step*

After the sorption step rinsing of the cation exchange column is performed not only in order to displace the solution which is left in the column but also to remove acids and non-electrolytes which might be reversibly adsorbed in the column. A prerequisite for the utilization of the ion exchange method for separating cations from anions is that the anions, if adsorbed, can be removed without desorption of cations.

Rinsing is usually performed with distilled water. The possibility that retained cations are displaced during the washing step has been discussed by Samuelson (32). In principle such a displacement will occur (Donnan hydrolysis), but as far as sulfonic acid resins are concerned this factor is of less importance. Only in systems where a considerable hydrolysis will occur, e.g. when cations have been taken up from alkaline solution by a weakly acid resin, will a marked displacement occur during the washing step. Losses may be prevented by increasing the column length so that the ions displaced from the upper parts of the column are resorbed in the lower parts.

The flow rate may conveniently be the same as in the sorption step. Little time is saved by working at extremely high speed. The time required for complete displacement of the anions is largely dependent upon their diffusion velocities in the resin phase.

In some analyses other solutions are recommended for washing. In phosphate analysis Samuelson (35) found that because of hydrolysis a slight precipitation of iron phosphate and aluminum phosphate occurred in the column when washing was carried out with pure water. This source of error was eliminated by rinsing with dilute hydrochloric acid (0.015 N) instead of water. No losses of the cations resulted at this extremely low concentration.

Certain organic compounds may be strongly adsorbed on the resin; in such cases rinsing with other solutions than water, e.g. alcohol, may be used to complete desorption.

As discussed in Chapter II:2 B, certain acids may be adsorbed on cation exchange resins. The acid adsorption means that the washing step must be performed more slowly and with greater amounts of water than in investigations where no adsorption occurs. However, even if strongly adsorbable acids, such as phosphoric acid or acetic acid, are present, they may be obtained quantitatively in the effluent after rinsing with a somewhat greater amount of water than is usual (34). An increased temperature may also be useful in such systems. The failure of certain authors to obtain quantitative washing seems to be due to excessive speed of washing; a further complication was the over-large particle size of the ion exchanger. Small resin particles and a low concentration in the solution to be analyzed should be used in order to avoid errors through adsorption. In certain troublesome cases it is suitable to wash with a water-miscible solvent, e.g. ethyl alcohol (47).

Control of the completeness of washing does not usually cause any trouble and should not be neglected when using the ion exchange method. In series analysis, e.g. routine production control, such a check need not be carried out every time if a safety margin is allowed which is determined beforehand in each case.

When only the effluent from the ion exchanger is to undergo analysis, it would seem simpler to ignore washing and instead, as soon as the water originally in the resin bed has been replaced by the sample solution, to take out a certain volume of the effluent for analysis. This procedure may be used in many cases without any significant errors being obtained. The author does not recommend this procedure for general use, however, since in many analyses interference may occur because of adsorption. Even the water adsorption (swelling) can cause certain errors, since its magnitude depends on the ions in the ion exchanger and is therefore changed in the sorption step (32). If it is desired to use this procedure in series analysis, conditions should be adjusted so that these sources of error are eliminated as far as possible.

F. *The Elution (Regeneration) Step*

As already mentioned, H^+-charged cation exchangers are generally employed and the regeneration is carried out with an acid. Hydrochloric acid is usually chosen as a regenerant, because it has several advantages: it is a strong acid, it is cheap (even in very pure qualities), it is easy to evaporate, and it does not oxidize the ion exchanger. When the cation solution is to be subjected to continual analysis, it is often advantageous for it to contain chloride ions. Ordinarily other regenerants are used only if the system contains ions giving insoluble chlorides.

A systematic work on the regeneration of cation exchange columns for analytical purposes has been published by Djurfeldt and Samuelson (11). Some of the regeneration curves are reproduced in Chapter V:6.

It was shown that the volume of acid and the time for the regeneration of the column increase greatly when the particle size is increased. The concentration of the regenerant acid is also of utmost importance. Moderately concentrated acid has been found to give a maximum speed of regeneration. When concentrated acid is used the regeneration is slower. In certain cases it is practically impossible to obtain quantitative regeneration if the concentration is too high. This is a fact which, if not observed, may cause considerable error and discredit the ion exchange method. Therefore a concentration of hydrochloric acid not higher than 4 N is recommended. In most cases 3–4 N acid is the most suitable, but for removing easily desorbable ions, e.g. Na^+ and K^+, the regeneration may also be performed at lower concentration, such as 1 N HCl.

The experiments referred to in Chapter V:6 show that the time of regeneration is ordinarily a more important factor than the amount of regenerant used. The regeneration may be started by passing acid through the column at a fairly high flow rate in order to replace the water in the void space so that the acid will penetrate the whole resin column. Then the flow rate is preferably diminished to low values. For common filters, e.g. of the height 100 mm, a flow rate of 1–2 ml sqcm^{-1} min^{-1} is recommended. For this filter the regeneration is complete after 5–30 min, depending upon the cation in question.

It might be thought that ions that have been retained for a very long time would be difficult to remove from the resin because they would have had time to diffuse deeply into very narrow and difficultly approachable capillaries. Djurfeldt and Samuelson (11) studied the effect of time between sorption and regeneration for ferric iron and found that the regeneration curve was the same whether the regeneration was made after about 30 min or after 20 days.

If complexing agents can be present in the cation solution without interfering with determination of the cations, it may be practical to use a complexing agent as eluant instead of hydrochloric acid. As an example the removal of iron (III) by means of potassium oxalate and the subsequent polarographic determination of iron may be mentioned (39). In such cases the regenerant volume may be lowered in comparison to regeneration with hydrochloric acid.

It may also be pointed out here that the tetravalent metals, zirconium, hafnium, niobium, protactinium, and thorium, are very difficult to remove by regeneration with hydrochloric acid. Therefore these metals may be separated from other cations by desorbing the latter by means of acid. Subsequently the tetravalent metals may be easily eluted by treating the resin with a complexing agent such as oxalic acid (3, 12).

Gustavson (18) observed difficulties in the complete removal of chromium retained from complex solutions and ascribed them to secondary reactions of the complex with the phenolic structure of the resin (sulfonated phenol-formaldehyde type). Especially after contact with solutions of hexa-urea-chromic chloride, chromium is bound so strongly to the resin that hardly any chromium can be removed by treatment with hydrochloric acid (1:1).

In the case of silver ions regeneration may be performed by means of nitric acid. As highly concentrated acid attacks the resin, 1 N or in certain cases 2 N nitric acid is recommended. According to Ekedahl, Högfeldt, and Sillén (13), the last amounts of silver are very difficult to remove.

4. SEPARATIONS BY MEANS OF ANION EXCHANGERS

A. *The Choice of Resin*

Strongly basic resins will, as already mentioned, operate over a much wider pH range than weakly basic resins.

In acid medium it is possible to use either the weakly or the strongly basic type. Important examples are removal of inorganic and organic acids from different solutions containing non-electrolytes. Extremely weak acids, such as carbonic acid, boric acid, and silicic acid, cannot be retained by resins of weakly basic type, whereas a complete uptake may be achieved by means of the free-base form of a strongly basic resin. Phenols (21), aldehydes containing phenolic groups (17), and even sugars may be taken up by the strongly basic type of resin.

In most work with neutral solutions, it is preferable to use resins of strongly basic type, but resins of medium basic strength have also been used. An example is the conversion of alkali sulfate solution into chloride.

In alkaline medium only the strongly basic type of resin is applicable. The free-base form may be used to convert a common salt, e.g. sodium chloride, into the corresponding base (sodium hydroxide).

Both types of resin have been used for the uptake of amino acids.

For the separation of low-molecular-weight anions from high-molecular-weight anions the commercial highly cross-linked type of resin is suitable. The availability of resins with varying degrees of cross-linking will increase the possibilities of separating anions of different ionic sizes. Such resins are produced by the Dow Chemical Company and Rohm and Haas Company.

The stability of anion exchangers at room temperature seems to be satisfactory for most analytical purposes. Complications are most likely to arise in those analyses where a slight dissolution of nitrogenous compounds may interfere, e.g. in the separation of amino acids. Cannan (9) found that, when 50 g of Amberlite IR-4 was stirred with 0.5 N hydrochloric acid for 5 1/2 hr, about 20 mg of solids containing 2 mg of nitrogen was dissolved. Wiklander (51) reported that the anion exchanger Wofatit M showed inferior stability compared with cation exchange resins.

An attack on resins of weakly basic type by chromate (45) and permanganate (24) in acid as well as alkaline medium has been reported.

New resins of weakly basic type are now available (cross-linked polystyrene) which are more stable against water and ethanol solutions than the older resins. Experiments performed in the author's laboratory showed that these resins (Dowex 3 and Amberlite IR-45) could be used at elevated temperature (40° C) without serious dissolution.

Wheaton and Bauman (48) have published some data concerning the chemical stability of the strongly basic resins Dowex 1 and Dowex 2 (Nalcite SAR). The free-base form is shown to be the least stable form of this resin type, but at room temperature there is only a slight capacity drop even when operating the hydroxyl cycle. At 95° C the capacity drops over 50 % in 30 days, whereas the chloride form exhibits no detectable change. Dowex 1 is reported to be somewhat more stable than Dowex 2. The authors state that the resins are particularly resistant to oxidation (active chlorine), as compared with resins of phenolic type. As observed by Atteberry and Boyd (2), the resins are attacked by permanganate.

According to Lindsay and D'Amico (23), Dowex 2 is insoluble in all common solvents, including aliphatic and aromatic hydrocarbons. Unpublished experiments made in the author's laboratory show, however, that a slight dissolution which occurs in ethyl alcohol solutions may interfere with spectrophotometric investigation of the effluent from columns filled with resins of strongly basic type.

The strongly basic resins used by the present author (Amberlite IRA-400, Dowex 1, and Dowex 2) are all yellow. The color changes when different ions are displaced by others, which may give some guidance to the operator. Among the weakly basic resins Wofatit M is almost black, Amberlite IR-4B red-brown, and Amberlite IR-45 light yellow. A darkening is observed when the resins are transformed from the chloride form into the free-base form.

The resins are used either in the free-base form or in the salt form, e.g. chloride, bicarbonate, or formate form. By choosing a proper pretreatment of the resin before the sorption step, it is possible to effect a separation of acids of different strength from each other. For example, only dicarboxylic amino acids are retained by anion exchangers in the chloride form, whereas neutral and even basic amino acids may be taken up when the free-base form is used (Chapter XX).

Certain complications were observed by Gabrielson and Samuelson (17) when anion exchangers were used in solutions containing aldehydes. The free-base form of weakly basic resins was found to react with aldehydes under the formation of condensation products of the same type as Schiff's bases. Complications due to a polymerization of several aldehydes interfered when a resin of strongly basic type was operated instead. Glyoxal was found to be quantitatively taken up by the strongly basic type of resin. This is due to the fact that this aldehyde undergoes Cannizzaro's reaction even at room temperature under formation of glycolic acid which is retained by the resin. For the separation of acids from aldehydes by means of anion exchangers the authors recommended that the resin be used in the bicarbonate form.

B. *Grinding and Purification*

Most anion exchangers are not available in the desired particle size and purity. Operation is facilitated considerably when a low particle size is used. For most analytical purposes the sieve fraction 0.12–0.30 mm may be recommended. In the investigation of solutions of high viscosity coarser resin particles may be used in order to avoid too high resistance against flow.

Grinding and separation may be performed in the same manner as described for cation exchange resins.

Ordinarily it is necessary to purify the resin in order to avoid the occurrence of resin-derived products in the solution. The treatment may be accommodated to the properties of the resin and the special field of application. As a standard procedure it is recommended that the resin be conditioned, before use, by a number of alternating treatments with acid (1 N HCl) and alkali (0.5 N NaOH).

C. *The Sorption Step*

The technique of anion exchange operation is largely the same as that already described for the application of cation exchangers. The same factors seem to be of importance, but systematic investigations are still scarce. The data presented in Chapter V:7 may provide some guidance, but it must be emphasized that when new methods are worked out the proper conditions should be determined in every special procedure.

The apparatus and flow rate may be the same as in cation exchange operation. The concentration of the solution should in most cases be low, but the uptake of certain complex anions may advantageously be performed at extremely high total electrolyte concentration (see Chapters IX:2 and XIII:2).

D. *The Washing Step*

Washing of the anion exchange column after the sorption step is in most cases performed with distilled water at room temperature. Generally speaking, the anion exchange resins hitherto available are more difficult to wash out than most cation exchange resins. Among resins used in the author's laboratory those of strongly basic type have proved more convenient in this respect. The particle size is of utmost importance; a small size should be chosen, especially in those cases where it is important to achieve a complete washing within a short time and without diluting the effluent too much.

The filtration rate during the washing step may be about the same as during the sorption. Working at higher speed will shorten the time of washing to only a limited extent.

The weakly basic anion exchangers of phenolic type are difficult to free from alkali because of the presence of phenolic groups (Chapter II:5). The washing may be facilitated by saturating the water with carbon dioxide.

Washing by means of complexing agents may also be of importance in certain analyses to avoid decomposition of retained complex anions (Chapter IX:2).

E. The Elution (Regeneration) Step

Anion exchange resins may be eluted by treatment with alkaline, neutral, or acid solutions, e.g. sodium hydroxide, sodium carbonate, sodium chloride, or hydrochloric acid. When it is not desired to achieve a chromatographic separation in the elution step, a high concentration is usually suitable, e.g $1 N$ solutions or higher.

A low particle size is a prerequisite for a rapid elution. A normal flow rate is 2–5 ml sqcm^{-1} min^{-1}. Suitable conditions must be determined in every special case, as the experimental material hitherto available is too scarce to make general conclusions as to the optimum conditions possible.

Under conditions where gas is evolved regeneration of ion exchangers is preferably performed in a batch system instead of column operation, as the gas bubbles cause channeling in the column. Examples are resins containing carbonate, sulfide, and sulfite (42).

When anion exchangers are used only to remove anions and consequently no separate elution of the retained anions from the column is required, it may be practical to collect the resin from several columns and regenerate and wash a large amount of resin simultaneously. The resin prepared in the desired form is stored under water for subsequent work. When the resin is to be used again, the column is filled in the ordinary way and washed with a slight amount of water. This is in many cases less time consuming than separate regeneration of each column (16, 42).

a. STRONGLY BASIC RESINS

As shown by the elution curves reproduced in Fig. 21, 1.25 mmol th
be displaced quantitatively from a resin in the chloride form by means
sodium chloride in about 20 min. When the elutriant concentration wa
1 N the corresponding figures were about 20 % higher. With 0.5 N solution the en
was considerably lower. A similar behavior has also been demonstrated in the removal
of sulfate.

Difficulties in the removal of tetrathionates from a strongly basic resin by elution
with sodium chloride were observed by Regestad and Samuelson (28). In order to make
a quantitative elution possible it was found necessary to convert the retained tetrathionate into thiosulfate by treating the resin with a sulfite solution (Chapter XVIII: 4).

Some data on the regeneration of anion exchangers of the strongly basic type
(Dowex 2) reported by Osmun and Wirth (27) may be of interest also from an analytical
point of view. These authors found that it was difficult to remove retained silica by
means of 0.5 N sodium hydroxide at room temperature but that satisfactory results
were obtained at 95°C on prolonged contact (1.5 hr).

b. WEAKLY BASIC RESINS

As demonstrated in Chapter V: 8, the regeneration of anion exchangers of the weakly
basic type is performed much more easily by means of alkaline solutions than by neutral
solutions. If there is no risk of complications, 0.5 N sodium hydroxide or ammonia,
e. g., may be recommended. In many cases it is also possible to use, for instance, sodium chloride or hydrochloric acid.

Certain regenerations are extremely difficult. Gustavson (19) found that the complex chromium thiocyanate anion, $[\mathrm{Cr(CNS)_6}]^{3-}$, could be taken up quantitatively
by means of an anion exchanger of weakly basic type but that only a small part of the
chromium could be eluted by means of 5 N hydrochloric acid. This was explained
by secondary reactions taking place between the chromium complex and the resin.

5. DEIONIZATION

The isolation, identification, and analytical estimation of several non-
electrolytes may frequently be facilitated if both cations and anions are
removed from the solution to be investigated. Such a deionization may
be performed by a combination of a cation exchanger (free-acid form) and
an anion exchanger (free-base form). This method is most important in
those cases where a separation by means of distillation or extraction is
difficult or impossible. Solutions containing carbohydrates and proteins
are important examples.

It must, however, be borne in mind that cations and anions of large
dimensions, e.g. colloidal ions, cannot be retained by resins of ordinary
(strongly cross-linked) type. The term deionization is therefore not strictly

correct in all cases, but if this important exception is kept in mind the use of this term may be practical. Furthermore it must be noticed that the resins may retain not only cations and anions but also potential ions, i.e. un-ionized substances which when brought into contact with the resins are converted to cations or anions. Amino acids are the most important members of the group which may be designated as potential cations.

The methods for deionizing solutions for analytical purposes are in principle the same as for large-scale operation, e.g. deionization of water. Three alternative separation schemes are of actual interest.

A. *Two-Step Deionization*

The deionization may be performed in two steps, the solution first being passed over a cation exchanger saturated with hydrogen ions and in a second step over an anion exchanger in the free-base form (cf. Chapter I, Scheme III S). The reactions involved in the two steps may be represented as follows, using sodium chloride as a typical salt:

(I) $$Na^+ + Cl^- + H^+ SO_3^- R_s \rightarrow Na^+ SO_3^- R_s + H^+ + Cl^-.$$

(II) $$H^+ + Cl^- + NH_2 \cdot R_s \rightarrow Cl^- NH_3^+ R_s.$$

If no complications occur, the effluent from the second column will after washing contain all non-electrolytes but no cations and anions, either inorganic or organic. By regenerating the columns two further fractions are obtained. Consequently this method gives a fractionation of the original solution into three different fractions: (*a*) deionized solution, (*b*) cation solution, (*c*) anion solution.

Such a fractionation is indeed of great value, especially when dealing with complex mixtures. It may give a great deal of information and many leads. Furthermore the analysis of the fractions is in most cases much simpler than a direct analysis of the original mixture.

In this scheme the first step should always be performed as a column operation. In a batch system the acids liberated would usually prevent the complete uptake of cations. Resins of sulfonic acid type are used in this step.

The second step may be operated as a column process or batchwise by stirring the solution with the free-base form (in certain cases the carbonate form) of the resin. The anion exchange resin may be of either weakly or strongly basic type.

For certain purposes it may be desirable to perform a deionization by a combination of a cation exchanger of weakly acid type and an anion exchanger of weakly basic type, an example being the removal of electrolytes from neutral amino acids, as studied by Brenner and Frey (6). In order to complete the uptake of electrolytes the solution has to be recirculated through the columns several times. An automatic apparatus has been devised by these authors.

B. *Reverse Deionization*

The capacity of strongly basic anion exchangers to split neutral salts, i.e. convert them into the corresponding bases, is utilized in the first step in so-called reverse deionization. In a second step the bases may be removed by means of a cation exchanger in the hydrogen form. The reaction formulae may be written:

(I) $Na^+ + Cl^- + OH^-(CH_3)_3 \cdot N^+ \cdot R_s \rightarrow Cl^-(CH_3)_3N^+ R_s + Na^+ + OH^-$.

(II) $Na^+ + OH^- + H^+ SO_3^- \cdot R_s \rightarrow Na^+ SO_3^- \cdot R_s + H_2O$.

Reverse deionization is of particular advantage where low solution pH must be avoided at all times, e.g. when precipitation or decomposition would occur in acid medium.

In reverse deionization also, the first step must be performed as a column operation, whereas the second step may alternatively be operated in a batch system. The cation exchanger may be either of carboxylic acid type or of sulfonic acid type. In those cases where the solution is extremely sensitive to acids, the weakly acid type of exchanger is to be preferred, as the contact with the strongly acid resin phase may cause a decomposition.

C. *Mixed-Resin Deionization*

The simplest and also most effective way to perform a deionization is to use a mixture of a cation exchanger and an anion exchanger. The cation exchanger may be the free-acid form of a sulfonic acid resin and the anion exchanger the free-base form of either strongly or weakly basic type. If the anion exchanger is of strongly basic type, all salts are converted to their corresponding bases and consequently the cation exchanger may instead be of carboxylic acid type. Complete deionization may be achieved by either batch or column operation.

Unlike the other deionization methods, the mixed-resin operation is performed in neutral solution, which is a great advantage as far as substances are concerned which are sensitive towards acid or alkali, e.g. protein solutions (cf. Chapter XXIV). However, it must be remembered that the contact between the resin and the solution may cause undesirable catalytic reactions even if the external solution is neutral (Chapter II:1).

From an analytical point of view mixed-resin deionization is most interesting in those cases where it is necessary to remove the electrolytes from a solution of non-electrolytes but not to determine in separate fractions the cations and anions removed by the resin. The separation of the original solution into three fractions, which is easily performed by two-step deionization or reverse deionization, would require a physical separation of the cation exchanger and the anion exchanger before regeneration. Such a separation may be achieved, e.g., by screening if different particle sizes are used for the two resins. With resins of different densities a hydraulic separation may be performed. This mode of operation seems to be of great actual interest as far as water deionization and similar procedures are concerned but for analytical purposes the resin is usually discarded after use in the mixed-resin process. Only the non-electrolyte fraction is used for further analysis.

BIBLIOGRAPHY

1. Applezweig, N.: *Ind. Eng. Chem.*, Anal. Ed., **18**, 82 (1946).
2. Atteberry, R. W., and Boyd, G. E.: *J. Am. Chem. Soc.*, **72**, 4805 (1950).
3. Ayres, J. A.: *J. Am. Chem. Soc.*, **69**, 2879 (1947).
4. Ayres, J. A.: *Ind. Eng. Chem.*, **43**, 1526 (1951).
5. Bauman, W. C., Skidmore, J. R., and Osman, R. H.: *Ind. Eng. Chem.*, **40**, 1350 (1948).
6. Brenner, M., and Frey, R.: *Helv. Chim. Acta*, **34**, 1701 (1951).
7. Boyd, G. E., Myers, Jr., L. S., and Adamson, A. W.: *J. Am. Chem. Soc.*, **69**, 2849 (1947).
8. Boyd, G. E., Schubert, J., and Adamson, A. W.: *J. Am. Chem. Soc.*, **69**, 2818 (1947).
9. Cannan, R. K.: *J. Biol. Chem.*, **152**, 401 (1944).
10. Djurfeldt, R., Hansen, J., and Samuelson, O.: *Svensk Kem. Tid.*, **59**, 14 (1947).
11. Djurfeldt, R., and Samuelson, O.: *Acta Chem. Scand.*, **4**, 165 (1950).
12. Dyrssen, D.: *Svensk Kem. Tid.*, **62**, 153 (1950).
13. Ekedahl, E., Högfeldt, E., and Sillén, L.-G.: *Acta Chem. Scand.*, **4**, 1471 (1950).
14. Frizzell, L. D.: *Ind. Eng. Chem.*, Anal. Ed., **16**, 615 (1944).
15. Gabrielson, G., and Samuelson, O.: *Svensk Kem. Tid.*, **62**, 214 (1950).
16. Gabrielson, G., and Samuelson, O.: *Svensk Kem. Tid.*, **62**, 221 (1950).
17. Gabrielson, G., and Samuelson, O.: *Acta Chem. Scand.*, in press.
18. Gustavson, K. H.: *J. Am. Leather Chemists' Assoc.*, **44**, 388 (1949).
19. Gustavson, K. H.: *Svensk Kem. Tid.*, **62**, 164 (1950).
20. Ketelle, B. H., and Boyd, G. E.: *J. Am. Chem. Soc.*, **69**, 2800 (1947).

21. Kunin, R., and McGarvey, F. X.: *Ind. Eng. Chem.*, **41**, 1265 (1949).

22. Kunin, R., and Barry, R. E.: *Ind. Eng. Chem.*, **41**, 1269 (1949).

23. Lindsay, F. K., and D'Amico, J. S.: *Ind. Eng. Chem.*, **43**, 1085 (1951).

24. Lur'e, Yu. Yu., and Filippova, N. A.: *Zavodskaya Lab.*, **13**, 539 (1947); **14**, 159 (1948).

25. Nydahl, F.: *Proc. Int. Assoc. Theor. Applied Limnology*, **11**, 276 (1951).

26. Orlova, L. M.: *Zhur. Anal. Khim.*, **5**, 370 (1950).

27. Osmun, R., and Wirth, L.: *Ind. Eng. Chem.*, **43**, 1076 (1951).

28. Regestad, S. O., and Samuelson, O.: to be published.

29. Riches, J. P. R.: *Nature*, **158**, 96 (1946); *Chemistry & Industry*, **1947**, 656.

30. Runeberg, G., and Samuelson, O.: *Svensk Kem. Tid.*, **57**, 250 (1945).

31. Samuelson, O.: *Z. anal. Chem.*, **116**, 328 (1939).

32. Samuelson, O.: *Svensk Kem. Tid.*, **51**, 195 (1939).

33. Samuelson, O.: *Svensk Kem. Tid.*, **52**, 115 (1940).

34. Samuelson, O.: *Svensk Kem. Tid.*, **52**, 241 1940).

35. Samuelson, O.: *Svensk Kem. Tid.*, **54**, 124 (1942).

36. Samuelson, O.: *Svensk Kem. Tid.*, **56**, 277 (1944).

37. Samuelson, O.: *Svensk Kem. Tid.*, **57**, 158 (1945).

38. Samuelson, O.: *Tek. Tid.*, **76**, 561 (1946).

39. Samuelson, O.: *Iva*, **17**, 9 (1946).

40. Samuelson, O.: *Iva*, **17**, 5 (1946).

41. Samuelson, O., Djurfeldt, R., and Scholander, A.: *Elementa*, **30**, 107 (1947).

42. Samuelson, O., and Gärtner, F.: *Acta Chem. Scand.*, **5**, 596 (1951).

43. Samuelson, O., and Hartler, N.: to be published.

44. Schubert, J., and Richter, J. W.: *J. Am. Chem. Soc.*, **70**, 4259 (1948).

45. Sussman, S., Nachod, F. C., and Wood, W.: *Ind. Eng. Chem.*, **37**, 618 (1945).

46. Tompkins, E. R.: *J. Chem. Education*, **26**, 32, 92 (1949).

47. Vaïsman, G. A., and Yampol'skaya, M. M.: *Zavodskaya Lab.*, **16**, 621 (1950).

48. Wheaton, R. M., and Bauman, W. C.: *Ind. Eng. Chem.*, **43**, 1088 (1951).

49. Wickbold, R.: *Z. anal. Chem.*, **132**, 242 (1951).

50. Wickbold, R.: *Z. anal. Chem.*, **132**, 321 (1951).

51. Wiklander, L.: *Diss.*, Uppsala, 1946.

CHAPTER VII

Technique of Ion Exchange Chromatography

1. GENERAL CONSIDERATIONS

According to the terminology adopted in this book, ion exchange chromatography denotes exclusively mutual separations of exchangeable ions. Separations of different cations from each other are based on differences in exchange potentials on cation exchangers, which may be utilized to effect a quantitative separation if proper conditions are chosen. Similarly anion exchangers may be used for mutual separation of different anions. Only chromatographic separations by means of ion exchange resins will be considered.

In chromatography, a sorbent which functions through only one type of sorption mechanism is desirable. Generally ion exchange resins are well adapted in this respect. It is advisable to choose monofunctional resins as far as possible. In those cases where the solutes to be separated have a tendency to be retained in the resin by a combination of salt linkages and van der Waals' adsorption forces, it may be of utmost importance to select a resin for which the van der Waals' forces are as small as possible. The non-ionic adsorption is considerable for weakly ionized organic substances such as carboxylic acids and amino acids and is most marked for aromatic substances (Chapters II: 2 B and XX). Working at elevated temperature reduces the influence of the non-ionic forces (Chapter XX: 5).

As mentioned in a short communication by Weiss (32), the non-ionic adsorption on ion exchangers may be utilized to effect separation between certain organic substances, e.g. dyestuffs. Acid dyestuffs may be taken up by a cation exchange resin of weakly acid type in its undissociated state (acid solution). By addition of alkali the adsorbed molecules as well as the resin will be dissociated, and consequently the electrolytic forces will cause a desorption of the dyestuff. Similarly basic dyestuffs may be adsorbed on weakly basic resins in alkaline medium and desorbed on addition of acid.

A direct observation of colored zones on the ion exchange column is possible only in special cases where it may give some guidance to the operator. When work is done with radioactive ions, these may be recognized directly on the columns by means of radioactivity detectors (20, 10, 31, 8, 11, 13, 30), thus facilitating the operation.

The technique used in ion exchange chromatography is generally the so-called liquid chromatogram, which means that the effluent from the column is investigated either in small fractions or continuously by observing some convenient physicochemical property related to the concentration of the effluent.

It is helpful to distinguish between two main types of chromatography, namely, (a) frontal analysis (break-through method) and (b) elution analysis. Displacement analysis and carrier displacement analysis are limiting cases which might be referred to the (b) main group. The principles of these separations were discussed in Chapter V. The present chapter will deal only with the factors which are of importance for the performance of the separation and with the technique. Frontal analysis is of secondary importance in ion exchange chromatography and will therefore not be taken into consideration.

2. FACTORS AFFECTING SEPARATION

The variables which determine the separation of exchangeable ions in the elution step may be classified into two groups:
  A. Factors which determine the equilibrium separation, i.e. the statical ion exchange equilibrium.
  B. Factors affecting column efficiency.

According to the terminology adopted in the plate theory, the factors in the first group are those which determine the separation for each exchange; the factors in the second group have an influence upon the number of exchanges that the ions make as they travel down the column (14).

A. *Factors Affecting the Equilibrium Separation*

Variables affecting the ion exchange equilibrium have been discussed in Chapter III. It was pointed out that from dilute solutions containing ions of different valence the ions of higher valence are preferentially held by the resin and that the differences in affinity increase on dilution of the solution. Separations of ions of different valence are therefore improved by diluting the solution. Furthermore the separation of ions, independent of the valence, is better for resins with high total ion concentration in the resin phase, i.e. for ion exchangers with high exchange capacity per unit volume.

On the other hand Tompkins *et al.* (24, 10, 25, 26) have shown that separation is most efficient when the amount of the ions to be separated in the resin phase is low. Complexing agents are therefore conveniently used as elutriants, since they reduce the fractions of the solutes in the exchangeable form [cf. (8, 20)].

Another reason why complexing agents are preferred as elutriants is that these agents may be used to shift the ion exchange equilibrium in such a

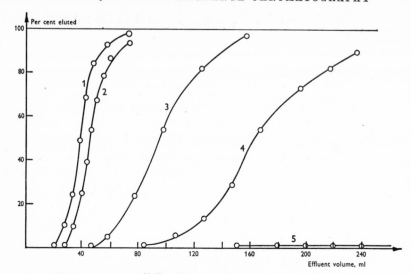

FIG. 29.   Elution of tracer $Sr^{89, \ 90}$ by 2% citrate and the effect of pH.
Column: 11.3 × 100 mm; Amberlite IR–1 [H$^+$; 0.25–0.36 mm].
Elutriant: 2% citric acid, converted to pH shown with ammonia.
Flow rate: 1 ml sqcm^{-1} min^{-1}.

Curve	1	2	3	4	5
pH	8.0	6.0	5.0	4.5	4.0

[from (24)]

direction that the separation is favored. The ideal situation would be to
have a specific complexing agent for each ion, which would form an extremely strong non-exchangeable complex with it but would not form any
complexes with the other ions. In this special case, however, it would be
unnecessary to apply the chromatographic technique, as such separations
may be performed according to the ion exchange method simply by adding
the complexing agent to the solution to be analyzed. Although this principle is applicable for some mixtures of dissimilar ions, e.g. separation of
iron or cobalt from alkali metals after addition of hydrocyanic acid (Chapter
IX: 1 Ac), it cannot be used for separating similar ions.

However, also in the separation of very similar ions, as the rare earths,
complexing agents are helpful because of differences in dissociation constants of the complexes. Those ions which show the greatest replacing
power in a complex-free solution have frequently been demonstrated to
give the weakest complexes. Thus the separation effects of the exchanger
and the complexing agent supplement each other (25, 12).

In the work performed under the Plutonium Project concerning the separation of the fragments formed during fission of the heavy elements, citrate

buffers were used as elutriants in most of the published investigations, but other complexing agents also were shown to be useful (25). For such complexing agents as citrate, in which the complex equilibrium depends upon the pH of the solution, the course of elution is markedly influenced by the pH (24, 20, 21, 10, 12, 25). The choice of pH is therefore of utmost importance for a successful separation. A striking example from a paper by Tompkins, Khym, and Cohn (24) is reproduced in Fig. 29. Variables affecting the equilibrium separation, such as different elutriants, pH, and concentration (24, 20, 1, 25), may be studied most readily by preliminary batch experiments (1, 25). It must be emphasized that the optimal conditions may vary from one resin to another, depending, for instance, upon the concentration in the resin phase (10, 12).

B. *Factors Affecting Column Efficiency*

Generally the separation will be improved when the column is operated under such conditions that equilibrium is approached between the solution and the ion exchanger in different parts of the column (24, 1, 14). Under these conditions the number of exchanges (theoretical plates) per unit length of the column is the highest possible. The variables affecting the column efficiency are in the main the same factors as those which have an influence upon the shape of the break-through curves and the regeneration curves (see Chapter V).

The particle size is of prime importance for an effective separation. It is common practice to use finer particles in ion exchange chromatography than in the application of ion exchangers for other purposes. To illustrate this fact some data from experiments by Ketelle and Boyd (12) are reproduced in Fig. 30. From these data, as well as from data published by other authors, it may be concluded that the particle size should not exceed 0.1 mm. Too small particles will of course effect too high resistance against flow and must therefore be avoided. It is necessary to remove the fines by screening or decantation. Only in those separations where large differences in exchange potentials exist is it permissible to increase the particle size to make a higher flow rate possible. The fraction 0.2–0.3 mm may be used under such conditions. The flow rate has likewise a great influence. An increased flow rate means that the ions are carried at a faster rate down the column, so that they have less time to diffuse through the resin particles and thus are prevented from reaching all exchanging groups (27, 28, 29). Too high flow rate will cause a long trailing edge of the elution curves and thus an increased overlap of the curves for the ions to be separated. Some

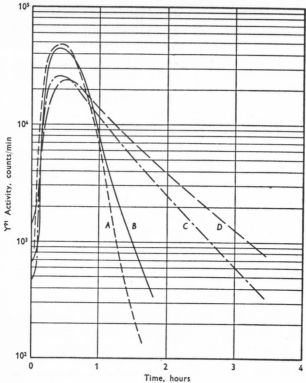

FIG. 30.   Effect of particle size of Amberlite IR–1 on the shape of the elution curve:
A, 0.044–0.055 mm; *B*, 0.074–0.088 mm; *C*, 0.25–0.29 mm; *D*, 0.36–0.50 mm.
[from (12)]

common flow rates for given particle sizes compiled from literature data
are reproduced in Table 6.

Moore and Stein found that the addition of a detergent (an ether of
polyethylene glycol) to the elutriant permitted faster flow rates without
broadening of the elution curves (15).

High temperature increases the diffusion rates and therefore the number
of exchanges in a given column. Improved separations were observed by
Ketelle and Boyd (12) when working at elevated temperature. When heated
columns are employed, it is recommended that air-free (boiled) solutions
be used in order to prevent the formation of bubbles in the column as the
temperature is raised.

The size of the liquid interstices between the resin particles (void space)
has also been shown to have a certain influence. Not only the size of the
resin particles but also the shape determines the void space (1).

TABLE 6

Flow rates commonly used in ion exchange chromatography

Resin	Solution	Particle Size, mm	Flow Rate, ml sqcm^{-1}min^{-1}	Reference
a Cation exchangers				
Amberlite IR–100	Yttrium group	0.074–0.088	1.2	12
Dowex 50	Cerium group	0.25 –0.36	0.2–0.4	10
Dowex 50	Yttrium group	0.112–0.125	2.2 (100 °C)	12
Dowex 50	Rare earths	0.044–0.055	1.0 (100 °C)	12
Zeo–Karb 215	Amino acids (aspartic acid, glycine, histidine)	0.25 –0.36	2.4	16, 17
b Anion exchangers				
Dowex 1	Adenosine polyphosphates	<0.074	<3.0	4
De–Acidite B	Amino acids (serine, glutamic acid, aspartic acid)	0.14 –0.17	1.2	18
Dowex 2	Amino acids (alanine, glycine)	0.074–0.14	0.14	19

In ion exchange chromatography a higher column is ordinarily required than in simple separations performed according to the ion exchange method, the ratio between length and diameter being as high as 100 : 1 or even 200 : 1 in certain cases. As already mentioned, the ions to be separated are lodged in a band near the top of the column. The separation occurs chiefly when the ions move down the column during the elution step. Depending on the differences in exchange potentials, a longer or a shorter resin bed is necessary to effect separation. At the beginning of most experiments, less than 10% of the exchange capacity (column length) is occupied for the uptake of the ions (cf. next section).

Within certain limits, the separation is improved by increasing the length of the resin bed. However, there is in many cases a critical bed length beyond which no improvement in separation can be gained. With non-linear isotherms a "steady state" is set up in the bed, after which no improvement in separation is obtained with increasing bed length. Symmetrical elution peaks (observed when linear isotherms hold) do broaden but the separation of the peaks is increased and the overlap of the elution curves is reduced (cf. Chapter V). A practical limitation, however, is the large volumes which must be collected.

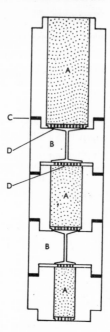

Fig. 31.   Coupled columns: *A*, ion exchange columns; *B*, constricted couplings; *C*, packing; *D*, perforated discs.   [from (9)]

C. *Coupled Columns*

Most authors have used ion exchange columns of the type reproduced in Fig. 23, Chapter VI. As shown by Claesson (3) and Hagdahl (9), improved chromatographic separations can be achieved by means of three or more coupled columns with decreasing diameters mounted one after the other. Between each pair of columns is mounted a small chamber in which a turbulent mixing occurs. Experiments reported by both Claesson and Hagdahl show that the fronts achieved with this arrangement are much sharper than those obtained with a simple column. The improvement is due to the fact that a front with a low concentration will move more slowly through the column than a front with a high concentration. If the solution which corresponds to an imperfect front (caused, e.g. by channeling) is mixed and spread over the whole area of a subsequent column, the more concentrated solution will in this column overtake the mixed, more dilute solution and a sharpening of the front will result. Hagdahl's column is shown schematically in Fig. 31. In ion exchange chromatography this method has been adopted by Partridge (see Chapter XX).

FIG. 32.   Automatic fraction collector (Shandon Scientific Company, London).

3. ARRANGEMENTS FOR ION EXCHANGE CHRO-
MATOGRAPHY

A general way of performing separations by means of ion exchange chromatography is to take up the effluent from the elution step in a large
number of fractions which are analyzed according to common methods.
The collection of these fractions is time-consuming, but automatic fraction
collectors (15) have been placed on the market. With these instruments
much time may be saved, and furthermore it is frequently possible to run
the experiment without attention, for instance, during the night. A fraction
collector of commercial type is shown in Fig. 32. Even with this equipment
the effective time of analysis is in many cases considerable, as the investigation of a large number of fractions may require much time.

In many separations the measurements may be simplified considerably by recording continuously some physical property of the effluent which is dependent on the composition of the solution (22). After passing through the ion exchange column the solution is allowed to flow through an arrangement for determining continuously the refractive index, light absorption, conductivity, pH value, or some other suitable property of the solution. The readings are plotted against the effluent volume.

Arrangements for continuous reading of the refractive index have been worked out by Tiselius (22, 23) and Claesson (2). Great accuracy is attained by means of an interferometric arrangement. A self-recording apparatus has also been constructed (2, 9, 6).

Drake (7) has described a polarographic (amperometric) arrangement for the automatic recording of the composition of the effluent. The voltage is fixed at a suitable value and the current continuously recorded as a function of time.

The interferometric and polarographic methods do not seem to have been applied in ion exchange chromatography as yet. On the other hand, pH measurements (17), as well as an automatic device for recording eluate composition by means of spot tests (5), have found practical use. More important in ion exchange chromatography is the conductometric method, and most significant of all the application of radioactive tracers. The technique used in chromatographic separation will be illustrated by the following example, in which the conductometric method has been adopted to record the composition of the effluent continuously.

A. Conductometric Technique

Arrangements for automatically recording the conductivity in flowing liquids have for a number of years found wide application for such purposes as the control of boiler feed water. An apparatus for continuous conductivity measurement of the effluent in ion exchange chromatography used by Wickbold (33) in investigations concerning the separation of alkali metals from each other is reproduced in Fig. 33. The separation of potassium and sodium (cf. Chapter V: 5) will be described here in more detail. The ion exchange column and experimental data are reproduced in Fig. 34. The comparison cell shown in the right part of the figure is filled with elutriant. By the device used in these investigations the influence of small variations in temperature is eliminated.

Before the elution the solution to be analyzed is introduced into the column, sodium and potassium ions being retained in a band near the top

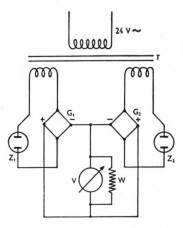

FIG. 33.   Circuit diagram of the conductivity-measuring arrangement: T, transformer;
Z_1, measuring conductivity cell; Z_2, comparison conductivity cell; G_1 and
G_2, two-way rectifiers in Graetz coupling; V, millivolt recorder; W, resistance.

[from (33)]

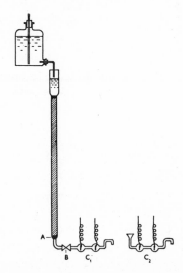

FIG. 34.   Experimental arrangement for continuous determination of the effluent
conductivity: A, sintered glass disc; B, adjustable stopcock; C_1, measuring
cell; C_2, comparison cell.

Column: 10×1100 mm; Wofatit KS [H^+; 0.25–0.3 mm].

Exchange capacity: 65 meq.

Column loaded with 13 meq $Na^+ + K^+$.

Elutriant: 0.1 N HCl.

Flow rate: 6 ml sqcm^{-1} min^{-1}.

[from (33)]

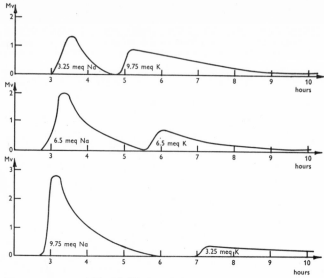

FIG. 35.   The separation of Na–K (Wofatit KS).   [from (33)]

of the column. Elution is performed with 0.1 N hydrochloric acid. The course of elution is illustrated in Fig. 35. First the solution left in the column after the sorption step is displaced. After a short time the effluent shows the same conductivity as the elutriant, and the millivoltmeter shows the value zero. After a certain time a difference in potential is indicated, which means that the conductivity of the effluent is lower than that of the elutriant because of the break-through of sodium ions. The potential curve passes through a maximum, and if proper conditions have been chosen the value will drop to zero. At this point the sodium ions have been quantitatively eluted. After a further amount of hydrochloric acid has been run through the column, the potassium ions appear in the effluent and the potential curve shows another maximum.

The separation may be utilized for analytical purposes by "cutting off" the effluent when the sodium ions have passed the column. This part of the solution is evaporated to dryness, and the sodium chloride determined gravimetrically or by titration with silver nitrate. The potassium ions are estimated in the latter part. In order to hasten this procedure the elution may be performed stepwise; i.e. the concentration of the hydrochloric acid may be increased to, e.g., 2 N after the sodium ions have been displaced from the column.

However, it is also possible to calculate the amount of sodium ions directly from the elution curve by planimetration, as the area between the

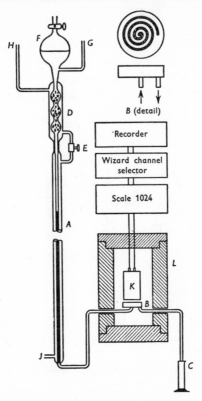

FIG. 36. Experimental arrangement employed in ion exchange column separations: *A*, ion exchange column; *B*, counting cell; *C*, receiver; *D*, Allihn condenser; *E*, throttle valve; *F*, gas entrainment bulb; *G*, elutriant inlet; *H*, thermostat fluid inlet; *K*, mica end-window Geiger-Mueller counting tube; *L*, 2-in. lead radiation shield. [from (12)]

curve and the abscissa is proportional to the amount of sodium ions. For this purpose the curve is drawn on a transparent paper, and the area between the curve and the abscissa is then cut out and weighed.

The sodium ions may be calculated by comparing the area (or the weight of the area cut out from the paper) obtained for the unknown sample with the results obtained in calibration experiments with known amounts of sodium ions.

A considerable drawback with this chromatographic method, as with most similar applications of ion exchange chromatography, is that the process is relatively lengthy. Not much attention is required, however, so that other work can be performed at the same time.

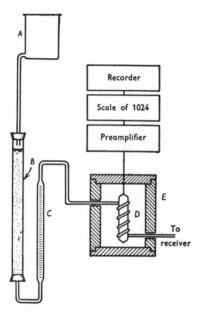

FIG. 37.   Experimental arrangement for ion exchange column studies: *A*, solution reservoir; *B*, ion exchange column; *C*, flowmeter; *D*, Geiger-Mueller counting tube; *E*, lead shield.   [from (1)]

B. *Radioisotopes in Ion Exchange Chromatography*

The use of radioisotopes as tracers frequently facilitates ion exchange chromatography. Continuous automatic recorders of radioactivity in the effluent were used by several workers in connection with the Plutonium Project for separation of the fission products from the uranium pile. This technique has been adopted in most subsequent works on ion exchange chromatography in inorganic chemistry. Experimental arrangements used by Ketelle and Boyd (12) and Boyd, Myers, and Adamson (1) are reproduced in Figs. 36 and 37. This radioactive-tracer technique and similar methods were later used by a large number of authors, and at present ion exchange chromatography may be considered a standard procedure in nuclear chemistry.

Most convenient are the separations in those cases where only tracer amounts are present, but the method will also work when larger quantities have to be separated. Where tracer amounts are involved, the elution characteristics of each ion may be conveniently investigated in separate columns. The results obtained by the use of parallel columns are applicable when all ions are on one column as long as no appreciable saturation of the resin results. In favorable cases this makes it possible to estimate the composition of the sample at least semiquantitatively by recording the activity continuously by means of a Geiger-Mueller counter. When the simple counting technique does not give sufficient information, the effluent has to be divided into fractions which may be analyzed according to common radiometric methods. Applications in ion exchange chromatography have been described in detail by Ketelle and Boyd (12) as well as by Spedding and associates (20).

C. *Simplified Procedure for Ions with Great Differences in Exchange Potentials*

In those separations where extremely large differences exist in exchange potentials between the ions to be separated, the operation may be simplified, as it may be unnecessary to divide the effluent into a great number of fractions or to analyze the effluent continuously. In the simplest case the ions which are most easily eluted are removed in one fraction by means of a proper elutriant, e.g. dilute hydrochloric acid, whereas the ions which under these conditions are held strongly by the resin are moved only a short distance in the column and do not appear in the effluent. These ions are eluted in a second step by means of a more effective elutriant, e.g. hydrochloric acid at high concentration.

It must, however, be emphasized that the success in many such operations is to a large extent dependent on the experimental conditions applied. If, for instance, too much of the first elutriant is used, other ions in addition to the desired species may appear in the effluent. Furthermore, the working conditions naturally have to be modified to the special resin used, and the operator should not use the procedures described in the literature without testing to ascertain that the method also works under his special conditions.

BIBLIOGRAPHY

1. Boyd, G. E., Myers, Jr., L. S., and Adamson, A. W.: *J. Am. Chem. Soc.*, **69**, 2849 (1947).
2. Claesson, S.: *Arkiv Kemi, Mineral. Geol.*, **A23**, No. 1 (1946).
3. Claesson, S.: *Arkiv Kemi, Mineral. Geol.*, **A24**, No. 16 (1947).
4. Cohn, W. E., and Carter, C. E.: *J. Am. Chem. Soc.*, **72**, 4273 (1950).
5. Drake, B.: *Nature*, **160**, 602 (1947).
6. Drake, B.: *Anal. Chim. Acta*, **3**, 452 (1949).
7. Drake, B.: *Acta Chem. Scand.*, **4**, 554 (1950).
8. Dyrssen, D.: *Svensk Kem. Tid.*, **62**, 153 (1950).
9. Hagdahl, L.: *Acta Chem. Scand.*, **2**, 574 (1948).
10. Harris, D. H., and Tompkins, E. R.: *J. Am. Chem. Soc.*, **69**, 2792 (1947).

11. Kayas, G.: *J. chim. phys.*, **47**, 408 (1950).
12. Ketelle, B. H., and Boyd, G. E.: *J. Am. Chem. Soc.*, **69**, 2800 (1947).
13. Kraus, K. A., and Moore, G. E.: *J. Am. Chem. Soc.*, **73**, 9 (1951).
14. Mayer, S. W., and Tompkins, E. R.: *J. Am. Chem. Soc.*, **69**, 2866 (1947).
15. Moore, S., and Stein, W. H.: *J. Biol. Chem.*, **176**, 367 (1948); **178**, 53 (1949); **192**, 669 (1951).
16. Partridge, S. M.: *Disc. Faraday Soc.*, **1949**, No. 7, 296.
17. Partridge, S. M., and Westall, R. G.: *Biochem. J.*, **44**, 418 (1949).
18. Partridge, S. M., and Brimley, R. C.: *Biochem. J.*, **44**, 513 (1949).
19. Partridge, S. M., and Brimley, R. C.: *Biochem. J.*, **49**, 153 (1951).
20. Spedding, F. H., Voigt, A. F., Gladrow, E. M., and Sleight, N. R.: *J. Am. Chem. Soc.*, **69**, 2777 (1947).
21. Spedding, F. H., Voigt, A. F., Gladrow, E. M., Sleight, N. R., Powell, J. E., Wright, J. M., Butler, T. A., and Figard, P.: *J. Am. Chem. Soc.*, **69**, 2786 (1947).
22. Tiselius, A.: *Arkiv Kemi, Mineral. Geol.*, **B14**, No. 22 (1940).
23. Tiselius, A., and Claesson, S.: *Arkiv Kemi, Mineral. Geol.*, **B15**, No. 18 (1942).
24. Tompkins, E. R., Khym, J. X., and Cohn, W. E.: *J. Am. Chem. Soc.*, **69**, 2769 (1947).
25. Tompkins, E. R., and Mayer, S. W.: *J. Am. Chem. Soc.*, **69**, 2859 (1947).
26. Tompkins, E. R., Harris, D. H., and Khym, J. X.: *J. Am. Chem. Soc.*, **71**, 2504 (1949).
27. Tompkins, E. R.: *J. Chem. Education*, **26**, 32, 92 (1949).
28. Tompkins, E. R.: *Disc. Faraday Soc.*, **1949**, No. 7, 232.
29. Tompkins, E. R.: *Anal. Chem.*, **22**, 1352 (1950).
30. van der Heijde, H. B., and Aten, Jr., A. H. W.: *J. Phys. & Colloid Chem.*, **55**, 740 (1951).
31. Vestermark, T.: Symposium of papers read on the Isotope Day (May 15, 1948) IVA, FKO 7, 31 (1948).
32. Weiss, D. E.: *Nature*, **166**, 66 (1950).
33. Wickbold, R.: Diss., Marl (Westf.),1950; *Z. anal. Chem.*, **132**, 401 (1951).

CHAPTER VIII

Determination of Total Salt Concentration

1. APPLICATION OF CATION EXCHANGERS

A. *General Considerations*

A very important field for the employment of the ion exchange method is the determination of the total salt concentration. Studies of this method, which is extremely rapid and accurate, were first reported by Samuelson (38). The cation exchanger should be the hydrogen form of a sulfonic acid resin.

The solution to be analyzed is merely passed through a column of the cation exchanger, and after washing with water, the resulting solution is titrated with standard alkali. The filtration and washing operations may be performed in 5 min, but in most cases it is an advantage to operate more slowly so that the time of filtration and washing totals 10–20 min. When acids are liberated which are strongly adsorbed by the exchanger (e.g. butyric acid), the washing takes a longer time. Afterwards the column is regenerated with 3–4 N hydrochloric acid; after being rinsed with water the column may be used again.

As an example of the use and accuracy of this method, Table 7 shows the results of several experiments on the determination of nitrate in acid, neutral, and alkaline nitrate solutions. The maximum deviation in these experiments was $\pm 0.2\%$.

Test solutions with a known nitrate content were prepared by the addition of various amounts of LiOH, NaOH, KOH, NH$_3$, Ca(OH)$_2$, Sr(OH)$_2$, Ba(OH)$_2$, CoCO$_3$, and NiCO$_3$ to nitric acid. Chemicals were of analytical standard and had been thoroughly purified. Volume of test solutions was about 50 ml. The ion exchanger, Wofatit K, in the hydrogen form had a particle size of 0.2–0.4 mm. The set-up is shown in Fig. 23, Chapter VI. The resin bed had a height of 130 mm and a diameter of 12 mm, corresponding to a total exchange capacity of ca. 10 meq. Total time for filtering and washing with about 75 ml water was around 10 min. The accumulated filtrate and washing water were titrated with 0.1 N sodium hydroxide with methyl red as indicator. After the final washing a further 50 ml of water was passed through the filter. An obvious yellow color was produced with a drop of sodium hydroxide solution after the addition of methyl red. Similar accuracy has been obtained with a series of various cations and anions.

TABLE 7

Analysis of Various Nitrates

Added, mmols				Found, mmols HNO_3		
2.98	LiOH	2.566	HNO_3	2.569	2.570	2.567
2.03	LiOH	2.566	HNO_3	2.568	2.568	2.566
2.11	NaOH	2.566	HNO_3	2.567	2.570	2.568
2.56	NaOH	2.566	HNO_3	2.570	2.568	2.570
3.02	NaOH	2.566	HNO_3	2.569	2.567	2.567
2.17	KOH	2.566	HNO_3	2.566	2.568	2.569
2.91	KOH	2.566	HNO_3	2.568	2.566	2.570
2.00	NH_3	2.566	HNO_3	2.566	2.567	2.567
2.57	NH_3	2.566	HNO_3	2.567	2.568	2.566
4.00	NH_3	2.566	HNO_3	2.568	2.569	2.571
1.00	$Ca(OH)_2$	2.566	HNO_3	2.567	2.569	2.570
1.25	$Ca(OH)_2$	2.566	HNO_3	2.568	2.568	2.566
1.03	$Sr(OH)_2$	2.566	HNO_3	2.570	2.567	2.565
1.27	$Sr(OH)_2$	2.566	HNO_3	2.569	2.571	2.567
1.09	$Ba(OH)_2$	2.566	HNO_3	2.570	2.570	2.569
1.23	$Ba(OH)_2$	2.566	HNO_3	2.571	2.568	2.569
0.99	$CoCO_3$	1.985	HNO_3	1.983	1.980	1.982
0.99	$NiCO_3$	1.985	HNO_3	1.982	1.986	1.981

One source of error which, if neglected, may sometimes lead to excessively high values is contamination of the distilled water used in making up solutions or in diluting, and for washing. In certain laboratories the distilled water does not come up to required standards. The quality of the water in question may be determined by filtering a certain amount through the hydrogen-saturated ion exchanger. Methyl red is added to the effluent, and titration with sodium hydroxide carried out. If one drop (0.03 ml) 0.1 N NaOH produces an obvious yellow color with an effluent volume of 100 ml, the purity may be considered satisfactory for most purposes. If the quality of the water is not up to standard, then the distillation apparatus should be improved or possibly combined with deionization with the help of ion exchangers (cf. Chapter XXVI: 1). If the extent of contamination is constant, a correction may instead be used.

The effect of the CO_2 content of the water must be taken into consideration as in normal analysis, especially when titrating at a high pH value, e.g. against phenolphthalein. It may be suitable here to use CO_2-free water, but in many cases it is simpler to drive off the CO_2 by the use of

CO_2-free air, when the solution and washing water have passed through the column.

Non-electrolytes such as sugar, ethyl alcohol, and glycerol have no influence upon the determination (42).

The method has been proved suitable for microscale work by Wiesenberger (58, 59) and Samuelson (47). Solutions of rubidium and cesium salts were examined by Samuelson. Some results are presented in Table 8.

TABLE 8

Analysis of Rubidium and Cesium Salts

	Added, meq	Found, meq	
RbNO$_3$	0.162	0.162	0.162
CsNO$_3$	0.162	0.163	0.163
RbClO$_4$	0.187	0.187	0.187
CsClO$_4$	0.187	0.187	0.187

Column: Fig. 26; 6×40 mm; Wofatit KS [H$^+$; < 0.3 mm]. The volume of the solution to be analyzed was 15 ml and the column was rinsed with 15 ml water. The time for filtration and rinsing was about 10 min. After removal of CO_2 the solution was titrated with 0.05 N NaOH against methyl red.

The practical applications of this principle are numerous. The analysis of many substances may be simplified when the constituent to be determined is the only anion present. For example, the procedure is most helpful for standardizing solutions that are prepared from pure salts, especially if the salts cannot be dried to a definite weight with reasonable accuracy. The method is of course of greater importance for solutions containing anions which are difficult to determine according to other methods, such as sulfate, nitrate, perchlorate, and acetate, than for solutions containing e.g. chloride, bromide, and iodide. Also in the case of the last-mentioned anions the method may sometimes be advantageous. As practical examples may be mentioned determinations of the concentration of polarographic and colorimetric standard solutions.

This procedure may also be applied to determinations of the concentration of different technical liquors and substances in factory operation. If trace amounts of other anions are present the figures may be corrected. Sometimes it is not necessary to determine the concentration of the impurities in all samples, as the variations are frequently small.

The method is also of importance for medical and pharmaceutical analyses, an example being the determination of total base in blood serum.

To determine the total amount of salt in a solution by titration of the liberated acid, the quantity of acid present in the original solution must be subtracted from the value obtained by titration of the effluent. The original acidity may be determined in the same sample or in a separate sample.

On the other hand, hydroxides, carbonates, and bicarbonates do not release an equivalent amount of acid in this process. In analyses concerned with the determination of the total amount of cations it is therefore necessary to titrate the original solution for alkalinity before passage through the column. With bisulfite solutions certain difficulties are encountered, partly with respect to the volatility of sulfur dioxide, and partly in obtaining a definite end-point in alkalimetric titration. In this case the problem is solved by adding a small excess of hydrochloric acid to the solution and boiling to drive off the sulfur dioxide. The excess of hydrochloric acid is determined by titration with alkali, and the sample then passed through a hydrogen-saturated ion exchanger. The effluent is titrated with alkali. The difference between the amounts of alkali used in the two titrations is equivalent to the amount of cation in the original solution (45).

Another interesting example is the application of this principle to the determination of esters. The esters are saponified by means of excess alkali, and after removal of the alkali with a cation exchanger the liberated acid is determined by titration (59).

Examples of the use of the method as a research tool may be mentioned here. For the determination of equivalent weights, for the identification of various salts, and for making possible the recording of potentiometric neutralization curves for salts of various acids the method is extremely valuable. It not only may be used for low-molecular-weight acids but also becomes significant with high polymer acids. One example is the determination of the concentration of sodium polymetaphosphate (Graham's salt) in solutions and the neutralization curves for the corresponding acid (44). As another example may be mentioned research on potentiometric and conductometric titration curves of sulfite waste liquor and ligninsulfonic acid after the cations are exchanged for hydrogen ions (cf. Chapter XVIII).

In various laboratory experiments, e.g. determination of solubility and rate of dissolution of salts the solubility of which is not too low, this method is excellent. Work by Scholander on the rate of dissolution of calcium sulfate may be cited as an example (52).

Nietsch and Heinrichs (31) determined the total amount of water-soluble salts in soils by shaking a water extract with a cation exchanger in the hydrogen form and subsequently titrating the filtrate with 0.01 N NaOH against phenolphthalein. In order to obtain complete uptake it is necessary to use a large excess of ion exchanger. Column operation is to be preferred for this analysis also.

B. *Chlorides, Bromides, Iodides, Nitrates, Perchlorates, and Chlorates*

Samuelson (38, 46, 47, 48, 49) studied solutions containing chloride, bromide, iodide, nitrate, perchlorate, chlorate, and the following cations: Li^+, Na^+, K^+, NH_4^+, Rb^+, Cs^+, Mg^{2+}, Ca^{2+}, Sr^{2+}, Ba^{2+}, Zn^{2+}, Mn^{2+}, Co^{2+}, Ni^{2+}, Cd^{2+}, Al^{3+}, Cr^{3+}, Fe^{3+}.*

In all cases the cations could be quantitatively exchanged for hydrogen ions, and the acid liberated determined simply in the same way as in experiments shown in Table 7. In nitrate solutions Cu^{2+} has also been examined. Experiments with copper chloride and lead nitrate have been published (33, 57).

Complications have been encountered only in extremely dilute solutions containing ferric ions where, as mentioned in Chapter VI, an irreversible hydrolysis occurs, which means that part of the quantity of iron introduced passes the filter as a colloid. In this way erroneous values are obtained. The same phenomenon occurs with ferric salt solutions to which alkali has been added.

It is remarkable that in no case does complex formation have a disturbing effect. Strong complexes are known, e.g. between cadmium and iodide ions, but, in spite of this, complete separation takes place without difficulty. With chromium salts experiments were carried out partly with solutions containing the violet ion $Cr(H_2O)_6^{3+}$ and partly with solutions which had been previously warmed. In this way, as is known, complexes are formed, and the color is changed to green. With solutions containing chloride, bromide, iodide, nitrate, perchlorate, or chlorate no complications occur because of previous warming. As observed by Gustavson, the separation is not complete in certain solutions containing basic chromic chloride (cf. Chapter XXV). According to Wickbold (57), mercuric ions are not taken up from chloride solutions because of the strong complexes existing in the solution.

According to Frizzell (15), solutions of potassium iodide are oxidized when filtered through a column containing an ion exchanger prepared by the sulfonation of coal (Zeo-Karb H). In Samuelson's experiments (48) a

---

* Iodide solutions containing Fe^{3+} naturally oxidize and cannot, therefore, be determined by this method.

sulfonated resin of phenol-formaldehyde type was used. In this way no complications are encountered.

Berggren and Björling (4) applied the method to the determination of ionic bromine in N, N-dibenzylamino-β-bromoethane hydrobromide. In order to prevent the hydrolysis of the cation, accompanied by a formation of hydrobromic acid, the ion exchange was performed in alcoholic solution. The resin used (Amberlite IR-100) was found to react slowly, prolonged contact (about 20 min) being required to effect a quantitative uptake of the cation. This was probably due to the large dimensions of the cation compared to the meshes in the network structure of the resin. A more rapid separation might probably be achieved by using a resin with a lower degree of cross-linking.

C. Determination of Nitrate in Explosives

Samuelson (46) applied the ion exchange method for the determination of potassium nitrate in black powder. The method was shown to be extremely rapid and accurate.

Procedure: Ten grams of the finely divided sample is treated with hot water several times. The solution is filtered and collected in a 500-ml-volume flask. After cooling, the flask is filled to the mark. Twenty-five milliliters of the solution is percolated through an H^+-cation exchange column (total exchange capacity ca. 10 meq). After washing with water the effluent is titrated with standard alkali.

The same procedure has been applied (46) for determination of ammonium nitrate in explosives consisting of TNT (trinitrotoluene) and ammonium nitrate. In this process the solution is cooled before filtration, as TNT melts in hot water. The method is also of importance for control of the quality of technical ammonium nitrate, since the direct determination of the moisture content is difficult.

D. Sulfates

Different cations are rapidly exchanged for hydrogen ions in sulfate solutions. Samuelson (38, 39, 40, 42, 47, 49) and Wiesenberger (58) analyzed solutions containing different cations and obtained a quantitative separation without any complications in the presence of the following cations: Li^+, Na^+, K^+, NH_4^+, Rb^+, Cs^+, Mg^{2+}, Ca^{2+}, Zn^{2+}, Fe^{2+}, Ni^{2+}, VO^{2+}, Cd^{2+}, Cu^{2+}, Al^{3+}.

Samuelson (46) found that with Fe^{3+} a source of error occurs with solutions which do not contain free acid, e.g. pure solutions of ferric ammonium sulfate. Basic ferric sulfate may be precipitated on the phase boundary between the trial solution and the washing water. A certain amount of sulfate (about 1%) can remain on the filter, especially if the column is operated at low speed. At a high flow rate no precipitation could be detected. This source of error may also be eliminated by shaking the solution to be analyzed with a certain amount of the resin in the acid form (e.g. 2 g) and then transferring the solution and the ion exchanger to the top of the column. The solution is afterwards passed through the column in order to complete the uptake, and washing is performed in the usual way.

With chromium sulfate solutions Samuelson showed (40) that quantitative transformation could be carried out in the normal way when the violet hexaquo-ion was concerned. Such a quantitative transformation does not occur in solutions containing green (complex) chromium sulfate. The experiment showed that, while part of the amount of sulfate remained in the column as complex cations, part of the chromium passed through the resin bed in the form of complex anions. The amount of sulfate taken up by the resin or the amount of chromium passing through the column depends, among other things, on the time taken for filtration and washing, the amount of ion exchanger, and the concentration of the trial solution. Even if these factors are taken care of by maintaining the most favorable possible conditions, the error is still so significant that the method cannot be used in practice.

According to Goehring and Darge (17), the method produces quantitative transformation also with solutions of chromium sulfate. These authors neutralized the free acid present before commencing their experiments. Samuelson (43) has not succeeded in confirming these results, finding instead that, under these conditions, about 15% of the amount of sulfate is taken up by the ion exchanger.

Gustavson studied solutions containing basic chromium sulfate and maintained that also here the separation was incomplete (cf. Chapter XXV).

Wickbold (57) found that the method can also be used for solutions containing sodium persulfate.

Rapid and accurate methods for analyzing different salts of technical grade, e.g. aluminum sulfate (39), cobalt sulfate (42), Glauber's salt (43), and zinc sulfate (42), have been worked out and used in practice by Samuelson. Excellent results have been obtained. In the case of zinc sulfate a correction had to be made for a slight amount of chloride present in the technical-grade salt. The method has also been applied to the determination of total sulfate in spinning baths for viscose rayon (43).

Futterknecht (16) used the method for the determination of sodium sulfate in dye baths. Before the ion exchange the solution was decolorized by means of active carbon. Chloride was determined in a separate sample according to the usual Volhard method, and the value was subtracted from the total salt concentration determined by the ion exchange method.

E. *Phosphates*

With alkalimetric titration of orthophosphoric acid the end-point cannot be determined with the same accuracy as in the determination of simple strong acids. Titration of phosphoric acid should be carried out in as small a volume as possible. This means that, when the ion exchange method is used, the collected filtrate and washing water from the ion exchanger before titration should be evaporated to a small volume. It must also be remembered that phosphoric acid has a pronounced tendency to be adsorbed on certain types of cation exchangers, and therefore larger quantities of washing water are required than in the washing of, e.g., sulfuric acid.

Samuelson showed that the separation of phosphoric acid was quantitative with the following cations (38, 41, 42, 46): Li^+, Na^+, K^+, NH_4^+, Rb^+, Cs^+, Mg^{2+}, Ca^{2+}, Sr^{2+}, Ba^{2+}, Zn^{2+}, Mn^{2+}, Co^{2+}, Ni^{2+}, Cd^{2+}, Al^{3+}, Fe^{3+}.

With solutions containing chromium phosphate (green) separation is incomplete because the complexes are too strong. A small amount of phosphoric acid is taken up by the ion exchanger, whereas a considerable amount of the chromium passes through the column (46).

The method may be used even if the salts are not soluble in water (41). In the cases of aluminum and iron phosphate or substances containing these compounds as contaminants, the phosphate may be dissolved in hydrochloric acid (possibly +nitric acid). After the excess acid has been disposed of by evaporation, the solution is diluted and filtered through a hydrogen-saturated cation exchanger. The effluent is evaporated to drive off the volatile acids, after which the sample is titrated with alkali against phenolphthalein. Determination may also take the form of two-step titration, in which disposal of the volatile acids is not necessary (cf. Chapter IX).

With phosphates which are soluble at a low acidity Samuelson (46) showed that a determination may be made without dissolving the sample in acid. When a suspension of such a phosphate is shaken with a hydrogen-saturated ion exchanger, dissolution quickly takes place. To obtain complete transformation the solution obtained should be passed through a column of hydrogen-saturated ion exchanger. This method has been tried with phosphates of the following divalent ions: Ca, Sr, Ba, Mn, Zn, Co, and Ni.

Example: In two experiments 1.79 mmol $BaHPO_4$ were agitated in water together with a well-washed hydrogen-saturated cation exchanger. The amount of moist ion exchanger corresponded to an exchange capacity of about 6 meq. After agitation for 2 min the sample had completely dissolved. The solution was filtered off and passed through a column, and after washing with a total of about 150 ml water, the collected filtrate and washing water were evaporated to a volume of about 15 ml and titrated with 0.5 N sodium hydroxide solution against phenolphthalein. In the two experiments an alkali consumption was obtained of 3.58 and 3.59 meq (calculated 3.58).

The time for filtering and washing was about 20 min. Barium could not be detected in the effluent, and in the cation solution, obtained by treating the ion exchanger with 150 ml of 5 N hydrochloric acid, phosphate could not be detected.

It should be pointed out that this modification is very suitable for pure substances but not for accurate analysis of technical-quality substances containing iron phosphate or other phosphates which are first dissolved at high acidity.

The ion exchange method has also been successful with solutions containing sodium pyrophosphate (57) and sodium polymetaphosphate (44). With solutions containing pyrophosphate or metaphosphate complexes of trivalent ions (Al^{3+}, Fe^{3+}, La^{3+}), the conversion is not quantitative (41, 42, 44, 50). The amount of the trivalent metals retained depends on the amount of phosphate present as well as on the rate of filtration and the size of the resin bed.

Complexes between divalent ions and metaphosphate are weaker, and in this case a quantitative uptake of the divalent ions may be achieved (50). Because of the complexes existing in these solutions a higher column length is required than with complex-free solutions. This is demonstrated in Fig. 7 A (Chapter V).

The free acids may also be liberated by means of sulfonic acid resins from the sodium salts of phosphorous acid and triphosphoric acid ($H_5P_3O_{10}$) and from the potassium salt of monoamidophosphoric acid (26).

F. *Bromates, Iodates, and Periodates*

In experiments with bromate and iodate, using an exchanger of the sulfonated carbon type, Frizzell (15) observed that the liberated acids were reduced by the exchanger. Similar results were obtained when a sulfonated resin of phenol-formaldehyde type was employed (48). However, when cation exchangers of sulfonated hydrocarbon type (Dowex 50) were used (22), good agreement was observed between calculated and observed values for solutions containing potassium bromate, iodate, and periodate.

G. *Thiocyanates*

The application of the ion exchange method to thiocyanates has not been investigated in detail. Wickbold (57) found that the method was suitable for converting the potassium salt into the free acid, which can be determined alkalimetrically in the effluent. The same method has also been used for the ammonium salt (50) and is probably feasible for several other thiocyanates.

Lur'e and Filippova observed that ferric iron could be quantitatively retained even in the presence of excess thiocyanate (28).

Chromium, on the other hand, forms extremely stable thiocyanate complexes of the type $K_3Cr(CN)_6$. Gustavson observed that, when a solution of this salt was percolated through a cation exchanger of sulfonic acid type, the total amount of chromium was found in the effluent (20).

H. *Borates*

In investigations by Frizzell (15), Brunisholz and Bonnet (7), as well as by Martin and Hayes (30), the method was applied to solutions containing borate. Quantitative separation was obtained with solutions containing the following cations: ammonium, beryllium, magnesium, calcium, zinc, cadmium, iron (II), nickel, cobalt, copper (II), mercury (II), aluminum, iron (III), thorium, tin (IV), titanium, uranium, and zirconium.

The last-mentioned authors found that the determination of boric acid in the effluent, accomplished by a modification of the familiar titration in the presence of invert sugar, permits the presence of moderate amounts of silicate, arsenate, phosphate, and molybdate. Synthetic standards simulating steel, ferroboron, a casting alloy, and nickel plating solutions with a boron content ranging from 0.025 to 20% were analyzed. The method is more rapid than conventional distillation procedures. The maximum relative error for determination of amounts of boron exceeding 2 mg was 1.0% and the standard deviation of a single value was 0.3%.

I. *Calcium in Sulfite Cooking Acid*

A method for the determination of the total lime content in sulfite cooking acid (raw acid) has been published by Samuelson (45). The method has been used in practice for many years.

To the liquor, which contains calcium bisulfite, excess sulfur dioxide, and a small amount of sulfate, a slight excess of hydrochloric acid is added and the solution is boiled for some minutes in order to decompose the bisulfite and to drive off SO_2. The free acid is titrated with standard alkali.

The metal cations are then exchanged for hydrogen ions. The acids liberated are titrated with NaOH. The lime content is calculated from the difference between these titrations. The analysis may be carried out in 20–30 min, and the error is less than 0.5% of the value obtained.

The method is considerably less time-consuming and, especially for less qualified workers, is more accurate than the usual precipitation as oxalate with subsequent titration with permanganate. If the acid contains other cations besides calcium, e.g. magnesium and sodium, these are included in the analysis. This is not a disadvantage, as the total amount of cations is of the greatest importance for the digestion process, but it is of secondary significance if part of the cations consist of, e.g., magnesium. The method has also been applied to sodium bisulfite cooking acids.

Procedure: Five milliliters raw acid is accurately measured out with a pipette and boiled in an Erlenmeyer flask with 5 ml 0.5–0.55 N hydrochloric acid until the smell of SO_2 has disappeared. Boiling time is about 5 min. The solution is then titrated with 0.1 N sodium hydroxide solution against methyl red (a ml used). It is passed through a layer of hydrogen-saturated cation exchanger and replaced by water until the washing water is neutral. Filtrate + washings are titrated with 0.1 N sodium hydroxide against methyl red (b ml used).

g CaO/100 ml cooking acid: $(b-a)$ $N \cdot 0.56$ where N is the normality of the sodium hydroxide solution.

Suitable dimensions for the filter layer, when Wofatit KS (0.2–0.4 mm) is used, are height 80 mm; diameter 10 mm. Required wash water is about 75 ml.

After the experiment the filter is regenerated with 100 ml 3 N hydrochloric acid and washed with distilled water until it is free from acid. The filter is then ready for re-use. In a series of experiments it is better to set up several filters and regenerate them simultaneously, thus saving time. Regeneration may be carried out in 10–15 min; about the same time is required for washing.

This method may also be combined with a determination of the total content of $SO_2 + SO_3$ and the "free sulfurous acid." The sample is first oxidized with pure hydrogen peroxide, after which the sulfuric acid obtained is determined by NaOH titration. This determination gives "free sulfurous acid." The metal cations are then removed by the ion exchange method and again titrated (total $SO_2 + SO_3$). The difference corresponds to the calcium content of the sample. The sample solution must be diluted so that gypsum is not precipitated in the oxidized solution.

J. *Acetates*

Acetate solutions containing different inorganic cations have been investigated by Wiesenberger (59), Samuelson (43, 49), and Djurfeldt, Hansen, and Samuelson (11). Quantitative separation was obtained in solutions containing the following cations: Li^+, Na^+, K^+, NH_4^+, Mg^{2+}, Ca^{2+}, Sr^{2+}, Ba^{2+}, Zn^{2+}, Mn^{2+}, Co^{2+}, Ni^{2+}, Al^{3+}, Fe^{3+}, Cd^{2+}, Cu^{2+}, Pb^{2+}.

The separation was quantitative even in samples containing excess acetic acid. Because of the tendency of acetic acid to be adsorbed on the ion exchanger, washing should not take place too quickly; it is equally important that the particle size of the ion exchanger be not too great.

Solutions containing chromium acetate (green) were studied. Complete separation could not be obtained in this way (11). The same statement applies to solutions of basic chromium acetate (and chromium formate) (21).

In experiments performed by Djurfeldt, Hansen, and Samuelson, the sample solutions contained a total of 2.4–2.9 meq. The resin bed (13×140 mm; Wofatit KS [H^+; 0.2–0.4 mm]) had a total capacity of 16 meq. The time for filtration and rinsing (100 ml water) was about 20 min. The maximum deviation between the calculated and observed NaOH consumption was 0.5%. In most experiments the deviation was considerably lower. The fact that Erler (12) did not obtain complete transformation must be due to the fact that the working conditions were such that washing was not complete (13).

Titration of the effluent is most convenient against phenolphthalein. Atmospheric carbon dioxide naturally has a disturbing effect. Therefore CO_2-free distilled water is used, or the carbon dioxide is removed from the effluent before titration.

K. *Determination of Esters*

The application of the ion exchange method for the determinations of esters has been carefully investigated by Wiesenberger (59). Ordinarily the ester is saponified by boiling with alkali, and the amount of alkali not consumed is back-titrated with acid. In the ion exchange method, the ester is saponified and subsequently the solution is passed through an ion exchange column containing an H^+-cation exchange resin (sulfonic acid type). The total effluent is titrated with standard alkali against phenolphthalein. Before the equivalent point is reached, carbon dioxide is removed from the solution.

The advantage of the ion exchange method over the older method is that the results are more accurate, as only one titration has to be made and carbon dioxide does not interfere. Another advantage is that it is possible to work with a much higher alkali concentration, which means that the saponification is performed more quickly. This is of the utmost importance when working on a microscale, where, according to the older method, the use of a low alkali concentration should be necessary if high accuracy is required.

In Wiesenberger's method, the solution obtained after saponification is shaken with the cation exchanger and subsequently passed through an ion exchange column. If cation exchange resins which are resistant against alkali are available, the ion exchange may be performed more simply as a single-column operation. This modification has been used in practice in the author's laboratory for analysis of ethyl acetate, butyl acetate, and similar simple esters. Excellent results have been obtained.

Wiesenberger's publication contains detailed instructions for the micro-determination of acetyl groups in different organic compounds, e.g. carbohydrate derivatives. The acetyl derivatives are saponified by means of p-toluenesulfonic acid in alcohol solution. The ester-alcohol solution is distilled and subsequently saponified with alkali.

L. *Oxalates*

In investigations concerning different chromium complexes Gustavson (20) found that, on passing a solution of $Na[Cr(C_2O_4)_2]$ through a bed of cation exchange resin in the hydrogen form, no uptake of chromium occurs. This is due to the formation of extremely strong anionic complexes in this solution. In other solutions containing chromium and oxalate a certain uptake may be obtained, but the retention has in all cases been incomplete (21).

Frizzell (15) studied the analysis of sodium oxalate according to the ion exchange method. The exchanger was of the sulfonated coal type (Zeo-Karb). The determination required a correction for a blank determination. However, Djurfeldt, Hansen, and Samuelson (11), working with an ion exchange resin, found excellent agreement without any correction with oxalate solutions containing a number of monovalent and divalent cations: Li^+, Na^+, K^+, NH_4^+, Mg^{2+}, Ca^{2+}, Sr^{2+}, Ba^{2+}, Zn^{2+}, Mn^{2+}, Co^{2+}, Ni^{2+}, Cd^{2+}, Cu^{2+}. In the experiments the same conditions prevailed as in the previously described work with acetate solutions. Naturally, for oxalates which are soluble to only a slight extent, e.g. calcium and copper, the accuracy is somewhat less because of the fact that the end-point in the titration is difficult to determine accurately, since the solution must be very dilute.

Under the same conditions, i.e. in spite of a great excess of ion exchanger, with solutions containing aluminum or ferric salts, incomplete separation was obtained because of the stable anion complexes in these solutions. Consequently the method cannot be used for oxalate solutions containing aluminum, iron, or chromium. Data are shown in Table 9.

TABLE 9

Uptake of Al^{3+} and Fe^{3+} from Solutions Containing Oxalate

Added, meq			Uptake by the Resin in Per Cent of the Added Amount
$AlCl_3$	$FeCl_3$	$(COOH)_2$	Al^{3+} and Fe^{3+}
1	0	0	100
1	0	0.5	89.8
1	0	1	70.8
1	0	2	42.0
1	0	5	22.5
0	1	0	100
0	1	0.5	86.5
0	1	1	68.7
0	1	2	34.5
0	1	5	8.05

M. *Salts of Other Organic Acids*

Björling (5) and Wickbold (57) found that the ion exchange method could be used for alkalimetric determination (indicator phenolphthalein) of a number of other organic salts. The investigations demonstrated the usefulness of the principle for analysis of pharmaceutical preparations. Satisfactory results were obtained with the following salts: sodium formate (57), sodium tartrate (5), sodium-potassium tartrate (57, 18), sodium citrate (5, 57), sodium and calcium lactate (5), sodium sulfosalicylate (5), sodium benzenesulfonate (57), calcium gluconate, calcium glycerophosphate, Novalgin (the sodium salt of amidopyrine methanesulfonic acid), sodium menadiol sulfate (2-methyl-1.4-naphthylene-disodium-disulfate) (5).

Under the working conditions used the method failed with propionic and benzoic acids, part of the acids being retained in the filter (5). Vaïsman and Yampol′skaya recommend washing with ethyl alcohol to remove benzoic acid and salicylic acid from the column (56). When a resin of sulfonated hydrocarbon type of the proper particle size (0.2–0.4 mm) is used, propionic acid and benzoic acid may be displaced by washing with water. As could be expected, the aromatic acid requires the larger amount of water (50).

The ion exchange method has further been utilized for the determination of sulfoguaiacolic acid (methyl orange) (56), the preparation of methyl-methanetrisulfonic acid from the potassium salt (37), and the liberation of the free acid from the sodium salt of cellulose-ethanesulfonic acid (53, 35) and hyaluronic acid (25).

N. *Total Salt Content of Vegetable Tanning Liquors*

Cheshire, Brown, and Holmes introduced the ion exchange method in the determination of salt in tanning liquors (10). Their method involves potentiometric titrations of the solution before and after percolation through a cation exchanger in the hydrogen form. The first titration is used to calculate the acidity. The salt content is obtained as a difference between the titrations. In the determination of the acidity the same dilution should be used as that obtained after percolation through the cation exchange column [cf. (32, 8, 55)].

Cheshire *et al.* used the method also for the determination of bound acid in leather. The finely divided leather is extracted with water and subsequently with alkali. The acidity is determined in the former solution, and the total amount of anions according to the ion exchange method. Balfe (3) elaborated the ion exchange method by using conductometric titration to determine salts of strong and weak acids.

As discussed in Chapter II:2 B, organic acids may be adsorbed on cation exchange resins. This may cause considerable errors in the determination. When a suitable resin is selected and dilute solutions and an extremely high flow rate are used, at least 97% of the cations present in tanning liquors will be titrated as H^+ ions in the effluent from the column (2, 54, 27).

O. *Application in Water Analysis*

Several authors have adopted ion exchange procedures for the determination of total salt content of natural waters (29, 14, 23). The water to be investigated is percolated through a cation exchange column containing a sulfonic acid resin in the hydrogen form. After removal of carbon dioxide by bubbling CO_2-free air through the effluent or by boiling, the acids liberated are titrated with standard alkali.

Many natural waters contain chloride as well as sulfate, but in many cases only traces of other anions stable in acid solution (e.g. nitrate) are present. The most practical procedure seems to be to report the result as NaOH consumption in milliequivalents per liter. If chloride is determined by titration with silver nitrate, sulfate may be calculated as the difference, provided only negligible quantities of other anions are present. In certain waters the NaOH consumption may be recalculated into permanent hardness.

Blumer (6) determined the alkalinity of water by titration with 0.1 N HCl (n_1 ml) until $pH = 5.1$ (bromocresol green + methyl red). Afterwards the water was passed through an H^+ exchanger and titrated with standard alkali (n_2 ml). n_1 corresponds to the alkalinity (or bicarbonate hardness); n_2, to the total hardness (provided no sodium ions are present).

The ion exchange method is most convenient for field investigations. It is not necessary to use distilled water for washing, as the determination can be performed with an aliquot of the effluent. In this special case it is practical to use a column of higher capacity than is necessary for one analysis and to re-employ the column several times without regeneration between the determinations.

In the case of waters which contain considerable amounts of alkali metals, except calcium and magnesium, the determination of total salt concentration may be used for an indirect estimation of the alkali metals. This is done by a separate determination of the hardness and calculation of the alkali metals by difference (24).

Robertson and Nielsen (36) employed the method for the determination of total salt concentration in boiler water. These authors used a batch procedure to liberate the acids.

P. *Total Salt Concentration in Blood Serum*

The determination of total base in blood serum has been shortened considerably by Polis and Reinhold (34), utilizing the technique already described. Two-tenths milliliter serum is passed through a microcolumn filled with a sulfonic acid resin in the hydrogen form. The column is washed with water, and the effluent, which contains hydrochloric acid, phosphoric acid, carbon dioxide, protein, etc., is aerated with CO_2-free air to remove the carbon dioxide present and is titrated with standard alkali to the pH of a control sample of serum which has been aerated but not treated with the ion exchanger. Since the base present as bicarbonate is not included in this titration, a separate determination of the CO_2-combining capacity is performed by gasometric measurement.

The results achieved with the ion exchange method agreed closely with those obtained by the time-consuming electrolytic method.

A similar method has been used by Gorter and van Royen (19). These authors take up the effluent from the cation exchange column in a flask containing excess 0.1 N sodium hydroxide. After the column is washed with CO_2-free water, the excess alkali is back-titrated with acid against bromothymol blue. According to Gorter and van Royen, it is not necessary, for practical purposes, to correct for pH differences between the end-point of the titration and the original serum.

2. APPLICATION OF ANION EXCHANGERS

In principle it is possible to use for the determination of total salt concentration an anion exchange resin of a strongly basic type instead of a cation exchanger as described above. By means of the free-base form of the resin, neutral salts, e.g. a sodium sulfate solution, can be converted quantitatively into the free base. The sodium hydroxide formed can be determined by titration in the effluent from the ion exchange column.

This technique has been used by Samuelson and Schramm (51) in studying the following alkali salts: chloride, sulfate, sulfite, orthophosphate, vanadate, and tungstate. The resin Dowex 2 was found to be superior to Amberlite IRA-400 for this special purpose. Excellent results were obtained, the relative error in most experiments being less than 0.1%. In this respect the method is comparable to the cation exchange method. However, the regeneration of the resin and the washing operation are more time-consuming. Consequently there is no reason to use anion exchangers in determinations which can be performed instead by titrating the acids liberated by means of cation exchangers.

In certain analyses where complications occur when using cation exchangers the anion exchange method may be of the utmost interest. Examples are solutions in which the acids corresponding to the anions are unstable or almost insoluble. In analyses of solutions in which the corresponding acids are difficult to estimate accurately by means of titration the method may also be of practical importance. It is therefore obvious that the cation and anion exchange methods supplement each other. The choice between them is usually rather simple. Solutions containing, e.g. alkali sulfates or nitrates are most conveniently analyzed by means of cation exchangers. If cations which give insoluble hydroxides are present, e.g. magnesium or iron, the total salt concentration can be determined by means of cation exchangers but not anion exchangers. On the other hand, the anion exchange method may be preferred for alkali phosphate solutions, since it may be difficult to establish the end-point accurately when cation exchangers are used (without evaporating the bulk of the water). For alkali sulfites, too, the anion exchange method of operation is more simple. With some solutions, such as those containing alkali vanadates, the simple cation exchange method fails, but the problem may be solved in a satisfactory way with the anion exchange technique.

It is obvious that the application of the method is limited to solutions in which the free hydroxides corresponding to the cations present in the original solution are sufficiently soluble and also stable in water or other solvents which may be used. Furthermore, due consideration must be given to the fact that high-molecular-weight anions are not taken up by resins of the common highly cross-linked type. In analyses where high-molecular-weight anions pass quantitatively into the effluent, the method may be used for estimating the cations corresponding to low molecular anions, provided the end-point of the titration can be properly established.

An interesting method which may be referred to in this chapter is a technique devised by Jindra for the determination of alkaloids. According to this author, a weakly basic resin is used to convert alkaloidal salts into the free bases, which are subsequently determined by titration with acid (see Chapter XIX).

BIBLIOGRAPHY

1. Andersson, S.: *Farm. Revy*, **47**, 433 (1948).
2. Atkin, W. R., and Burton, D.: *J. Soc. Leather Trades' Chemists*, **33**, 52 (1949).
3. Balfe, M. P.: *J. Soc. Leather Trades' Chemists*, **32**, 39 (1948); **33**, 197 (1949).
4. Berggren, A., and Björling, C. O.: *Farm. Revy*, **50**, 537 (1951).
5. Björling, C. O.: *Farm. Revy*, **48**, 281 (1949).
6. Blumer, M.: *Experientia*, **9**, 351 (1948).
7. Brunisholz, G., and Bonnet, J.: *Helv. Chim. Acta*, **34**, 2074 (1951).
8. Burton, D., and Lee, G.: *J. Intern. Soc. Leather Trades' Chemists*, **29**, 204 (1945).
9. Burton, D., and Harrison, J. M.: *J. Soc. Leather Trades' Chemists*, **34**, 22 (1950).
10. Cheshire, A., Brown, W. B., and Holmes, N. L.: *J. Soc. Leather Trades' Chemists*, **25**, 254 (1941).
11. Djurfeldt, R., Hansen, J., and Samuelson, O.: *Svensk Kem. Tid.*, **59**, 14 (1947).
12. Erler, K.: *Z. anal. Chem.*, **129**, 209 (1949).
13. Erler, K.: *Z. anal. Chem.*, **131**, 106 (1950).
14. Federova, G. V.: *Izvest. VTI*, **15**, No. 2, 28 (1946).
15. Frizzell, L. D.: *Ind. Eng. Chem.*, Anal. Ed., **16**, 615 (1944).
16. Futterknecht, A.: *Teintex*, **14**, 191 (1949).
17. Goehring, M., and Darge, I.: *Z. anal. Chem.*, **125**, 180 (1943).
18. Golovatyï, R. N.: *Vinodelie i Vinogradarstvo SSSR*, **10**, No. 10, 24 (1950).
19. Gorter, E., and van Royen, A.: *Koninkl. Nederland. Akad. Wetenschap. Proc.*, **51**, 824 (1948).
20. Gustavson, K. H.: *Svensk Kem. Tid.*, **56**, 14 (1944).
21. Gustavson, K. H.: *J. Intern. Soc. Leather Trades' Chemists*, **30**, 264 (1946).
22. Hartler, N., and Samuelson, O.: unpublished.
23. Hilfiger, J. P.: *Chim. anal.*, **31**, 226 (1949).
24. Hoek, H.: *Chimia*, **2**, 227 (1948).
25. Jeanloz, R. W., and Forchielli, E.: *J. Biol. Chem.*, **186**, 495 (1950).
26. Klement, R.: *Z. anorg. Chem.*, **260**, 18 (1949).
27. Lee, H.: *J. Soc. Leather Trades' Chemists*, **34**, 150 (1950).
28. Lur'e, Yu. Yu., and Filippova, N. A.: *Zavodskaya Lab.*, **14**, 159 (1948).

29. Lur'e, Yu. Yu., and Stefanovich, S. N.: *Zavodskaya Lab.*, **13**, 660 (1947).
30. Martin, J. R., and Hayes, J. R.: *Anal. Chem.*, **24**, 182 (1952).
31. Nietsch, W. von, and Heinrichs, M.: *Kolloid-Z.*, **104**, 51 (1943).
32. Okell, R. L.: *J. Intern. Soc. Leather Trades' Chemists*, **29**, 56 (1945).
33. Orlova, L. M.: *Zhur. Anal. Khim.*, **5**, 370 (1950).
34. Polis, B. D., and Reinhold, J. G.: *J. Biol. Chem.*, **156**, 231 (1944).
35. Regestad, S. O., and Samuelson, O.: *Svensk Kem. Tid.*, **61**, 8 (1949).
36. Robertson, R. S., and Nielsen, M. F.: *Power*, **95**, No. 2, 87 (1951).
37. Samén, E.: *Acta Chem. Scand.*, **4**, 397 (1950).
38. Samuelson, O.: *Z. anal. Chem.*, **116**, 328 (1939).
39. Samuelson, O.: *Svensk Kem. Tid.*, **51**, 195 (1939).
40. Samuelson, O.: *Svensk Kem. Tid.*, **52**, 115 (1940).
41. Samuelson, O.: *Svensk Kem. Tid.*, **52**, 241 (1940).
42. Samuelson, O.: *Svensk Kem. Tid.*, **54**, 124 (1942).
43. Samuelson, O.: Diss., Tekn. Högskolan, Stockholm, 1944.
44. Samuelson, O.: *Svensk Kem. Tid.*, **56**, 277 (1944).
45. Samuelson, O.: *Svensk Papperstidn.*, **48**, 55 (1945).
46. Samuelson, O.: *Svensk Kem. Tid.*, **57**, 158 (1945).
47. Samuelson, O.: *Tek. Tid.*, **76**, 561 (1946).
48. Samuelson, O.: *IVA*, **17**, 5 (1946).
49. Samuelson, O.: *Svensk Kem. Tid.*, **58**, 247 (1946).
50. Samuelson, O.: unpublished.
51. Samuelson, O., and Schramm, K.: *Svensk Kem. Tid.*, **63**, 307 (1951).
52. Scholander, A.: *Svensk Papperstidn.*, **53**, 681 (1950).
53. Timell, T.: *Svensk Papperstidn.*, **51**, 254 (1948); Diss., Tekn. Högskolan, Stockholm, 1950.
54. Tolliday, J. D., Thompson, G. W. H., and Forman, G.: *J. Soc. Leather Trades' Chemists*, **32**, 291 (1948); **34**, 221 (1950).
55. Tweddell, G. H., and May, M.: *J. Soc. Leather Trades' Chemists*, **32**, 268 (1948).
56. Vaĭsman, G. A., and Yampol'skaya, M. M.: *Zavodskaya Lab.*, **16**, 621 (1950).
57. Wickbold, R.: *Z. anal. Chem.*, **132**, 241 (1951).
58. Wiesenberger, E.: *Mikrochemie ver. Mikrochim. Acta*, **30**, 176 (1942).
59. Wiesenberger, E.: *Mikrochemie ver. Mikrochim. Acta*, **30**, 241 (1942).

CHAPTER IX

Removal of Interfering Ions in Inorganic Analysis

1. APPLICATION OF CATION EXCHANGERS

The separation of interfering ions of opposite charge by means of cation exchange resins is one of the most important applications of the ion exchange method in inorganic analysis. Ordinarily sulfonic acid resins are employed. These resins are used in the free-acid form except in special cases where complications occur in acid medium; in these separations the salt form (e.g. NH_4^+) is substituted. Resins of carboxylic type have not found application in this field as yet.

A. *Determination of Alkali Metals in the Presence of Different Anions*

It is a well-known fact to any analyst that many anions interfere in the determination of the alkali metals. A number of separation methods, chiefly by precipitation, have therefore been used to remove different interfering anions. Most of the methods are time-consuming, and errors often occur because of coprecipitation. The precipitates often have to be dissolved and reprecipitated in order to avoid too great a loss of the cation to be determined. These methods require great skill if accurate results are to be obtained.

Many of the separations may easily be performed according to the ion exchange method. This fact has been demonstrated in papers by Samuelson and Runeberg (27, 23, 24, 25, 32).

A separation of sulfate and phosphate from potassium and sodium can readily be performed by means of a cation exchanger in the hydrogen form. The cations retained in the column are removed by treating the exchanger with hydrochloric acid. The same procedure has been adopted for solutions containing different complex cyanides.

For solutions containing vanadate, chromate, molybdate, tungstate, and phosphomolybdate a cation exchanger in the hydrogen form cannot be used, as part of the anions are retained because of transformation into cations, reduction or precipitation. The separation may be easily performed, however, with a column containing a cation exchanger in the ammonium form.

Permanganate is reduced even by the ammonium form of the resin, and therefore the ion exchange method cannot be used to determine alkali in the presence of permanganate.

The separation of sulfate and phosphate from potassium and sodium has also been performed by passing the solution through an anion exchange column filled with a resin in the chloride form (cf. section 2).

a. POTASSIUM IN THE PRESENCE OF SULFATE

For samples which contain potassium as the only cation the potassium content is easily determined by running the solution through a cation exchange column in the hydrogen form and titrating the effluent with standard alkali as described in Chapter VIII.

Gravimetric determination of potassium is ordinarily employed for solutions which, besides potassium, contain other cations such as sodium and magnesium. In most cases the precipitation is made as perchlorate. Sulfate ions interfere with the determination and are therefore removed before the precipitation of potassium perchlorate. Earlier, the usual procedure was the removal of sulfate as barium sulfate. When potassium is determined gravimetrically as K_2PtCl_6, the solution should also be free from sulfate. Runeberg (23) made a thorough investigation of the utilization of cation exchange resins for this separation. Mixtures containing known amounts of K^+, Na^+, Mg^{2+}, SO_4^{2-}, and Cl^- were analyzed for K^+. For 16 determinations a maximum relative error of 0.6% was obtained.

The method was also applied for determination of potassium in kainite and other potash salts for fertilizer purposes. Good agreement was obtained between the ion exchange method and the precipitation method described above. The ion exchange method is simpler and more rapid in operation and shows better reproducibility. The method has been accepted as the standard procedure for the Agricultural Chemical Control Stations in Sweden.

The manner of operation is illustrated by the following example. Twenty-five milliliters solution containing 0.500 g potash salt is percolated through a column containing 12–15 meq of a sulfonic acid resin in the hydrogen form. The column is rinsed with water until the effluent is neutral (100–150 ml). The total time required for these operations is about 20 min. The ions retained by the column are eluted by passing 100 ml 4 N hydrochloric acid. The effluent is evaporated to dryness, and potassium ions are determined according to the perchlorate method.

b. SODIUM AND POTASSIUM IN THE PRESENCE OF PHOSPHATE

In the determination of alkali metals as chloride or sulfate the phosphoric acid must be eliminated. When precipitating sodium in the form of sodium-uranyl-zinc acetate, it is essential that the solution be free from phosphate. Potassium can be precipitated from a pure solution of a potassium salt by using platinum chloride even in the presence of phosphoric acid; but in the separation of potassium and sodium by the platinum method the removal of the phosphoric acid is usually prescribed. If potassium is determined by the perchlorate method, the phosphoric acid is usually eliminated first (cf. W. F. Hillebrand and G. E. F. Lundell, *Applied Inorganic Analysis*, New York, 1929).

The quantitative separation by the ion exchange method of sodium, potassium, and lithium from solutions containing phosphate was demonstrated by Runeberg and Samuelson (24). The procedure has great advantages compared to the usual methods of precipitating phosphate by addition of ferric, zinc, barium, or calcium salts. The ion exchange method is not only more rapid but also considerably more accurate. When this method is used, complications arising from the presence of sulfate are also avoided.

Analysis by the ion exchange method is best carried out by passing the sample solution through a filter layer of hydrogen-saturated ion exchanger, the alkali ions being taken up quantitatively during the passage. After water is passed through, the alkali metals are displaced by an excess of hydrochloric acid. The effluent obtained, the cation solution, containing only chloride anions, is evaporated to dryness. The chlorides are determined either by weighing or by titration with silver nitrate. When only one alkali metal is present, the titration is preferable, since rapid evaporation may be carried out in a glass beaker of such a type that the disposal of ammonium salts, which possibly will be present, may be carried out in the beaker itself.

In the presence of several alkali metals, the total may be determined gravimetrically, after which separation may take place in a straightforward manner by the usual precipitation methods. If metallic cations other than the alkali metals are present, it may in certain cases be necessary, as in earlier procedures, to remove these by usual precipitation methods. When the ion exchange method is used in connection with the separation of the disturbing anions, certain metals, such as iron and cobalt, may also be eliminated by binding them in anionic complexes, e.g. as cyanides. The complexes are so stable that these metals pass the column quantitatively, whereas the alkalies are taken up entirely (see next section).

Use of the ion exchange method in the analysis of technical products has also been studied. As an example was chosen the determination of sodium in technical disodium phosphate and so-called salt phosphate (a mixture of disodium phosphate and sodium chloride). Ion exchange determinations were carried out by the evaporation of the cation solution in a beaker followed by titration with silver nitrate. Another example studied was the determination of potassium in a mixed fertilizer consisting of superphosphate, ammonium sulfate, and potassium salt, by precipitation with platinum chloride.

The procedure already given for the determination of alkali metals in the presence of sulfate may be followed. If the ion exchanger shows a pronounced tendency to take up phosphoric acid, it may be necessary to increase the amount of water and the time taken in washing. The reproducibility in the ion exchange experiments was very good and in agreement with determinations after separation through precipitation, where dissolving and reprecipitation were used in the precipitation method.

The results of the analyses of salt phosphate, shown in Table 10, give some idea of the reproducibility and advantages of the ion exchange method.

TABLE 10

Determination of Na_2O in "Salt Phosphate" ($Na_2HPO_4 + NaCl$)

Gravimetric Determination as Na_2SO_4 after Removal of Phosphate as Basic Ferric Phosphate		Ion Exchange Method
% Na_2O after First Precipitation	% Na_2O Total	% Na_2O
21.05	21.94	21.98
20.88	21.78	21.98
20.94	21.90	22.00
21.00	21.90	21.92

c. Sodium and Potassium in the Presence of Complex Cyanides

Many cyanide complexes are so stable that they may be passed through a bed of cation exchange resin without decomposition. Samuelson (32) studied the cyanides listed in Table 11 and found that all the separations were complete with H^+ resins. The ion exchange was performed as described above. Potassium or sodium was determined according to three different methods:

1. Titration of the solution with alkali against methyl red after passage through a H^+ resin.
2. Weighing as chloride after evaporating the cation solution obtained after regeneration with hydrochloric acid.
3. Dissolving in water the chlorides obtained according to method 2 and passing them through a H^+ column. The effluent was titrated with standard alkali.

The results given in Table 11 are average values from two determinations.

TABLE 11

Determination of Alkali Metals in Complex Cyanides

Substance	% Potassium or Sodium			
	Calculated	Method 1	Method 2	Method 3
$K_3Fe(CN)_6$	35.63	35.65	35.71	35.68
$K_4Fe(CN)_6 \cdot 3H_2O$	37.03	36.96	37.10	37.09
$Na_2Fe(CN)_5NO \cdot 2H_2O$	15.44	15.42	15.49	15.46
$K_3Cr(CN)_6$	36.05	—	36.15	36.15
$K_3Co(CN)_6$	35.29	35.34	35.30	35.32
$K_4Mo(CN)_8 \cdot 2H_2O$	31.50	31.49	31.55	31.53
$K_4W(CN)_8 \cdot 2H_2O$	26.76	26.73	26.80	26.85

For complex chromium cyanide, method 1 cannot be adopted, as the liberated acid is not stable enough. However, the separation is quantitative, and methods 2 and 3 have given good agreement with the calculated value.

Complex zinc and nickel cyanides were also investigated. The separation was not complete.

By converting certain metallic cations to complex cyanides, a quantitative separation of the alkali metals from these ions may be carried out by the ion exchange technique. This method was studied by Samuelson, who determined sodium and potassium in the presence of iron or cobalt, or mixtures containing both iron and cobalt. The solutions were treated with ammonium sulfite to reduce the iron to a state of divalency. Hydrocyanic acid was added, corresponding to about 7 mols per mol of iron and cobalt, respectively. After the first precipitate had dissolved, the solution was oxidized with hydrogen peroxide and boiled for a few minutes. The solutions were then analyzed in the usual way with the ion exchanger. Deviations between calculated and found values were not higher than 0.3%. The method is most convenient in separations where the ion exchange method has to be used anyhow to remove interfering anions as sulfate or phosphate (32).

For chromium, molybdenum, and tungsten the method is of less interest, since separation is easily performed as chromate, molybdate, or tungstate, as will be described in the next section (cf. also section 2 B).

d. Sodium and Potassium in the Presence of Chromate, Molybdate, Vanadate, Tungstate, Phosphomolybdate, Phosphotungstate, and Silicotungstate

Samuelson (27) devised a rapid and accurate method for the determination of sodium and potassium in the presence of vanadium. The method has been used, with excellent results, for analysis of technical vanadium catalysts for a number of years [cf. (11)].

Vanadium not present as vanadate in the original sample is oxidized by hydrogen peroxide before separation can be carried out.

The separation is performed by passing the solution through a cation exchanger in the ammonium form. After rinsing with water, all vanadate ions are obtained in the effluent, whereas the alkali metals are quantitatively retained by the resin. When the resin is treated with hydrochloric acid, the alkali metals are quantitatively eluted and may be easily determined in the cation solution. Owing to the rather low solubility of ammonium vanadate the solution to be analyzed should not be too concentrated.

After the regeneration with hydrochloric acid and subsequent rinsing with water, the resin is transformed into the ammonium form by passing $0.5\,N$ ammonium chloride or ammonium sulfate solution through the column until the filtrate is neutral against methyl red. After rinsing with water the column is ready for use. The ion exchanger used in the first experiments — sulfonated butadiene rubber — had a very porous structure, and with this type of ion exchanger the transformation into the ammonium form could be performed in about 15 min. With ion exchangers of the technical strongly cross-linked type, which were used in later experiments, this step is rather time-consuming.

According to Runeberg and Samuelson (25), the transformation of the H^+ resin into NH_4^+ resin is carried out more simply by passing ammonia through the column until the effluent is alkaline. Afterwards the resin bed is rinsed with water. Excess ammonia is difficult to remove, but it is not necessary to remove the ammonia quantitatively. The treatment with ammonia and water can be made in a total of 10 min. The authors showed that the method previously used for vanadate solutions can also be adopted for solutions containing chromate, molybdate, tungstate, and some heteropolyacids, e.g. phosphomolybdate, phosphotungstate, and silicotungstate.

Lindquist (18) used this separation method in his investigations concerning the formulae of paramolybdates. Sodium was determined in the cation solution as $(UO_2)_3NaMg(CH_3CO_2)_9 \cdot 8H_2O$.

The accuracy of the ion exchange method may be seen from some results of Samuelson's experiments on vanadate solutions (Table 12). The cation solution was evaporated to dryness for analysis. The ammonium salts were eliminated, and the alkali chloride was titrated potentiometrically with 0.1 N silver nitrate.

TABLE 12

Determination of Alkali Metals in Vanadate Solutions

Solution to be Analyzed	% Alkali as Vanadate	Milliequivalents Na^+ or K^+ Added	Found
Sodium metavanadate	100	2.162	2.164; 2.160
Sodium metavanadate + sulfate	70	2.162	2.166; 2.160
Sodium metavanadate + chloride	50	2.162	2.159; 2.165
Potassium metavanadate	100	2.273	2.270; 2.268
Potassium metavanadate + sulfate	50	2.273	2.273; 2.270

Procedure: The solution to be analyzed is percolated through a cation exchange column: 12 × 140 mm; Wofatit KS [NH_4^+; 0.2–0.4 mm]. The total time of percolation and rinsing with 100 ml water may be about 20 min. The column is treated with 100 ml 4 N hydrochloric acid (about 15 min). The cation solution is evaporated and ammonium chloride driven off. The alkali chloride is weighed or titrated with silver nitrate. If more than one alkali metal is present, separation is performed as usual.

In order to make the column ready for a subsequent cycle, washing is performed with water to displace the greatest part of the hydrochloric acid. Afterwards 0.1 N ammonia is passed through until the effluent is alkaline. After being rinsed with 200 ml water the column can be used again.

B. *Determination of Sulfate in the Presence of Various Cations*

In the accurate determination of sulfate it is usually only the precipitation as barium sulfate which is considered. The composition of the barium sulfate precipitate is dependent to a high degree on the ions present in the test solution and their concentrations.

The conditions of precipitation, such as the temperature and concentration of the solution, as well as the way in which the barium chloride is added, are of the greatest importance. An effort should, naturally, be made to obtain the purest possible barium sulfate precipitate, but this point has not been stressed in most of the many investigations of this system which have been published. On the contrary, many authors have attempted to obtain barium sulfate which was more contaminated than necessary in order to compensate for errors resulting in a low precipitate value. When such methods are used, it is often difficult to obtain the same conditions as those under which the compensation method was worked out. Erroneous results are, therefore, often obtained. Instead, the determination should be carried out in such a way that the purest possible precipitate is weighed, and for the contamination and other sources of error which may be unavoidable a correction factor should be introduced.

Practically pure barium sulfate may be prepared, as is known, if a pure, sufficiently dilute sulfuric acid solution to which a little hydrochloric acid has been added is slowly precipitated dropwise, while boiling, with a barium chloride solution.

If, for instance, a solution containing ammonium salts is precipitated in the usual way dropwise with barium chloride solution, too low values are obtained, since ammonium sulfate is coprecipitated. In this case, as a compensation, precipitation is carried out rapidly, as a result of which barium chloride is coprecipitated. This compensation is, however, purely conditional and errors easily creep in. The quantity of ammonium sulfate depends on the concentration of ammonium ions, which often is not precisely known. Errors depend first and foremost on the reproducibility by different persons of a "rapid precipitation," especially since the degree of agitation has shown itself to be of the greatest importance.

One way to eliminate the possibilities of error by the influence of various cations is to remove or decrease the concentration of interfering ions before the actual sulfate determination. When complete removal of these ions is desired, precipitation has usually been employed. In many cases sulfate ions are coprecipitated, and thus losses easily occur. Therefore it is often necessary to redissolve and precipitate again.

Furthermore, through these operations other ions are usually carried into the test solution, and these may be coprecipitated with the barium sulfate. A classic example is Lunge's method for the determination of sulfate in solutions containing iron. According to this method, the iron salts are removed by precipitation with ammonia, this removal being carried out in a certain precise manner so that the formation of basic iron sulfate is prevented as much as possible. In the iron-free solution the sulfate cannot be accurately determined because of the ammonium salts introduced. Hintz and Weber's method of rapid precipitation is used here instead.

Samuelson (27, 28, 30) has shown that interfering cations in many cases may be removed from the sample by passing the solution through a column containing a cation exchanger (sulfonic acid type) in the hydrogen form. The effluent contains hydrogen ions as the only cation, and the determination may be carried out with great precision in this solution.

This method has its greatest importance with solutions containing calcium and iron, where errors occurring through direct precipitation are considerable and the method of separation is troublesome. However, it has not been possible to use this method with solutions containing green chromium salts, where, as mentioned in Chapter VIII: 1 D, an incomplete exchange occurs. According to Goehring and Darge, this method is not feasible with solutions containing bismuth and antimony, since these solutions must be maintained so acid that uptake does not occur (6).

When the test solution contains sulfate ions as the only anion, the sulfate ions are naturally determined by titrating the liberated acid. If, apart from sulfate, only anions for which the corresponding acids are volatile, e.g. hydrochloric acid and nitric acid, are present, then the determination may be carried out by titration instead of gravimetrically after the volatile acids have been removed by evaporation over a water bath.

a. Determination of Sulfur in Pyrites

Samuelson (28, 31) devised a method for the determination of sulfur in pyrites based on the principle just mentioned. The sample was dissolved in a mixture of hydrochloric and nitric acids. After dilution the solution was percolated through the H^+-cation exchange column, and after washing with water the sulfate was determined in the effluent as barium sulfate.

The reproducibility was extremely good, and the results were only slightly lower than those obtained with Lunge's method (Kastner's modification described in Lunge–Berl, *Chemisch-Technische Untersuchungsmethoden*, II, Berlin, 1932). Some results are presented in Table 13.

It may be pointed out that the ion exchange method is less time-consuming than Lunge's method and may be carried out with good results by analysts without extensive experience. Good results with Lunge's method are obtained only by skilled analysts with practical training.

TABLE 13

Determination of Sulfur in Pyrites

Pyrite Sample	% S According to the Ion Exchange Method	% S According to Lunge's Method
I	49.25; 49.29; 49.21; 49.20; 49.23	49.43; 49.34; 49.35
II	43.91; 43.89; 43.96	44.10; 44.00; 44.09

Procedure: Five-tenths gram of the finely divided pyrite sample is treated with 10 ml of a mixture of 3 vol nitric acid (sp. gr. 1.4) and 1 vol conc. hydrochloric acid. After evaporation on a steam bath the residue is dissolved in 5 ml conc. hydrochloric acid and evaporated again. After dissolution in 1 ml hydrochloric acid under heating, the solution is diluted to about 100 ml with hot water and filtered through a small filter.

The solution is percolated through a cation exchanger in the hydrogen form and displaced with water till the filtrate is neutral. The effluent is heated to boiling and precipitated by adding $BaCl_2$ solution slowly.

If an iron-free effluent is to be obtained, the ion exchanger should have a capacity of at least 30 meq and the filtration time must not be too short. About 60 min with an appropriate ion exchanger is a suitable time for filtration and washing. Another important point is that the acid concentration in the test solution must not be too high.

b. Determination of Sulfur in Nickel and Copper

A method for the determination of sulfur in nickel and copper which has been described by Lur'e and Filippova (21) is based upon the same principle.

The metal (4–5 g) is dissolved in nitric acid. The excess acid is driven off, and after dilution with 200 ml water the solution is passed through a sulfonic acid resin in the hydrogen form. In order to achieve a quantitative uptake, the authors recommend that the pH of the solution be adjusted to 5.5–6 by adding ammonia before the passage through the resin. After the column is washed with water, the effluent is evaporated. After dilution with 10 ml water and 0.5 ml concentrated hydrochloric acid the sulfate is precipitated with barium chloride.

c. Volumetric Determination of Sulfate

As already mentioned (Chapter I), the first application of ion exchange for inorganic analysis was Bahrdt's method for the determination of sulfate in natural waters (2). Bahrdt removed the calcium and magnesium ions by exchange with the sodium ions of a Permutit filter. Afterwards a measured volume of standard barium chloride was added, and excess barium ions were titrated with potassium palmitate against phenolphthalein. Some refinements in this method were introduced by Kehren and Stommel (12).

A similar procedure was adopted by Abrahamczik and Blümel (1) for the determination of sulfate by the rhodizonate method. The authors recommended the removal of interfering cations by sodium zeolite (Permutit). Experiments were made with zinc sulfate solution.

C. *Determination of Chloride in the Presence of Various Metal Ions*

In the determination of chloride by titration with silver nitrate (chromate indicator; Mohr), a series of various metallic cations interfere, e.g. copper, lead, and iron. Use has been made, therefore, of other titration methods, such as various modifications of Volhard's method. These are less accurate than Mohr's method. However, a potentiometric titration may be carried out to a high degree of accuracy also in the presence of various metallic salts which cause interference when titrating according to Mohr's method. Therefore the determination of chloride usually presents no difficulties.

If apparatus for potentiometric titration is not available, titration by Mohr's method is recommended after the interfering metallic cations have been removed by the ion exchange method. The fact that an exchange of various metallic cations for hydrogen ions in chloride solutions presents no difficulties has been pointed out in Chapter VIII: 1B. The liberated acid is neutralized with chloride-free alkali and titrated according to Mohr (after evaporating part of the water to increase the accuracy).

Sometimes it is possible to use a cation exchanger in the sodium form instead of the hydrogen form (26). In the former determination the effluent is neutral. However, it is usually preferable to use an H^+ resin and neutralize the effluent before titration, as by this technique the risk of complications due to hydrolysis is eliminated.

D. *Application to Phosphate Analysis*

One of the most important applications of the ion exchange method is to the analysis of phosphates. Samuelson has studied this application in several papers (26, 29, 30, 31) and the method has been used in practice since 1940. The metal cations are retained in a column containing a cation exchange resin in the hydrogen form and are in this manner separated from the phosphoric acid, which passes quantitatively into the effluent. The metal cations are eluted with 4 N hydrochloric acid and determined in the phosphate-free cation solution. The phosphoric acid can be determined in the effluent either gravimetrically or by titration. It may be pointed out that, whereas the separation is quantitative in the presence of orthophosphate, iron and aluminum are not quantitatively retained in solutions containing pyrophosphate or polymetaphosphate (29) (cf. Chapter VIII: 1 E).

The method has been used for the determination of calcium, magnesium, iron, aluminum, and phosphoric acid in phosphate rocks and commercial dicalcium phosphate.

In regard to the practical performance it should be observed that phosphoric acid has a marked tendency to be adsorbed on certain types of cation exchange resins. Therefore the use of a greater amount of wash water is necessary in the washing step than for solutions containing, e.g., chloride and sulfate (see Chapter II: 2 B). Furthermore a slight amount of iron phosphate and aluminum phosphate may be precipitated in the column during the washing step if washing is performed with water. To eliminate this source of error, slightly acidified water ($\sim 0.015\ N$ HCl) is recommended.

a. Calcium, Magnesium, Iron, and Aluminum in Phosphate Rock

Studies of the determination of iron, aluminum, calcium, and magnesium in known mixtures with phosphoric acid and in phosphate rock have been published by Samuelson (29, 30, 31). Excellent agreement was obtained. Most thoroughly studied was the determination of iron and aluminum in phosphate rock, where the ion exchange method was compared with the formerly customary method of Glaser and with the removal of phosphoric acid with molybdate. The ion exchange method was shown to be superior to the other methods.

Procedure: Weigh 5-g sample of ground material into a 400-ml beaker. Add 50 ml concentrated hydrochloric acid, cover with a watch glass, and boil gently for 1 hr. Add 15 ml concentrated nitric acid and evaporate to dryness on a steam bath. Add 15 ml concentrated hydrochloric acid, evaporate to dryness, and bake there for 1 hr to dehydrate the silica and expel hydrofluoric acid. Dissolve in 15 ml concentrated hydrochloric acid under heating. Part of the hydrochloric acid is evaporated during this process. (There should not be too much excess acid in the solution, or else an increased amount of ion exchanger will be required.) Dilute with water to about 50 ml and filter. The filtrate is collected in a 500-ml flask. After dilution to the mark, 50 ml of the solution (corresponding to 0.5-g sample) is passed through an ion exchange column containing a cation exchanger in the hydrogen form. With a suitable resin of sulfonic acid type (particle size 0.2–0.4 mm) an exchange capacity of about 25 meq is sufficient. The column is rinsed with 200–250 ml 0.015 N hydrochloric acid, the total time for filtration and rinsing being 60 min. Phosphoric acid can be determined in the collected effluent.

Regeneration is made with 4 N hydrochloric acid. About 150 ml is required for complete regeneration at a flow rate of 2 ml sqcm^{-1} min^{-1}. In the effluent — cation solution — iron and aluminum are determined by precipitation with ammonia, calcium is precipitated as oxalate, and magnesium is precipitated as magnesium ammonium phosphate.

Edelshteïn and Petatskiï (4) applied this method to the determination of calcium and magnesium hardness in boiler water containing phosphate. After the sorption step the cations are eluted with dilute hydrochloric acid; the eluate is neutralized with sodium hydroxide against phenolphthalein, and the hardness is determined by the oleate method. The excess of phosphates in the boiler water may be easily calculated if the total phosphate concentration is determined.

b. Phosphorus in Phosphate Rock

The effluent from the column obtained as described above contains all the phosphorus in the original sample as phosphoric acid. As no metal cations are present, the gravimetric determination as magnesium pyrophosphate can be performed with high accuracy (31).

A determination by titration with alkali can also be performed. The equivalence point may be determined by potentiometric titration or by the use of two indicators. First the hydrochloric acid is neutralized and phosphoric acid is titrated as a monobasic acid. After this point is reached, the second indicator is added and the titration continued to the second end-point. Since the change of the pH near the first equivalence point is not very pronounced, the equivalence point is difficult to observe. Therefore this method is less accurate than the gravimetric procedure mentioned above. If it is desired to make the determination by alkali titration, evaporation of the effluent to a small volume is recommended (30). Methyl orange and phenolphthalein may be used as indicators.

Helrich and Rieman (8) have suggested a rapid method for direct titration (without evaporation) with methyl red and phenolphthalein as indicators. The accurate adjustment of the solution to the designated pH values requires the aid of comparison buffers. For the analysis of two samples of phosphate rock obtained from the National Bureau of Standards a mean deviation of only 0.07 % is reported.

c. COLORIMETRIC DETERMINATION OF PHOSPHATE AFTER RE-
MOVAL OF IRON

Colorimetric methods are the most suitable for the determination of phosphate in low concentration. The most frequently used methods are determination of the phosphate as molybdophosphoric acid, sometimes after reduction to so-called molybdenum blue, and as molybdovanadophosphoric acid. Errors may be caused by the presence of various components in the samples, particularly iron and silica.

Interfering cations may be eliminated simply by their removal by means of cation exchangers. This method was used by Lagerström and Samuelson (16) in investigations on the colorimetric determination of phosphoric acid in sulfite waste liquor. The silica was removed by treatment with hydrofluoric acid. The colorimetric measurements were carried out according to the molybdovanadophosphoric acid method. According to Kortüm et al. (15), the method cannot be used for determination of phosphorus in steel. The authors report that it is impossible to wash out phosphoric acid quantitatively from the ion exchanger in the presence of a large excess of iron.

Procedure: Ten milliliters sulfite waste liquor is filtered through a column of sulfonic acid resin: 10 × 80 mm; Wofatit KS [H⁺; 0.2–0.4 mm]. The liquor is washed out with 15 ml distilled water. The total time for filtration and washing is 20 min. The effluent and the washing water are transferred to a platinum crucible and concentrated to a small volume by heating with an infrared lamp. After neutralization with 0.5 N sodium carbonate solution the sample is evaporated to dryness, and ashed at 600°C. One milliliter sulfuric acid 1:1 and 10 ml hydrofluoric acid are added to the ash, and the sample is then evaporated on a water bath. The sulfuric acid is removed by heating on an electric plate. The residue is ignited over a gas flame and fused with 0.5 g potassium-sodium carbonate for 20 min, after which the melt is dissolved in about 15 ml water. The sample is acidified with nitric acid (1:2) and transferred to a 100-ml standard flask. More nitric acid is added, making the total addition 12 ml, and the sample is heated in a steam bath for 30 min. After cooling, 10 ml 0.25% ammonium vanadate solution and 10 ml 5% ammonium molybdate solution are added and the solution is made up to the mark with distilled water. After 15 min the transmission is determined at 465 mμ with a photoelectric colorimeter.

E. *Colorimetric Determination of Silica after Removal of Iron*

Colorimetric methods for the determination of silica as silicomolybdic acid or reduction products of this acid are particularly important for products with low content of silica, e.g. water, but are also of interest for rapid analysis of products with high silica content.

It is a well-known fact that ferric salts and phosphate ions interfere with the determinations. The best method to eliminate the color of the phosphomolybdic acid seems to be the addition of certain organic acids, as oxalic or citric acids. These do not change the color of the silicomolybdic acid. However, an iron content of the same magnitude as the silica content has no observable effect on the colorimetric determination of silica as silicomolybdic acid.

In investigations concerning determination of silica in sulfite waste liquor, Lagerström, Samuelson, and Scholander (17) observed that even small amounts of iron cause errors, probably because of the simultaneous presence of phosphate ions. The authors removed the ferric ions by filtering the liquor through a column with cation exchanger in the hydrogen form. At the same time the calcium ions were removed, thus simplifying the continued work. The effect of phosphoric acid was eliminated by addition of citric acid before the colorimetric determination.

The method was controlled by analyzing solutions containing known amounts of silica. Some data are presented in Table 14. The method has been used in practice for analysis of sulfite waste liquor and cooking acid.

Procedure: The ion exchange is performed as described above (section 1: Dc). After · evaporation and burning, the ashes are fused with 1 g sodium-potassium carbonate for 20 min, after which the melt is dissolved in 15 ml water. The solution is neutralized with dilute hydrochloric acid, phenolphthalein being used as indicator, and transferred to a 100-ml flask, which is filled to the mark. Then 50 ml is transferred to another

TABLE 14

Determination of Silica after Percolation through an H^+ resin

Added, mg per liter			Found, mg per liter
Fe	P_2O_5	SiO_2	SiO_2
60	24	30	30
—	—	22	21
—	—	60	60

flask of the same volume. To both flasks are added 20 ml water and 2 ml dilute hydro-chloric acid (1:1). Afterwards 2 ml 20% ammonium molybdate is added to one of the flasks. It is left for 10 min; then 4 ml 10% citric acid is added to both flasks. The flasks are then filled to the marks, and after the solution is filtered through glass filter (Jena 3G4) the colorimetric determinations are immediately carried out at 18–22°C (440 mμ).

A similar method has been devised by Honda for the determination of silica in steel and iron (9).

Procedure: To 0.1–1 g of sample, dissolved in 6 N nitric acid on a water bath, a few ml H_2O_2 is added. After oxidation with 5 ml 1% $KMnO_4$ the solution is reduced with SO_2 and diluted to 100 ml. Then 5–20 ml is passed through a column containing sulfonic acid resin in the sodium form (capacity 1 g steel per 100 ml resin). Silica is determined colorimetrically in the effluent after addition of hydrochloric acid and ammonium molybdate.

F. *Separation of Fluoride from Iron, Aluminum, and Beryllium*

Several cations interfere in the colorimetric determination of fluoride in natural waters. Honda (10) found that the interfering ions can be removed by percolating the water through a resin of sulfonic acid type. Fluoride can be determined colorimetrically in the effluent, e.g. according to the aluminum-haematoxylin method. The procedure has been used also by Shimizu (37).

G. *Determination of Uranium in Silicate Rocks and Slags*

By extraction with ether small amounts of uranyl nitrate can be separated quantitatively from solutions containing large amounts of other elements, e.g. iron. The extraction method may be used in connection with determination of uranium in silicate rocks and metallurgical slags. Helger and Rynninger (7) found that phosphate and sulfate ions disturb the ether extraction and must be removed before it. The ion exchange method was found to be suitable for this separation.

Procedure: A 1–5-g rock sample is decomposed with hydrochloric and nitric acids. After centrifugation the solution is evaporated and the residue dissolved in 7 ml nitric acid and 20 ml water. The insoluble residue is treated with nitric and hydrofluoric acids. The hydrofluoric acid is driven off by repeated evaporations with nitric acid. The mass is dissolved as above.

The solutions are combined and passed through a sulfonic acid resin: 20 × 400; Wofatit KS [H$^+$; 0.2–0.4 mm]. The solution must be moderately acid (< 0.5 N). After rinsing with water till the effluent is neutral, the cations are eluted with 3 N hydrochloric acid until all the iron is liberated. The authors observed that uranium is eluted before iron, whereas titanium is even more difficult to remove than iron. About 200 ml hydrochloric acid is usually sufficient. The cation solution is evaporated, and nitric acid is added to remove the chloride ions.

After addition of nitric acid, saturated barium nitrate solution, and permanganate till the solution is distinctly pink, the solution is saturated with ammonium nitrate and extracted with ether. Extraction is performed for 2 hr in a special apparatus. Uranium is determined after evaporation of ether by precipitation as oxyquinolate or colorimetrically as ferrocyanide.

H. *Determination of Selenium*

Samuelson (33) found that iron, aluminum, cobalt, manganese, and zinc ions interfere in the polarographic determination of selenite according to Schwaer and Suchy. By means of an H$^+$ cation exchanger it is possible to separate these cations easily from the selenite. After the separation the selenite can be determined polarographically.

The ion exchange is performed in the usual way. Dissolved oxygen is removed by bubbling nitrogen through 5 ml of the effluent or by addition of sulfite. One milliliter of buffer solution (1 N NH$_3$ + 1 N NH$_4$Cl) and 0.02 ml of 2% solution of tylose are added, and the selenite concentration is determined polarographically.

A similar ion exchange procedure has been used by Yoshino (40) for the removal of interfering cations (Zn and Fe) before the colorimetric determination of selenium. The author reports that selenite ions pass quantitatively into the effluent at pH 0.7–5.0.

I. *Iodometric Determination of Arsenic*

Odencrantz and Rieman (22) devised a method for the iodometric determination of arsenate after the removal of interfering cations by means of cation exchange. The method was applied to the analysis of insecticides.

Procedure: A 0.2-g sample dissolved in concentrated nitric acid is oxidized with potassium bromate. After evaporation to dryness the residue is dissolved in 2 ml 6 N hydrochloric acid, diluted and filtered if there is any residue. The solution (about 40 ml) is passed through a column of cation exchange resin (sulfonic acid type) in the hydrogen form (e.g. 12 ml Dowex 50). After washing with water the combined filtrate and wash water is made 4 N with hydrochloric acid, 1 g sodium bicarbonate and 1 g potassium iodide are added, and after 5 min the solution is titrated with 0.05 N sodium thiosulfate.

J. *Determination of Arsenic and Phosphorus in Nickel and Copper*

Lur'e and Filippova (21) applied the ion exchange method to the determination of small amounts of arsenic and phosphorus in nickel and copper alloys. With samples containing less than 0.01% As or 0.005% P it is recommended that 2 g be dissolved in nitric acid and 20 mg Fe be added. After addition of ammonia the precipitate is separated and dissolved in sulfuric acid. The solution is diluted with water to 100 ml and passed through a cation exchanger in the hydrogen form to remove the cations. Arsenate and phosphate are determined colorimetrically in the effluent according to standard procedures (F. B. Snell and C. Snell, *Colorimetric Methods of Analysis*, New York, 1948–1949).

K. *Separation of Arsenic from Antimony and Tin*

According to Lur'e and Filippova (20) arsenic may be separated from antimony and tin by passing the acid solution through a cation exchanger of sulfonic acid type. Arsenic passes quantitatively through the resin, whereas antimony and tin are retained. Antimony and tin cannot be detected in the effluent, and no detectable quantities of arsenic are obtained in the cation solution after regeneration with 50 ml hydrochloric acid (1:1). The experimental conditions and results are summarized in Table 15.

TABLE 15

Separation of Arsenic from Antimony and Tin by Means of Wofatit P (10 g in the hydrogen form)

Original Solution				Found		
As, mg	Sb, mg	Sn, mg	Acidity	In Effluent As, mg	After Regeneration	
					Sb, mg	Sn, mg
7.0	0.5		1 N H$_2$SO$_4$		0.48–0.52	
1.0		1.0	0.6 N HCl	0.94–1.02		0.92–0.96

L. *Separation of Bismuth from Antimony*

Lur'e and Filippova report that bismuth may be separated from antimony as thiocyanate by means of a cation exchanger. The separation is made in a 6% solution of ammonium thiocyanate acidified with sulfuric acid to give 1 N concentration. Under these conditions bismuth passes the resin layer, whereas antimony is retained. If the thiocyanate concentration is lowered, bismuth is partially retained and for an increased concentration a certain amount of the antimony will pass into the effluent (20).

The authors recommend that, if all bismuth is to remain in solution and a slight amount of antimony is allowable, the concentration should be above 6%. If, on the other hand, antimony is to be determined and a little bismuth is permissible, the concentration should be below 6%.

M. *Separation of Molybdenum from Lead, Copper, Iron, and Vanadium*

An interesting application of the ion exchange method in the analysis of molybdenum ores and ferromolybdenum has been devised by Klement (14). Lead, copper, iron (III), and vanadium (as vanadyl ion) are taken up by a cation exchanger of sulfonic acid type, whereas molybdic acid which has previously been complexly bound by addition of citric acid passes into the effluent. About 1 g citric acid is used for 100–150 mg molybdenum. The resin is employed in the hydrogen form. After washing with water, molybdenum is determined in the effluent by using the hydroxyquinoline method.

The retained ions are displaced by means of acid and determined in the eluate. In the presence of lead elution is performed with dilute nitric acid (1:7). For copper or vanadium it is most convenient to use dilute sulfuric acid (1:9). To obtain a quantitative elution of iron the common treatment with 4 N hydrochloric acid is recommended.

Excellent results have been obtained both with solutions containing known amounts of the different components and with ores and ferromolybdenum, the relative error being in most experiments less than 0.5%.

N. *Removal of Contaminants in Tracers*

Cohn (3) reports the current usage of ion exchange columns to remove macroscopic quantities of cations, e.g. lanthanum from carrier-free P^{32} as phosphate and potassium from carrier-free S^{35} as sulfate. The cations are simply exchanged for hydrogen ions by means of a cation exchanger. Subsequently the liberated acids may be concentrated by evaporation.

O. *Separation of Amphoteric Metals from Non-Amphoteric*

Lur'e and Filippova (19, 20) found that zinc, aluminum, molybdenum, tungsten, and antimony can be quantitatively retained by cation exchangers of sulfonic acid type. Because of their amphoteric character the metals may be removed as anions if the resin is afterwards treated with alkali solutions. The authors report that molybdenum and tungsten may be extracted by means of a 2% solution of sodium hydroxide, and zinc and aluminum by means of a 5% solution, whereas a concentration of 10% is recommended for antimony. Tin is incompletely dissolved even if the concentration is increased to 20%.

In this manner it should be possible to separate the amphoteric metals mentioned above from metals which form insoluble hydroxides (e.g. iron and copper) on treating the cation exchanger with alkali after the sorption step. Excellent results have been reported for the separation of small amounts of molybdenum and tungsten from large amounts of iron (19). From a solution containing 10 mg aluminum and 10 mg iron, 9.79–9.87 mg aluminum could be recovered by first retaining the cations on Wofatit P (10 g) and subsequently extracting with 50 ml 5% sodium hydroxide. Only traces of iron were present in the effluent. For zinc a poorer recovery was reported. At a regenerant volume of 200 ml the recovery was 96–98% (20).

Experiments performed in the author's laboratory (with Amberlite IR-120) show that a quantitative extraction of zinc from resins which also contain cobalt is extremely difficult. Also, for the separation of aluminum from iron rather unsatisfactory results were obtained.

The method has been applied by Usatenko and Datsenko (39) to the determination of molybdenum in ferromolybdenum and by Shemyakin et al. (36) to iron-chromium-molybdenum alloys. Shemyakin and his associates report that the results are reproducible but are about 0.2% too low. These authors used the following procedure:

A 0.2-g sample is dissolved in 30 ml hydrochloric acid (1:1), and after addition of 1–2 ml nitric acid the solution is evaporated to sirup consistency. The residue is taken up in 7 ml hydrochloric acid (1:1), diluted with 50 ml water, and percolated through a sulfonic acid resin. After washing with water the resin is extracted with 3% sodium hydroxide. After acidification, reduction is performed with the Jones reductor and molybdenum determined by titration with 0.05 N permanganate.

2. APPLICATION OF ANION EXCHANGERS

When the removal of interfering anions is desired in order to facilitate the determination of different cations, it is in principle simpler to use anion exchangers than cation exchangers, as no elution step is needed with anion exchangers. Hence the introduction of a great excess of regenerant into the solution to be analyzed is prevented.

However, with the anion exchange resins previously available the washing and regeneration were more difficult to perform than with the available cation exchangers. As pointed out in Chapter II: 5, most anion exchangers of weakly basic type contain also a slight amount of phenolic groups. Their presence may cause errors as far as this type of separation is concerned.

The anion exchange resins of strongly basic type offer great advantages, but it must be remembered that most separations may be carried out as well by means of cation exchangers.

An interesting field of application which thus far has been only slightly explored is the separation of metals by means of anion exchangers after transformation of one of the metal ions into an anionic complex. The simple ion exchange technique may be applied only in separations where extremely stable complexes are formed. In cases where a decomposition of the complex occurs on rinsing with water, it may be advantageous to wash the column with the complexing agent after the sorption step (20). When only weak complexes are at hand, it is necessary to resort to chromatographic techniques.

A separation of different metals from each other may also be performed by percolating the solution to be analyzed through an anion exchanger saturated with anions which give strong complexes with certain metal ions present in the solutions. Those metals which form strong complexes may be quantitatively retained, whereas other metal ions may pass quantitatively into the effluent (35).

A. *Determination of Sodium and Potassium in the Presence of Sulfate and Phosphate*

The first application of anion exchange resins for the separation of sodium from phosphate was described by Klement and Dmytruk (13). Difficulties were encountered because a certain amount of sodium was retained by the resin, which was of weakly basic type (Wofatit M in chloride form). However, the authors found that under special conditions sodium could be accurately estimated in solutions containing phosphoric acid after removal of the phosphate ions by means of a column filled with the anion exchanger.

Gabrielson and Samuelson (5) used an anion exchange resin of the strongly basic type for the determination of potassium in the presence of sulfate and phosphate. The solution to be analyzed was percolated through a column filled with resin in the chloride form. Sulfate and phosphate ions were quantitatively exchanged for chloride ions, and the potassium ions passed quantitatively into the effluent. After washing with water, potassium could be accurately determined in the combined filtrate and wash water, e.g. as potassium perchlorate.

Experiments were made in pure water solutions ($pH = 6$) as well as after addition of ammonia ($pH = 9$) and hydrochloric acid ($pH = 3$). In fifteen experiments a maximum relative error of 0.4% was obtained. The accuracy of the method is about the same as that obtained in earlier investigations on the determination of potassium in solutions containing sulfate and phosphate after separation by means of a cation exchanger (cf. section 1 A).

Procedure: The anion exchanger Amberlite IRA-400 (particle size 0.12–0.30 mm), completely transformed to the chloride form and carefully washed with water before use, is placed in the ion exchange column and washed with an additional 25 ml water.

Dimensions of the resin bed: height 150 mm and diameter 9.8 mm. Then 0.2–1.3 g of the salt (K_2SO_4; $KCl + Na_2SO_4$ or $KCl + NaH_2PO_4$) dissolved in 50 ml water is percolated through the column at the flow rate 4 ml sqcm^{-1} min^{-1}. After washing with 75–100 ml water at the same flow rate, the combined effluents are analyzed.

B. *Separation of Alkali Metals from Various Cations*

Samuelson and Schramm (35) devised an accurate ion exchange method for the removal of various cations from solutions containing alkali salts. The method is based on the observation that a number of cations may be taken up by means of an anion exchanger saturated with anions which have the ability to form strong complexes (e.g. citrate). Cobalt (II), nickel (II), copper (II), iron (III), and vanadium (IV) are quantitatively retained by an anion exchanger in the citrate form, whereas the alkali metals pass through the column. After washing with water the alkali metals may be easily determined in the effluent. If only one alkali metal is present or if it is desired to estimate the total amount of alkali, the simplest way is to pass the effluent from the citrate-saturated anion exchange column through a second column filled with an anion exchanger in the free-base form. The latter column containing a resin of the strongly basic type converts the alkali citrate to alkali hydroxide, which may be accurately determined in the effluent from the second column by titration with standard acid. It is most convenient to have the columns coupled together from the beginning of the sorption step and let the solution to be analyzed and the water used for washing pass through both columns in series (Fig. 38). Some results are reproduced in Table 16.

TABLE 16

Sample Solution	Alkali Hydroxide, mmols	
	Calculated	Found
0.517 mmol $FeCl_3$ + 2.000 mmols KCl	2.000	2.004
0.517 mmol $FeCl_3$ + 2.000 mmols KCl	2.000	1.998
0.515 mmol V_2O_5 + 2.128 mmols NaOH + 1.000 mmol KCl	3.128	3.125
0.508 mmol V_2O_5 + 1.277 mmols NaOH + 1.000 mmol KCl	2.277	2.273
1.195 mmols $CoSO_4$ + 2.000 mmols KCl	2.000	1.996
0.598 mmol $CoSO_4$ + 2.000 mmols KCl	2.000	1.998
0.535 mmol $NiSO_4$ + 2.000 mmols KCl	2.000	2.000
0.535 mmol $NiSO_4$ + 2.000 mmols KCl	2.000	1.998
0.507 mmol $CuSO_4$ + 2.000 mmols KCl	2.000	1.997
0.507 mmol $CuSO_4$ + 2.000 mmols KCl	2.000	1.996

After the experiment the first column is regenerated with 1 N hydrochloric acid and may be used again after treatment with about 300 ml 1 M

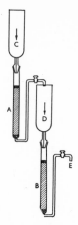

FIG. 38. Separation of iron from potassium.
    A. Anion exchange column: 9 × 140 mm; Dowex 2 [citrate; 0.2–0.3 mm].
    B. Anion exchange column: 9 × 140 mm; Dowex 2 [OH⁻; 0.2–0.3 mm].
    C. Influent (25 ml): 0.517 mmol $FeCl_3$ + 2.000 mmols KCl.
    D. Potassium citrate solution.
    E. Effluent: 1.998 mmols KOH.   [from (35)]

citric acid. The second column is transformed into the hydroxyl form by
regeneration with 1 *N* sodium hydroxide.

    It was found that chromium (III) ions [chrome alum and chromium
chloride (green) solutions] were not (or were only to a slight extent) taken
up by the citrate-saturated resin. Nor was it possible to achieve a quantitative uptake with a resin in the oxalate form. However, on addition of oxalic
acid and heating of the original solution the chromium ions were transformed into exchangeable complex ions, and a quantitative separation of
chromium from alkali ions could be easily achieved by means of an anion
exchanger in the oxalate form.

C. *Determination of Chromium in the Presence of Nickel*

A method for the separation of chromium from large amounts of nickel has
been suggested by Lur'e and Filippova (20). Chromium may be taken up as
chromate on an anion exchange resin in acid as well as alkaline medium
(*p*H 1–12). Elution is performed by means of a 2% NaOH solution. Some
reduction of the chromate may occur, and therefore a final extraction of
the resin by means of dilute sulfuric acid (1:9) may be recommended.

    Nickel is not retained in ammoniacal solution, and it is possible to sepa-
rate chromate from nickel in ammoniacal solution in which Ni:Cr is as high
as 60 : 1.

D. Determination of Bismuth in the Presence of Copper

Large amounts of copper interfere with the colorimetric determination of bismuth. In addition to a separation method based on cation exchange worked out by Lur'e and Filippova (see Chapter IX: 1 L), the same authors have also suggested a method for separation by means of a bed of anion exchanger (20). Bismuth is taken up either as iodide complex or as thiocyanate complex, whereas copper passes the filter as ammonium complex. Subsequently bismuth is eluted by means of 100 ml of 2% NaOH solution. The experimental data are summarized in Table 17.

TABLE 17

Separation of Bismuth from Copper in Ammoniacal Solution ($pH = 12$) by Means of Anion Exchange

Added 50 ml Solution Containing				Found
Bi, mg	Cu, mg	KI, g	NH_4CNS, g	Bi, mg
0.20	50.0	2	—	0.18
0.20	50.0	3	—	0.18
0.20	50.0	—	3	0.18
0.20	50.0	—	4	0.18

E. Determination of Aluminum in the Presence of Iron

Teicher and Gordon (38) report the separation of aluminum from iron (III) in solutions containing excess thiocyanate by the action of an anion exchange resin. Iron is retained as complex thiocyanate anion, whereas aluminum passes into the effluent. Aluminum is determined gravimetrically. Excellent agreement is reported for solutions containing 1–2 mg iron and 18–78 mg aluminum, the maximum error being 0.3 mg aluminum. The authors state that the technique may possibly be feasible when larger quantities of iron are present, but that it may be difficult to wash out all aluminum salts.

Procedure: An anion exchange resin of strongly basic type, previously treated with 3–4 N hydrochloric acid, is rinsed with 50 ml 0.3 M ammonium thiocyanate adjusted to pH 1.0 with hydrochloric acid, before the sorption step.

Fifty milliliters of a solution 0.0004–0.0008 M in iron (III), 1.5 M in ammonium thiocyanate, and containing varying amounts of aluminum is adjusted to pH 1.0 and passed through the column (13 × 250 mm) at a flow rate of 8–10 ml per minute. Washing is performed by means of 40–200 ml 0.3 M NH_4CNS at pH 1.0, the volume required being dependent on the amount of aluminum present. Aluminum is determined in the combined effluents.

After the washing step the column is regenerated with 4 N hydrochloric acid, so that it can be used again.

F. Separation of Arsenic from Antimony

Klement (14) showed that arsenate is taken up quantitatively by a strongly basic anion exchanger in the sulfate form, whereas antimonate passes into the effluent. A considerable amount of 0.1% potassium hydroxide is used to free the column from antimonate. After evaporation of the bulk of the water, antimony is determined iodometrically. Arsenate is eluted by 8% potassium hydroxide and determined by the iodometric method. Excellent results were obtained with mixtures of the pure potassium salts.

BIBLIOGRAPHY

1. Abrahamczik, E., and Blümel, F.: Mikrochim. Acta, 1, 354 (1937).
2. Bahrdt, A.: Z. anal. Chem., 70, 109 (1927).
3. Cohn, W. E.: Anal. Chem., 20, 498 (1948).
4. Edelshteïn, S. A., and Petatskiï, V. I.: Zavodskaya Lab., 15, 850 (1949).
5. Gabrielson, G., and Samuelson, O.: Svensk Kem. Tid., 62, 221 (1950).
6. Goehring, M., and Darge, I.: Z. anal. Chem., 125, 180, 373 (1943).
7. Helger, B., and Rynninger, R.: Svensk Kem. Tid., 61, 189 (1949).
8. Helrich, K., and Rieman, W.: Anal. Chem., 19, 651 (1947).
9. Honda, M.: J. Chem. Soc. Japan, 70, 103 (1949).
10. Honda, M.: J. Chem. Soc. Japan, 71, 59 (1950).
11. Kakihana, H.: Bull. Chem. Soc. Japan, 22, 242 (1949).
12. Kehren, M., and Stommel, H.: Chem. Ztg., 51, 913 (1927); 52, 163 (1928).
13. Klement, R., and Dmytruk, R.: Z. anal. Chem., 128, 106 (1948).
14. Klement, R.: to be published.
15. Kortüm, G., Kortüm-Seiler, M., and Finckh, B.: Angew. Chem., 58, 39 (1945).
16. Lagerström, O., and Samuelson, O.: Svensk Papperstidn., 53, 183 (1950).
17. Lagerström, O., Samuelson, O., and Scholander, A.: Svensk Papperstidn., 52, 113 (1949).
18. Lindquist, I.: Acta Chem. Scand., 2, 88 (1948).
19. Lur'e, Yu. Yu., and Filippova, N.A.: Zavodskaya Lab., 13, 539 (1947).
20. Lur'e, Yu. Yu., and Filippova, N. A.: Zavodskaya Lab., 14, 159 (1948).
21. Lur'e, Yu. Yu., and Filippova, N. A.: Zavodskaya Lab., 15, 771 (1949).
22. Odencrantz, J. T., and Rieman, W.: Anal. Chem., 22, 1066 (1950).
23. Runeberg, G.: Svensk Kem. Tid., 57, 114 (1945).
24. Runeberg, G., and Samuelson, O.: Svensk Kem. Tid., 57, 91 (1945).
25. Runeberg, G., and Samuelson, O.: Svensk Kem. Tid., 57, 250 (1945).
26. Samuelson, O.: Z. anal. Chem., 116, 328 (1939).
27. Samuelson, O.: Svensk Kem. Tid., 51, 195 (1939).
28. Samuelson, O.: Svensk Kem. Tid., 52, 115 (1940).

29. Samuelson, O.: *Svensk Kem. Tid.*, **52**, 241 (1940).
30. Samuelson, O.: *Svensk Kem. Tid.*, **54**, 124 (1942).
31. Samuelson, O.: Diss., Tekn. Högskolan, Stockholm, 1944.
32. Samuelson, O.: *Svensk Kem. Tid.*, **57**, 158 (1945).
33. Samuelson, O.: *IVA*, **17**, 5 (1946).
34. Samuelson, O.: *Tek. Tid.*, **76**, 561 (1946).
35. Samuelson, O., and Schramm, K.: to be published.
36. Shemyakin, F. M., Kharlamov, P. P., and Mitselovskiĭ, E. S.: *Zavodskaya Lab.*, **16**, 1124 (1950).
37. Shimizu, H.: *Chem. High Polymers (Japan)*, **7**, 108 (1950).
38. Teicher, H., and Gordon, L.: *Anal. Chem.*, **23**, 930 (1951).
39. Usatenko, Yu. I., and Datsenko, O. V.: *Zavodskaya Lab.*, **15**, 779 (1949).
40. Yoshino, Y.: *J. Chem. Soc. Japan*, **71**, 577 (1950).

CHAPTER X

Inorganic Colloids and High Polymer Electrolytes

1. APPLICATION OF CATION EXCHANGERS

A. *Inorganic Sols*

Ion exchangers have been utilized by Ryznar (5) both to prepare and to purify inorganic colloids. An analytical application is the separation of cations from a solution containing small amounts of silica by means of a cation exchange resin in the hydrogen form. These experiments were related in Chapter IX: 1 E. Samuelson (7) studied the uptake of iron from solutions of ferric chloride, ferric nitrate, and ferric perchlorate to which different amounts of sodium hydroxide had been added at room temperature. As shown by the results reproduced in Fig. 39, the retention was complete when no alkali was added, whereas with the highest amount of alkali only about 1% was retained.

The transformation of ferric iron into a stable sol, e.g. by addition of ammonia to the dilute solution at room temperature, does not make possible the complete separation of the iron, but the greater part of the iron passes into the effluent, a fact which may be of value in certain types of analyses.

Electrophoresis showed that the colloids were positively charged. The reason why they were not quantitatively taken up by the ion exchanger is that the dimensions of the colloidal ions do not permit them to penetrate into the network structure of the resin.

As already pointed out in Chapter VI: 3 D, the formation of a stable ferric hydroxide sol on dilution of solutions of ferric salts may cause complications when the ion exchange method is used. Aluminum hydroxide sols are known to be less stable, and in aluminum solutions to which alkali had been added the uptake was shown to be quantitative provided the flow rate was low (3).

If zirconium nitrate is dissolved, colloidal zirconium hydroxide is obtained. As found by Ayres (1), only a slight amount of zirconium is retained by a cation exchanger in the hydrogen form, whereas impurities such as Be^{2+} and La^{3+} are taken up. This would serve as a rapid method of purification of the zirconium salt and is also of interest from an analytical point of view. The removal of titanium and iron is not complete; about 80% and 95%, respectively, are removed in one passage through the column.

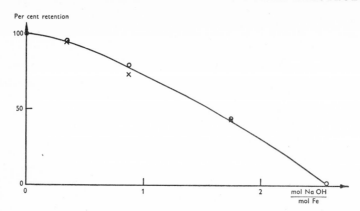

FIG. 39.   Retention of iron from ferric hydroxide sols by a sulfonic acid resin in the
hydrogen form.
○ Fe(ClO₄)₃ + NaOH.
× Fe(NO₃)₃ + NaOH.   [from (7)]

The slight amount of zirconium adsorbed in the column is very difficult
to remove by means of acid. Therefore it is possible to desorb other cations
that are simultaneously adsorbed without removing any appreciable
amount of zirconium (1) (cf. Chapter XIII: 1 A).

Hafnium, niobium, thorium, and protactinium behave in the same
manner as zirconium. The adsorption equilibrium of zirconium and niobium
from solutions containing tracer amounts has been studied by Schubert *et al.*
(9, 10, 11). In contradistinction to the uptake of cations by a cation exchanger the adsorption of zirconium and niobium ("radiocolloids") has
been found to remain unaffected or even to increase when the bulk cation
concentration increases. According to Schubert, "radiocolloids" may be
differentiated from cations by studying the adsorption equilibrium from
solutions containing different concentrations of bulk electrolyte. However,
as mentioned in Chapter VI: 3 F, iron (III) shows a behavior similar to
that of the "radiocolloids" in concentrated solutions of hydrochloric acid.
Further fundamental work is necessary to explain the behavior of different
trivalent and tetravalent elements in ion exchangers.

B. *Determination of Releasable Cations in Soils*

Wiklander (12) has adopted cation exchangers for the determination of
releasable cations in soils. Five grams H⁺-saturated resin (sulfonic acid
type) is shaken with 5 g soil suspended in 40 ml water. After 2–4 hr of
reaction the resin is separated by pouring the suspension through a silk

cloth which retains the resin particles but allows the soil suspension to pass through. After washing with water until the resin is free from soil particles, the resin is transferred to a glass tube and the retained ions replaced by percolating 2 N hydrochloric acid through the resin bed. In the eluate, containing only chloride as anion and free from silica and humus, the released cations can easily be determined. The procedure transforms the soil into the hydrogen form, and by investigating, e.g., the neutralization curve of the H^+ soil valuable information may be obtained as to the properties of the soil. Pratt (4) employed this technique to remove potassium ions from soils.

In a subsequent paper Wiklander (13) showed that for certain soil colloids column operation can be used instead of batchwise operation. In experiments with colloidal humus solution and bentonite suspensions ($<2\,\mu$) positive results were obtained. Bead-shaped resin particles made it possible to use finer resin fractions than if the particles were irregular. It was found that the column method is not suitable for kaolin and ground mica ($<2\,\mu$), as the material sticks in the column.

2. APPLICATION OF ANION EXCHANGERS

A. *Inorganic sols*

Anion exchangers are of great interest for the preparation of inorganic sols (5), e.g. ferric hydroxide sols. However, the ion exchange technique is not yet of any analytical significance in this field.

B. *Separation of Low-Molecular-Weight Phosphates from High Polymer Metaphosphate*

One of the earliest examples studied of the separation of low-molecular-weight anions from high polymer anions with the help of an ion exchanger is the separation of low-molecular-weight phosphate from high polymer metaphosphate. Sodium polymetaphosphate (Graham's salt) is prepared by melting monosodium orthophosphate at about 700° C and chilling the melt quickly. Earlier it was believed that the composition of the product corresponded to a hexametaphosphate $(NaPO_3)_6$. However, later investigations showed that the molecular weight was considerably higher than corresponded to this formula. The acid corresponding to Graham's salt is a strong one, but as a matter of fact a slight amount of alkali is consumed when the solution of the sodium salt, which is neutral against methyl red, is titrated against phenolphthalein. This alkali consumption was earlier ascribed to impurities (other phosphates).

Samuelson (6, 8) used anion exchange resins in his investigations concerning the constitution of Graham's salt. He found that orthophosphate as well as pyrophosphate could be taken up by an anion exchanger, whereas the solution of Graham's salt (or the corresponding acid) was under proper conditions unaffected. The metaphosphate solution had the same consumption of alkali between the titration against methyl red and the titration against phenolphthalein, after treatment with the anion exchanger as before. From these experiments the conclusion was drawn that the weak acid groups were not due to impurities but belonged to the high polymer anion itself and were the end groups in a linear polymer anion. By titrating the weak acid groups the molecular weight (number average) may be easily determined.

The experiments related constitute an example of the utilization of ion exchangers for investigations concerning the structure of complicated systems. However, the ion exchange method does not seem to be useful for a quantitative separation of low-molecular-weight phosphates from polymetaphosphate for practical analytical purposes, because of the instability of the polymetaphosphate anion. When polymetaphosphoric acid is percolated through a column containing a weakly basic resin in the free-base form, a slight amount of the acid is retained in the column. Deuel, Solms, and Anyas-Weisz (2) found that when the solution is hydrolyzed before the percolation the amount of acid retained in the column increases with increased time of reaction, a phenomenon which is explained by a depolymerization of the polymetaphosphate anions.

BIBLIOGRAPHY

1. Ayres, J. A.: *J. Am. Chem. Soc.*, **69**, 2879 (1947).
2. Deuel, H., Solms, J., and Anyas-Weisz, L.: *Helv. Chim. Acta*, **33**, 2171 (1950).
3. Djurfeldt, R., Hansen, J., and Samuelson, O.: *Svensk Kem. Tid.*, **59**, 14 (1947).
4. Pratt, P. F.: *Soil Sci.*, **72**, 107 (1951).
5. Ryznar, J. W.: *Ind. Eng. Chem.*, **36**, 821 (1944).
6. Samuelson, O.: *Svensk Kem. Tid.*, **56**, 343 (1944).
7. Samuelson, O.: *Svensk Kem. Tid.*, **57**, 158 (1945).
8. Samuelson, O.: *Svensk Kem. Tid.*, **61**, 76 (1949).
9. Schubert, J.: *J. Phys. & Colloid Chem.*, **52**, 340 (1948).
10. Schubert, J., and Conn, E. E.: *Nucleonics*, **4**, No 6, 2 (1949).
11. Schubert, J., and Richter, J. W.: *J. Colloid Sci.*, **5**, 376 (1950).
12. Wiklander, L.: *Annals Roy. Agr. Coll. Sweden*, **16**, 670 (1949).
13. Wiklander, L.: *Annals Roy. Agr. Coll. Sweden*, **18**, 154 (1951).

CHAPTER XI

Isolation of Trace Constituents

1. GENERAL CONSIDERATIONS

If a very dilute solution is passed through an ion exchange column, the exchangeable ions will be retained. The ions may then be desorbed, producing a solution of higher concentration by regenerating the column with a proper electrolyte solution. Through this application of the ion exchange method, the ions in many liters of solution can be concentrated with exceptional rapidity. The method may replace or supplement concentration by evaporation, a process that is often troublesome. The method is useful in many biological and technical investigations. In certain procedures, e.g. water analysis, the sorption step may conveniently be performed in the field to avoid the transport of large samples.

As mentioned in the Introduction, Kullgren used this principle for estimating copper in distilled water. Rather unsatisfactory results were reported in early experiments by Abrahamczik (1), who made an attempt to concentrate iron (II) (90% recovery) and radium (50% uptake) from natural waters by means of a synthetic zeolite.

More satisfactory results have been obtained by several authors using cation exchange resins of sulfonic acid type. Because of the risk of complications due to hydrolysis of certain ions, the resins should be employed in the hydrogen form. Furthermore, slightly acidified solutions may be advisable in some cases. It seems probable that for the most part the accuracy is not limited by the ion exchange process itself and that the rather large deviations reported by some authors are due to impurities in the chemicals and to difficulties in performing the microchemical estimations with highest accuracy. It must be emphasized that, when only small quantities are to be determined, special attention must be given to the purity of the regenerant. A redistillation in an all-glass still of the hydrochloric acid used for regeneration of cation exchangers is recommended.

Anion exchange resins have also been employed in some investigations on the determination of anions in extremely dilute solutions. The resins have been used in the free-base form and regeneration has been performed, e.g. by ammonia.

2. ANALYSIS OF NATURAL WATERS

Lur'e and Stefanovich (8) used a cation exchanger of sulfonic acid type to concentrate calcium and magnesium from natural waters. Elution was performed by means of hydrochloric acid. This principle was also used in a careful investigation by Nydahl (9), who extended the method to include Na^+, K^+, Ca^{2+}, Mg^{2+}, Fe^{3+}, Mn^{2+}, Cl^-, SO_4^{2-}, and PO_4^{3-}, the three last ions being retained by an anion exchanger of weakly basic type. The method was checked by analysis of "synthetic lake waters." Some typical results are reproduced in Table 18.

TABLE 18

Amount of "Synthetic Lake Water": 5 liters

Constituent	Added, mg	Found, mg
Na	3.61	3.65
K	1.33	1.39
Ca	12.72	12.73
Mg	2.12	2.12
SO_4	7.50	7.50

The recovery of iron, manganese, chloride, and phosphate was studied at different concentrations, equally high accuracy being achieved. For the uptake of iron, adjustment of the pH of the solution to about 2 is recommended.

When the method was applied to natural lake waters, a quantitative uptake and recovery were achieved with the following ions: Na^+, K^+, Ca^{2+}, Mg^{2+}, Mn^{2+}, Cl^-, SO_4^{2-}. Iron (III), occurring complexly bound to humus, was retained to only a slight extent. Phosphorus present as phosphate ions was retained by the anion exchanger, but in most waters considerable amounts passed into the effluent, because of the presence of non-exchangeable complexes. Humus passed into the effluent almost quantitatively.

A procedure for operation in the field is recommended by Nydahl. In order to save time the sorption step is carried out at extremely high flow rate. Before the cation exchanger is used for the first time, it must be thoroughly purified by means of 6 N hydrochloric acid until the effluent gives a negative test for iron. The resin is used in the hydrogen form. The anion exchange resin should be purified by alternating treatments with 1 N hydrochloric acid and 2 N ammonia. This resin is used in the free-base form.

Five liters of the water to be analyzed is run through two connected columns, the first containing 30 ml sulfonic acid resin and the second 30 ml weakly basic resin. The percolation may be performed in 30 min. The columns are taken apart and transported to the laboratory, where elution is performed by means of 100 ml 2.5 N hydrochloric acid and 100 ml 0.5 N ammonia, respectively. After being washed with water, the columns are ready for use again. In order to obtain a quantitative elution with these moderate amounts of elutriant it is necessary to perform the elution at extremely low speed (e.g. 0.15 ml per min). The direction of flow is reversed in the elution. The hydrochloric acid is introduced at the bottom of the cation exchange column. The anion exchange column is also eluted in countercurrent operation, but in that procedure the column is tipped and the ammonia (which has a lower specific gravity than water) is introduced at the top of the column.

3. DETERMINATION OF THE COMPOSITION OF ATMOSPHERIC PRECIPITATION

Egnér, Eriksson, and Emanuelsson (4) applied the ion exchange method to the analysis of atmospheric precipitations. Ions in rain water were retained by passing the water first through a column with H^+-saturated cation exchanger (Amberlite IR-100) and afterwards through a column with anion exchanger in the free-base form (Amberlite IR–4 B). Ammonium was shown to be quantitatively retained by the cation exchanger from a solution containing 0.50 mg NH_4-nitrogen per liter.

The method has great advantages over previously known procedures, as the precipitation can be filtered immediately, thus lessening the time of contact with vessels, dust, insects, and pollen. Furthermore the ions from the precipitations of any period of time (one month, for instance) may be preserved in a very small volume, which means considerable savings, as the water may be discarded.

The ion exchange resins used in this investigation showed some deficiencies in stability and activity, but with the improved resins now available and proper particle size more accurate results will probably be obtained.

4. ANALYSIS OF MILK, BEER, AND APPLE JUICE

Cranston and Thompson (3) devised a method for the determination of copper in milk by the use of a cation exchange resin. The copper in milk is transferred to cupric ions by addition of perchloric acid to pH less than 3.0. This accomplishes the precipitation of the protein, and fat will be carried into the curd. After filtration through a filter paper the solution is neutralized with dilute ammonia (to pH 5) and percolated through a column filled with a cation exchanger (sulfonic acid type) in the hydrogen form. Copper as well as other cations is retained in the column, and after washing with redistilled water the cations are removed from the column by regeneration with 3 N hydrochloric acid. After evaporation to dryness copper is determined polarographically.

As the copper content of milk is very low, 0.1–1 ppm, it is of importance that the resin and the filter paper be carefully purified by treatment with acid before use and that all solutions be of highest purity. The method was compared with a spectrophotometric procedure (sample wet-ashed) and a procedure in which the sample was first evaporated and ignited and copper determined polarographically. Excellent agreement was obtained. The ion exchange method is simple and rapid compared to earlier methods and will probably have wide application to the determination of traces of copper in various food products. About 2 hr is required to isolate the copper in a form suitable for the polarographic determination.

Preliminary experiments on the concentration of tin, copper, and iron from beer by means of cation exchange resins have been reported (11). Furthermore, the method has been successfully applied to the determination of sodium and potassium in apple juice (2).

5. DETERMINATION OF TRACES OF COPPER, CADMIUM, NICKEL, COBALT, ZINC, AND MANGANESE

Riches (10) has published some preliminary experiments on the uptake of copper, cadmium, nickel, zinc, and manganese at low concentration (4–8 mg per liter) from solutions containing ammonium chloride or ammonium phosphate in approximately decinormal concentration. The ions taken up by the sulfonic acid resin were eluted by means of 1 N hydrochloric acid and determined polarographically. For the ammonium phosphate solution the following recoveries were reported: 94% copper, 96% cadmium, 99% nickel, 95% zinc, and 87% manganese.

It seems probable that more accurate results may be achieved provided all precautions are taken to avoid losses.

Some data on the uptake of copper, nickel, and cobalt from dilute solutions and subsequent elution by means of acid to obtain a more concentrated solution were given in a paper by Lur'e and Filippova (7). A loss of 1–2% in the total cycle was reported [cf. (5, 6)].

BIBLIOGRAPHY

1. Abrahamczik, E.: *Mikrochemie ver. Mikrochim. Acta*, **25**, 228 (1938).
2. Bäckström, H. L. J.: unpublished.
3. Cranston, H. A., and Thompson, J. B.: *Ind. Eng. Chem.*, Anal. Ed., **18**, 323 (1946).
4. Egnér, H., Eriksson, E., and Emanuelsson, A.: *Kgl. Lantbruks-Högskol. Ann.*, **16**, 593 (1949).
5. Kostrikin, Yu. M.: *Zavodskaya Lab.*, **13**, 539 (1947).
6. Kot, A. A.: *Zavodskaya Lab.*, **16**, 493 (1950).
7. Lur'e, Yu. Yu., and Filippova, N. A.: *Zavodskaya Lab.*, **13**, 539 (1947).
8. Lur'e, Yu. Yu., and Stefanovich, S. N.: *Zavodskaya Lab.*, **13**, 660 (1947).
9. Nydahl, F.: *Proc. Intern. Assoc. of Theor. Applied Limnology*, **11**, 276 (1951).
10. Riches, J. P. R.: *Nature*, **158**, 96 (1946); *Chemistry & Industry*, **1947**, 656.
11. West, D. B., Evans, R. F., and Becker, K.: *Am. Soc. Brewing Chemists Proc.*, **1950**, 107.

CHAPTER XII

Inorganic Qualitative Analysis

1. SEPARATION OF INTERFERING IONS

The ion exchange method is of great importance also in the solving of more complicated analytical problems in qualitative inorganic analysis, above all for the removal of interfering ions (4). Qualitative cation analysis cannot be carried out in the usual way on a sample which contains phosphate, borate, or oxalate ions, without first removing these anions from the solution. This removal can be carried out simply in a single operation by using a cation exchanger of sulfonic acid type. The method is more rapid and, at least for inexperienced analysts, more reliable than usual earlier methods. At the Royal Institute of Technology in Stockholm the ion exchange method has been used in the basic analytical course for a number of years (5).

The following method of working has proved suitable. After precipitation of the metals belonging to Group 2 with hydrogen sulfide, the filtrate is evaporated to near dryness so that only a slight amount of hydrochloric acid is left in the sample. The residue is diluted with water and percolated through a column filled with a cation exchange resin (sulfonic acid type) in the hydrogen form. After the column is washed free from acid, it is treated with 3–4 N hydrochloric acid to obtain a cation solution free from interfering anions. It is recommended that part of the hydrochloric acid be removed from the cation solution by evaporation.

Compared with the earlier usual procedures, the ion exchange method has the following advantages:

1. *Less work.* In a single ion exchange cycle all the anions in the sample are exchanged for chloride ions. Former methods required different procedures for each different anion, which was laborious and troublesome.

2. *Saving of time.* The ion exchange method requires in many cases two evaporations, but these take care of themselves. By a suitable choice of acid concentration in regeneration and by abstaining from quantitative operation (being, instead, content with 95–99%) the volume of the cation solution may be considerably reduced.

3. *Simpler analysis procedure.* The cation solution obtained by the ion exchange method is a pure chloride solution, and in the analysis all the metals are therefore precipitated by their group reagents. The metals of Group 4,

calcium, strontium, and barium, as well as magnesium from Group 5, were precipitated in former methods, together with the metals of Group 3 if phosphate, etc., was present. With insufficient phosphate these metal ions are precipitated at two stages, a fact which may easily be overlooked. Oxalate may result in the precipitation of Group 3 metals chromium and aluminum, together with the Group 4 metals. Cobalt was precipitated by former methods, partly as the almost insoluble sulfide, and partly as phosphate, which dissolved later in dilute acids, constituting a great disadvantage when analysis was further continued. In the ion exchange technique cobalt is precipitated only as sulfide, which is insoluble in dilute acids.

The disadvantage of the ion exchange method is that the metals occurring as strong negatively charged complexes can pass through the ion exchanger. In qualitative analysis this means that Cr^{3+}, Al^{3+}, and Fe^{3+}, which form quite stable complexes with oxalic acid, can partially pass through and appear in the effluent. Cr^{3+} forms also with phosphate and sulfate complexes, which hinder a quantitative uptake of chromium. Since the greater part of Fe^{3+} and Al^{3+} are taken up in the cation exchanger provided that oxalate is not present in large excess, this factor does not limit seriously the use of the ion exchange method. Both Cr^{3+} and Fe^{3+} may easily be detected in the effluent.

Past experience with the ion exchange method shows that it means a saving in both time and work, as the analysis procedure is rendered simpler and more easily controlled.

The method not only has been used on a macroscale but has also been employed to advantage for semimicroscale work (6).

According to Klement and Dmytruk (2), this method is also suitable for the separation of tartaric acid in qualitative analysis procedure.

2. PRECIPITATION OF GROUP 2 IONS AS SULFIDES

The utilization of gaseous hydrogen sulfide as a precipitant has certain disadvantages due to the odor and poisonous properties.

Gaddis (1) suggested that gaseous hydrogen sulfide be replaced by an anion exchange resin in the sulfide form. She found that the resin (Amberlite IR-4) could take up 12% of its weight of hydrogen sulfide. After saturation with hydrogen sulfide the resin is stored in well-stoppered bottles and may be substituted for hydrogen sulfide as a precipitant for the Group 2 ions. The method is claimed to be suitable for semimicroqualitative analyses, but the accuracy does not seem to be the best. For detailed information the reader is referred to the original paper.

It may also be mentioned that, according to Kunin (3), the cyanide form of a strong base anion exchanger may be used as a precipitant for such ions as nickel, cobalt, zinc, and copper.

BIBLIOGRAPHY

1. Gaddis, S.: *J. Chem. Education*, **13**, 327 (1942).
2. Klement, R., and Dmytruk, R.: *Z. anal. Chem.*, **128**, 109 (1949).
3. Kunin, R.: *Anal. Chem.*, **21**, 87 (1949).
4. Samuelson, O.: *Z. anal. Chem.*, **116**, 328 (1939).
5. Samuelson, O., Djurfeldt, R., and Scholander, A.: *Elementa*, **30**, 107 (1947).
6. Scholander, A., and Scholander, H.: *Kvalitativ oorganisk analys i halvmikroskala*, Stockholm, 1948.

CHAPTER XIII

Chromatographic Separations in Inorganic Chemistry

Most work on ion exchange chromatography in inorganic chemistry has been performed by means of the tracer technique. The fission products from the uranium pile have been isolated in a pure condition for preparative, nuclear physical as well as biological purposes. Furthermore, the method has led to the isolation of transuranic elements and to several other interesting discoveries. The investigations show, moreover, that ion exchange chromatography is of the utmost importance in inorganic analytical chemistry, especially for separations which are difficult or fallible by classical methods. Only a few investigations have been performed with the aim of applying the technique to practical analytical purposes.

1. APPLICATION OF CATION EXCHANGERS

A. *Group Separations*

In the work performed under the Plutonium Project, Russell (44) showed that the tetravalent ions could be selectively eluted from a sulfonic acid resin by means of oxalic acid, the explanation being that oxalic acid forms extremely strong complexes with these ions. This principle has been used in group separations of fission-produced radioisotopes. Thus, from a mixture containing zirconium, hafnium, and niobium as well as rare earths and alkaline earths retained on the top of a column, the tetravalent ions may be easily eluted with 0.5% oxalic acid without appreciable movement of the other ions down the column (70, 10). Subsequently the tri-, di-, and monovalent ions can be separated by means of citrate buffers. At pH 3, a 5% citrate solution displaces the trivalent species; at pH 5 the remaining divalent and monovalent cations are removed from the column (70, 10). The ions belonging to a single group may afterwards be separated by resorption and chromatographic elution with citrate buffers.

In this connection, it may be mentioned that other reagents have also been suggested for a separation of cations into different groups. As an example, it is possible to displace monovalent cations by means of dilute hydrochloric acid (0.1 N) without an interfering movement of divalent and trivalent ions in the column. The latter groups may subsequently be eluted, e.g. by means of acid at higher concentration or with salt solutions or complexing agents [cf., e.g., (18)].

B. *Alkali Metals*

The separation of the alkali metals from each other by chromatographic elution was first studied by Cohn and Kohn, who worked with a neutron-activated mixture of sodium, potassium, rubidium, and cesium (9). Elution was performed by means of 0.15 N hydrochloric acid. A similar technique was used by Kayas (24, 25).

An interesting improvement was introduced by Buser (5), who performed the elution by means of uramildiacetic acid, which has the ability to form stable complexes with lithium and sodium but not with potassium; as could be expected from theoretical considerations, an improved separation of the bands was obtained. The separation was performed in alkaline medium, using a sulfonic acid resin pretreated with either dimethylamine or tetramethylammonium hydroxide.

The separation of sodium and potassium by Wickbold, using the conductometric technique, has been described in detail (Chapter VII: 3 A). Experiments with lithium are included in this report. Excellent separations of sodium, potassium, and magnesium by chromatographic elution have been reported by Beukenkamp and Rieman (2). All these investigations are of analytical interest.

C. *Rare Earths*

One of the most difficult processes in inorganic chemistry has been the separation of the rare earths from each other. This problem has been solved by the application of ion exchange chromatography; the historical development of this solution has been traced by Johnson, Quill, and Daniels (23). The first successful separations were those of Tompkins, Khym, and Cohn (70), by means of chromatographic elution with tartrate and citrate buffers, which followed the earlier observations of Russell (44) with respect to the complexing of tetravalent ions by oxalic acid, described above. Subsequent refinements of method and technique were made by Ketelle and Boyd (26, 27), Mayer and Tompkins (41), and others (16, 74, 78, 75, 76, 17, 13, 14). The method has been applied to the production of large amounts of fission-produced radioisotopes (10), to the isolation and first positive chemical identification of element 61 (promethium) by Marinsky, Glendenin, and Coryell (40), and to the production of large amounts of the rare earths from natural sources by Spedding *et al.* (53–62, 15).

The elution method may be used for analytical purposes to detect and estimate quantitatively extremely small amounts of impurities in different salts. This application has been demonstrated in a striking way by Ketelle

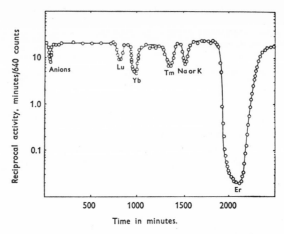

Fig. 40.   Neutron activation analysis of spectrographically pure erbium oxide.
Column: 5.8 × 970 mm; Dowex 50 [H⁺; 0.044–0.055 mm].
Flow rate: 0.5 ml sqcm⁻¹ min⁻¹.
Elutriant: 5% citrate buffer at pH 3.2.   [from (26)]

and Boyd (26), who were able to determine difficultly recognizable impurities in spectrographically pure erbium oxide. A 5-mg sample was irradiated
in a neutron chain reactor and then taken up on top of a cation exchange column. Elution was performed by means of 5% citrate buffer at pH 3.2;
temperature 100°C. Lutecium, ytterbium, thulium, and sodium could be
easily detected (Fig. 40). By radiometric methods it was found that the
sample contained not more than 0.001% thulium.

D. *Transuranic Elements*

Of utmost interest are the separations and isolation of the transuranic elements, performed in recent years by Seaborg and associates (64, 65, 66, 39).
Even though the half-lives of some of these elements are extremely short, a
number of their chemical characteristics have been determined.

The transuranic elements are first separated from the rare earths by
elution of the former group from a sulfonic acid resin by means of 13.3 N
hydrochloric acid. Subsequently, the transuranic elements are separated
from each other by resorption and elution with citrate solution.

E. *Miscellaneous Applications*

A few separations of divalent ions other than fission products from each
other have been reported (43, 69, 73). The results seem to be of only limited
interest from an analytical point of view. Blanco and Perkinson (3) have

prepared gallium citrate by the elution of gallium from a cation exchanger of sulfonic acid type with sodium citrate. Street and Seaborg (63) have reported the separation of hafnium and zirconium by elution with hydrochloric acid from a sulfonic acid resin. An improved method for stepwise elution with sulfuric acid and oxalic acid has been devised by Lister (36) (cf. section 2).

A simple method for the quantitative separation of titanium, zirconium, and thorium by stepwise elution with citrate buffers of progressively increasing pH has been developed by Brown and Rieman (4). Column: 30×70 mm; Dowex 50 [H^+; 0.125–0.14 mm]. The authors believe that a partial separation of the natural isotopes of titanium was achieved during the experiment.

F. *Isolation of Radioelements from Urine*

As an example of the application of a simplified technique for ion exchange chromatography, a method by Schubert, Russell, and Farabee (50) for the determination of radioelements in urine will be described in detail. By this method, the amount of dangerous radioelements which may have accumulated in the body of an exposed individual is conveniently ascertained.

Experiments were performed with carrier-free radioactive yttrium (Y^{91}) which was retained from 1 liter urine and concentrated by means of a cation exchanger in a solution free from salts which interfere in radiometric analyses. Before the sorption step the urine is acidified (0.1 N in hydrochloric acid) in order to prevent the precipitation of calcium salts and to keep the yttrium in exchangeable ionic form. The ion exchange column is filled with 70 g Amberlite IR-1. Calcium and other inorganic cations as well as adsorbed organic matter are removed by percolating 1500 ml 0.4 N hydrochloric acid through the column. It is stated that a total loss of about 5% yttrium is obtained in the effluents from these operations.

Yttrium is eluted with 1000 ml 7 N hydrochloric acid. After evaporation to near dryness the remaining organic matter is destroyed by wet-ashing with nitric acid. The residue is evaporated to dryness, and the radioactivity measured with a Geiger-Mueller counter.

Before the column can be used again, it must be washed with water, 95% alcohol to remove organic matter, and finally with water again.

If the radiations from a particular radioelement are not very penetrating, it may be necessary to remove the last traces of salts. This may be done by dissolving the residue in water and repeating the ion exchange procedure. The second ion exchange column may be much smaller than the column used in the first run.

Recoveries of 85–95% are reported when only one column operation is needed, and an over-all recovery of $85 \pm 5\%$ if the process includes a further purification step.

In a subsequent paper, Schubert (47) stated that the method could be improved by adsorbing the radioelement batchwise and then placing the resin containing yttrium on a previously prepared resin bed. A similar procedure has been devised by Russell, Lesko, and Schubert (45) for the determination of radium in urine.

G. Separation of Uranium and Thorium

Another example which illustrates the application of the simplified technique is the separation of uranium and thorium according to a method worked out by Vestermark (72) and Dyrssen (12) [see also (52)].

Thorium (Th^{234}) is retained very strongly at the top of a cation exchange column when a concentrated uranyl nitrate solution is percolated through it. Afterwards the uranyl ions and various contaminants, such as Fe^{3+}, Al^{3+}, Ca^{2+}, Mg^{2+}, and Cu^{2+}, can be desorbed with 2 N hydrochloric acid, whereas Th^{234} is shifted in the column to a minor extent only. Subsequently Th^{234} is eluted from the column with 0.5 M oxalic acid.

H. Separation of Titanium and Iron

Yoshino and Kojima (79) have used a cation exchange resin of sulfonic acid type to remove the bulk of iron from solutions containing small amounts of titanium. A sample solution with high iron concentration is treated with a 50% potassium or sodium cyanide solution. Part of the iron is converted into ferricyanide complex, whereas another part is precipitated as ferric hydroxide. Titanium is coprecipitated quantitatively as titanium hydroxide. The precipitate is filtered off and dissolved in dilute sulfuric acid. After dilution with water the solution is passed through a cation exchange column in the hydrogen form. Iron is eluted with 2 N KCN solution, while titanium remains in the column. Finally titanium is eluted by means of a 10% sulfuric acid solution and determined colorimetrically by the hydrogen peroxide method.

In those cases where the iron concentration is relatively low it is possible to perform the analysis without separating the precipitate from the solution. Instead, the precipitate is dissolved by addition of sulfuric acid and the solution passed directly through the cation exchanger.

The method has been applied to the determination of titanium in limonite. Excellent results have been reported.

I. Separation of Bismuth from Copper and Lead

Lur'e and Filippova (38) observed that bismuth can be easily eluted from a cation exchange resin by means of a 1% solution of potassium iodide to which sulfuric acid has been added to a concentration of 0.1 N. Under the experimental conditions chosen only traces of copper are eluted, which do not interfere with the direct colorimetric determination of bismuth in the eluate even if copper is present in excess in the original solutions (Cu : Bi = 40 : 1). According to these authors, the separation of bismuth from lead is complete even for Pb : Bi = 100 : 1. Not more than 10 mg lead should be used for the analysis (8 g cation exchange resin). Otherwise the elution of bismuth is prevented.

Wofatit P in the potassium form was used in the experiments. The pH of the original solution was 1.8–2.2, and the amount of bismuth in all experiments was 0.10 mg.

In experiments on elution of antimony by means of acidified iodide solution the recovery was incomplete.

J. Determination of Calcium and Magnesium in Iron Ore

Usatenko and Datsenko (71) report a method for the determination of calcium and magnesium in iron ore. Iron and aluminum are complexly bound by addition of citric acid or tartaric acid. On filtration through a column containing a sulfonic acid resin in the hydrogen form, calcium and magnesium are quantitatively retained, whereas iron and aluminum reportedly pass into the effluent. After rinsing with water, the calcium and magnesium ions are desorbed with hydrochloric acid and determined in the cation solution.

The working conditions used by these authors were as follows:

A 0.5-g sample is dissolved by heating with 15 ml concentrated hydrochloric acid. After evaporation to sirup consistency the solution is diluted with 30 ml hot hydrochloric acid (1 : 4) and filtered. After washing with acidified water the filtrate is evaporated to 2–3 ml. It is very important for the subsequent sorption step that only a moderate amount of hydrochloric acid be present. Thirty milliliters of water and 20 ml of 20% tartaric acid are added, and the solution is passed through a column containing 60–65 ml Wofatit P in the hydrogen form at the flow rate of 5 ml per minute.

Experiments performed in the author's laboratory show that not only calcium and magnesium but also iron and aluminum are taken up by the resin. Therefore the chromatographic technique must be adopted; i.e. it is necessary to establish the point where aluminum and iron are displaced quantitatively from the column. Only after proper conditions for a certain resin have been worked out can the method be employed for routine analysis. It is advisable to run the sorption step under conditions where a certain uptake of the trivalent ions occurs and to elute these.

2. APPLICATION OF ANION EXCHANGERS

Ion exchange chromatography by means of anion exchangers has been used in several investigations on separations of metals which form negatively charged complexes. Anion exchange resins are particularly useful with metal ions which would precipitate if not complexed.

Kraus and Moore (29, 30) showed that this principle could be used for separation of zirconium and hafnium, as well as niobium and tantalum. The metals were dissolved in HCl-HF mixtures, taken up on top of the column (strongly basic resin), and subsequently eluted by means of HCl-HF solution. The zirconium-hafnium separation has also been performed by Huffman and Lilly (19, 21). Detailed information on the separation of zirconium and niobium is given in a subsequent paper by Kraus and Moore (33). It is interesting to note that the separation is excellent in extremely concentrated solutions (e.g. 9 N HCl–0.5 N HF). An almost complete separation of niobium, tantalum, and protactinium from each other by stepwise elution has also been achieved (31, 33, 34, 22) [cf. also (77)].

Another application of the elution technique is the separation of tracer amounts of promethium and europium, which has been reported by Huffman and Oswalt (20). These authors performed the elution with 0.0125 M citric acid.

Atteberry and Boyd have demonstrated the separation of fluoride, chloride, bromide, and iodide from each other, as well as the separation of perrhenate from pertechnetate (1). An anion exchange resin has also been used to effect a rapid separation of ferrocyanide and ferricyanide (8).

Most interesting results on the removal of iron from solutions containing hydrochloric acid at high concentration by means of an anion exchanger are reported in a communication by Moore and Kraus (32). The fact that iron is strongly taken up, e.g. from 3 N hydrochloric acid, is ascribed to a formation of negatively charged complex ions. Metal ions which do not form anionic complexes (e.g. alkali metals and alkaline earths) are not retained. The trivalent ions tested (aluminum, chromium, and rare earths) were found to be practically unadsorbed from strong hydrochloric acid solution. The authors report the successful removal of an iron impurity (30 mg per liter) from 2 M aluminum chloride solution in 3 N hydrochloric acid.

Similarly, protactinium may be freed from various contaminants by sorption from 8 N hydrochloric acid (31). Subsequently protactinium may be eluted by means of hydrochloric acid at lower concentration (less than 4 N).

Recently Moore and Kraus (35) report that gallium behaves in the same manner as iron. Nickel is not taken up by the anion exchanger from strong hydrochloric acid, whereas cobalt is strongly retained from $9 N$ hydrochloric acid. The cobalt band has a characteristic blue color on the resin which is sufficiently intense to permit detection of traces. Excellent separation of cobalt from nickel has been achieved.

BIBLIOGRAPHY

1. Atteberry, R. W., and Boyd, G. E.: *J. Am. Chem. Soc.*, **72**, 4805 (1950).
2. Beukenkamp, J., and Rieman III, W.: *Anal. Chem.*, **22**, 582 (1950).
3. Blanco, R. E., and Perkinson, Jr., J. D.: *J. Am. Chem. Soc.*, **73**, 2696 (1951).
4. Brown, W. E., and Rieman III, W.: *J. Am. Chem. Soc.*, **74**, 1278 (1952).
5. Buser, W.: *Helv. Chim. Acta*, **34**, 1635 (1951).
6. Butement, F. D. S.: *Nature*, **167**, 400 (1951).
7. Coates, J. I., and Glueckauf, E.: *J. Chem. Soc.*, **1947**, 1308.
8. Cobble, J. W., and Adamson, A. W.: *J. Am. Chem. Soc.*, **72**, 2276 (1950).
9. Cohn, W. E., and Kohn, H. W.: *J. Am. Chem. Soc.*, **70**, 1986 (1948).
10. Cohn, W. E., Parker, G. W., and Tompkins, E. R.: *Nucleonics*, **3**, No. 5, 22 (1948).
11. Duncan, J. F., and Lister, B. A. J.: *J. Chem. Soc.*, **1949**, 3285.
12. Dyrssen, D.: *Svensk Kem. Tid.*, **62**, 153 (1950).
13. Fitch, F. T., and Russell, D. S.: *Can. J. Chem.*, **29**, 363 (1951).
14. Fitch, F. T., and Russell, D. S.: *Anal. Chem.*, **23**, 1469 (1951).
15. Gladrow, E. M.: *Iowa State Coll. J. Sci.*, **25**, 224 (1951).
16. Harris, D. H., and Tompkins, E. R.: *J. Am. Chem. Soc.*, **69**, 2792 (1947).
17. Higgins, G. H., and Street, Jr., K.: *J. Am. Chem. Soc.*, **72**, 5321 (1950).
18. Honda, M.: *J. Chem. Soc. Japan*, **71**, 118 (1950).
19. Huffman, E. H., and Lilly, R. C.: *J. Am. Chem. Soc.*, **71**, 4147 (1949).
20. Huffman, E. H., and Oswalt, R. L.: *J. Am. Chem. Soc.*, **72**, 3323 (1950).
21. Huffman, E. H., and Lilly, R. C.: *J. Am. Chem. Soc.*, **73**, 2902 (1951).
22. Huffman, E. H., Iddings, G. M., and Lilly, R. C.: *J. Am. Chem. Soc.*, **73**, 4474 (1951).
23. Johnson, W. C., Quill, L. L., and Daniels, F.: *Chem. Eng. News*, **25**, 2494 (1947).
24. Kayas, G.: *Compt. rend.*, **228**, 1002 (1949).
25. Kayas, G.: *J. chim. phys.*, **47**, 408 (1950).
26. Ketelle, B. H., and Boyd, G. E.: *J. Am. Chem. Soc.*, **69**, 2800 (1947).
27. Ketelle, B. H., and Boyd, G. E.: *J. Am. Chem. Soc.*, **73**, 1862 (1951).
28. Kozak, R., and Walton, H. F.: *J. Phys. Chem.*, **49**, 471 (1945).
29. Kraus, K. A., and Moore, G. E.: *J. Am. Chem. Soc.*, **71**, 3263 (1949).
30. Kraus, K. A., and Moore, G. E.: *J. Am. Chem. Soc.*, **71**, 3855 (1949).
31. Kraus, K. A., and Moore, G. E.: *J. Am. Chem. Soc.*, **72**, 4293 (1950).
32. Kraus, K. A., and Moore, G. E.: *J. Am. Chem. Soc.*, **72**, 5792 (1950).
33. Kraus, K. A., and Moore, G. E.: *J. Am. Chem. Soc.*, **73**, 9, 13 (1951).
34. Kraus, K. A., and Moore, G. E.: *J. Am. Chem. Soc.*, **73**, 2900 (1951).
35. Kraus, K. A., and Moore, G. E.: *J. Am. Chem. Soc.*, **74**, 843 (1952).
36. Lister, B. A. J.: *J. Chem. Soc.*, **1951**, 3123.

37. Lister, B. A., and Smith, M. L.: *J. Chem. Soc.*, **1948**, 1272.
38. Lur'e, Yu. Yu., and Filippova, N. A.: *Zavodskaya Lab.*, **14**, 159 (1948).
39. Magnusson, L. B., Thompson, S. G., and Seaborg, G. T.: *Phys. Rev.*, **78**, 363 (1950).
40. Marinsky, J. A., Glendenin, L. E., and Coryell, C. D.: *J. Am. Chem. Soc.*, **69**, 2781 (1947).
41. Mayer, S. W., and Tompkins, E. R.: *J. Am. Chem. Soc.*, **69**, 2866 (1947).
42. Peterson, S.: *J. Chem. Education*, **28**, 22 (1951).
43. Reid, A. F.: *Ind. Eng. Chem.*, **40**, 76 (1948).
44. Russell, E. R., cited by Tompkins *et al.: J. Am. Chem. Soc.*, **69**, 2769 (1947).
45. Russell, E. R., Lesko, R. C., and Schubert, J.: *Nucleonics*, **7**, No. 1, 60 (1950).
46. Russell, R. G., and Pearce, D. W.: *J. Am. Chem. Soc.*, **65**, 595 (1943).
47. Schubert, J.: *Anal. Chem.*, **22**, 1359 (1950).
48. Schubert, J.: *Natl. Nuclear Energy Ser.*, Div. VIII-1, Anal. Chem. Manhattan Project, 693 (1950).
49. Schubert, J., and Richter, J. W.: *J. Am. Chem. Soc.*, **70**, 4259 (1948).
50. Schubert, J., Russell, E. R., and Farabee, L. B.: *Science*, **109**, 316 (1949).
51. Schuler, R. H., Boyd, Jr., A. C., and Kay, D. J.: *J. Chem. Education*, **28**, 192 (1951).
52. Schweitzer, G. K., and Whitney, I. B.: *Radioactive Tracer Technique*, New York, 1949.
53. Spedding, F. H.: *Disc. Faraday Soc.*, **1949**, No. 7, 214.
54. Spedding, F. H., Voigt, A. F., Gladrow, E. M., and Sleight, N. R.: *J. Am. Chem. Soc.*, **69**, 2777 (1947).
55. Spedding, F. H., Voigt, A. F., Gladrow, E. M., Sleight, N. R., Powell, J. E., Wright, J. M., Butler, T. A., and Figard, P.: *J. Am. Chem. Soc.*, **69**, 2786 (1947).
56. Spedding, F. H., Fulmer, E. I., Butler, T. A., Gladrow, E. M., Gobush, M., Porter, P. E., Powell, J. E., and Wright, J. M.: *J. Am. Chem. Soc.*, **69**, 2812 (1947).
57. Spedding, F. H., Fulmer, E. I., Ayres, B., Butler, T. A., Powell, J. E., Tevebaugh, A. D., and Thompson, R.: *J. Am. Chem. Soc.*, **70**, 1671 (1948).
58. Spedding, F. H., Fulmer, E. I., Butler, T. A., and Powell, J. E.: *J. Am. Chem. Soc.*, **72**, 2349 (1950).
59. Spedding, F. H., Fulmer, E. I., Powell, J. E., and Butler, T. A.: *J. Am. Chem. Soc.*, **72**, 2354 (1950).
60. Spedding, F. H., and Dye, J. L.: *J. Am. Chem. Soc.*, **72**, 5350 (1950).
61. Spedding, F. H., Fulmer, E. I., Powell, J. E., Butler, T. A., and Yaffe, I. S.: *J. Am. Chem. Soc.*, **73**, 4840 (1951).
62. Spedding, F. H., and Powell, J. E.: *J. Am. Chem. Soc.*, **74**, 856, 857 (1952).
63. Street, Jr., K., and Seaborg, G. T.: *J. Am. Chem. Soc.*, **70**, 4268 (1948).
64. Street, Jr., K., and Seaborg, G. T.: *J. Am. Chem. Soc.*, **72**, 2790 (1950).
65. Thompson, S. G., Cunningham, B. B., and Seaborg, G. T.: *J. Am. Chem. Soc.*, **72**, 2798 (1950).
66. Thompson, S. G., Street, Jr., K., Ghiorso, A., and Seaborg, G. T.: *Phys. Rev.*, **78**, 298 (1950).
67. Tiselius, A.: *Arkiv Kemi, Mineral. Geol.*, **B14**, No. 22 (1940).
68. Tiselius, A., and Claesson, S.: *Arkiv Kemi, Mineral. Geol.*, **B15**, No. 18 (1942).

69. Tompkins, E. R.: *J. Am. Chem. Soc.*, **70**, 3520 (1948).
70. Tompkins, E. R., Khym, J. X., and Cohn, W. E.: *J. Am. Chem. Soc.*, **69**, 2769 (1947).
71. Usatenko, Y. I., and Datsenko, O. V.: *Zavodskaya Lab.*, **14**, 1323 (1948).
72. Vestermark, T.: Symposium of papers read on the Isotope Day (May 15, 1948), IVA, FKO 7, 31 (1948).
73. Wickbold, R.: Diss., Marl (Westf.), 1950; *Z. anal. Chem.*, **132**, 401 (1951).
74. Wilkinson, G.: *Phys. Rev.*, **75**, 1370 (1949).
75. Yang, J.-T.: *Anal. Chim. Acta*, **4**, 59 (1950).
76. Yang, J.-T.: *J. chim. phys.*, **47**, 805 (1950).
77. Yang, J.-T.: *Compt. rend.*, **231**, 1059 (1950).
78. Yang, J.-T., and Haissinsky, M.: *Bull. soc. chim. France*, **1949**, 546.
79. Yoshino, Y., and Kojima, M.: *Bull. Chem. Soc. Japan*, **23**, 46 (1950).

CHAPTER XIV

Isolation of Low-Molecular-Weight Organic Acids

1. SEPARATION FROM VARIOUS CONTAMINANTS

Several commercial processes have been suggested which call for the use of anion exchange resins for the uptake of organic acids from fruit extracts (5). A number of analytical applications of this principle have also been proposed. By the uptake of low-molecular-weight organic acids on anion exchange resins, different types of contaminants which interfere with the characterizing and quantitative determination may be removed. Among removable substances may be mentioned alcohols, sugars, aldehydes, ketones, and other non-electrolytes, high polymer acids, amino acids, and cations.

A resin of strongly basic type saturated with carbonate ions has been utilized by Bryant and Overell (1) for the isolation of citric, malic, succinic, and fumaric acids from plant-tissue extracts. In this manner several impurities which interfere with the identification and estimation of the different carboxylic acids by paper chromatography can be removed. Among the impurities removed are inorganic cations, sugars, and pigments.

The carboxylic acids are displaced by elution with sodium carbonate or ammonium carbonate solution. In the former elution the effluent naturally contains a high concentration of sodium carbonate, which may be removed by addition of a sulfonic acid resin in the free-acid form or by electrolytic desalting. Ammonium carbonate may be removed during concentration.

Column: 8×250 mm; Amberlite IRA-400 [CO_3^{2-}].

Capacity: 1 liter solution containing 150 mg total of citric, malic, and succinic acids.

Flow rate: 2–3 ml sqcm^{-1} min^{-1}.

A preliminary separation of the carboxylic acids from each other can be achieved by elution with 0.1 N sodium carbonate. It was found that malic and succinic acids were quantitatively eluted in the first 300 ml, but citric acid was not detected until a further 300 ml of the elutriant had passed the column. In those cases where no separation was required, 250 ml 1 N sodium carbonate was used to displace all retained acids quantitatively.

Wilson (11) has made a careful investigation concerning the application of the ion exchange method for the determination of l-malic acid in maple sirup, mixed maple sirups, and apple juice. The method is based on a deionization in two steps (Chapter VI: 5 A). The second column (the anion exchanger Duolite A 4 in free-base form), which retains the acids, is subsequently regenerated by means of alkali. The eluate is passed through a cation exchanger to remove the sodium ions before the polarimetric determination in the presence of uranium acetate. Some preliminary experiments with synthetic samples containing tartaric acid and citric acid are included in Wilson's article.

The determination of galacturonic acid in fruits and fruit juices has been shortened considerably by Winkler (12) and Mills (8), utilizing a technique similar to the one already described. An anion exchanger of strongly basic type was found to be most satisfactory in the second step. The acids retained by the resin were eluted by hydrochloric acid (1–2 N) and galacturonic acid determined spectrophotometrically after addition of naphthoresorcinol.

A similar ion exchange technique has been employed by Porter, Buch and Willits (9) to isolate the non-volatile acid fraction from maple sirup. Subsequently the acids were identified by paper chromatography.

Two-step deionization of wine and must has been suggested by Guntz (6) in connection with the characterization and analysis of these products. The amount of extract (chiefly glycerol, sugar, and coloring matters) is determined in the deionized solution. The application of the principle of total salt determination (Chapter VIII) was also suggested by the author.

Haas and Stadtman (7) described a method of fractionating apricot concentrates into three different fractions. The water solution was passed first over a sulfonic acid resin (H^+ form) and in a second step over an anion exchanger of weakly basic type (free-base form). After washing with water, the effluent from the second column contained 98% of the sugars. The first column was regenerated with 2 N hydrochloric acid, and the cation solution obtained was found to contain the inorganic cations and 81% of the nitrogenous constituents. From the anion fraction prepared by eluting the second column with 1 N sodium hydroxide, 88% of the acids other than amino acids and acidic proteins were recovered.

2. SEPARATION FROM ALDEHYDES AND KETONES

As mentioned in Chapter VI: 4 A, aldehydes and ketones react with anion exchangers in the free-base form. Therefore the use of resins in the bicarbonate form is recommended (4) to take up acids from solutions containing

TABLE 19

Added		Found	
Formic Acid	Formaldehyde	Formic Acid	Formaldehyde
g	g	g	g
0.138	0.280	0.138	0.277
0.173	0.277	0.172	0.277
0.173	0.197	0.174	0.197

In these experiments the total amount of anion exchanger was 20 ml: Amberlite IRA-400 [HCO_3^-; 0.12–0.30 mm]. The elution was performed with 100 ml 0.1 M sodium carbonate solution.

aldehydes and ketones. Experiments with formaldehyde, acetaldehyde, furfural, benzaldehyde, crotonic aldehyde, glyoxal, acetone, and methyl ethyl ketone showed that with this procedure the carbonyl compounds remain quantitatively in solution. Only aldehydes containing phenolic hydroxyl groups (salicylaldehyde and vanillin) were found to be retained by the resin, and consequently the method cannot be applied for separation of acids and carbonyl compounds when aldehydes of this type are present.

A combined operation, e.g. first shaking the solution to be analyzed with the resin and subsequently transferring the solution and the resin into a column containing a short resin layer, was found suitable for this separation. After washing, the aldehydes may be estimated in the effluent. The acids are conveniently eluted by means of dilute sodium carbonate solution; they are liberated in the eluate by a combined batch and column operation, using a sulfonic acid resin in the hydrogen form. The aldehydes are determined colorimetrically and the acids by titration with standard alkali. Some typical results are reproduced in Table 19.

3. CHROMATOGRAPHIC SEPARATION OF ORGANIC ACIDS

The separation of several organic acids from each other has been studied by Stark, Goodban, and Owens (10), working with sugar-beet liquors. In order to convert the salts to the corresponding acids and simultaneously to remove the amino acids, the liquor was first passed over a sulfonic acid resin in the hydrogen form. The liberated acids were taken up on the top of an anion exchange column, e.g. in the chloride (or formate) form. The amount of acid was chosen so as to load only the first few centimeters of the column. After washing with water, the acids were eluted by means of hydrochloric or sulfuric acid at pH 1.5. This pH was chosen because maximum differences in the degree of dissociation of the different acids exist near this pH. An improved separation was obtained when the flow rate was lowered from 1 to 0.1 ml sqcm^{-1} min^{-1}. The eluate was collected in a great number of fractions. Selected fractions were studied by means of paper chromatography. Furthermore, the total amount of acid was determined by titration with alkali, and chloride was estimated according to Volhard. Lactic, glycolic, pyrrolidone carboxylic, malic, citric, and oxalic acids were identified, and some of them estimated semiquantitatively.

Of great interest is the observation that organic acids can be taken up also from non-aqueous solutions (e.g. ether) by means of anion exchangers of the strongly basic type [OH$^-$ form] (2). Cason and Sumrell (3) used this procedure to isolate acids of phthioic type from the tubercle bacillus.

BIBLIOGRAPHY

1. Bryant, F., and Overell, B. T.: *Nature*, **167**, 361 (1951).
2. Cason, J., Sumrell, G., and Mitchell, R. S.: *J. Org. Chem.*, **15**, 850 (1950).
3. Cason, J., and Sumrell, G.: *J. Biol. Chem.*, **192**, 405 (1951).
4. Gabrielson, G., and Samuelson, O.: *Acta Chem. Scand.*, in press.
5. Griessbach, R.: *Austausch-Adsorbentien in der Lebensmittelindustrie*, Leipzig, 1949, p. 64.
6. Guntz, A. A.: *Chim. anal.*, **32**, 246 (1950).
7. Haas, V. A., and Stadtman, E. R.: *Ind. Eng. Chem.*, **41**, 983 (1949).
8. Mills, P. A.: *J. Assoc. Offic. Agr. Chemists*, **33**, 513 (1951).
9. Porter, W. L., Buch, M. L., and Willits, C. O.: *Food Research*, **16** (No. 4), 338 (1951).
10. Stark, J. B., Goodban, A. E., and Owens, H. S.: *Proc. Am. Soc. Sugar Beet Technol.*, **1950**, 578; *Ind. Eng. Chem.*, **43**, 603 (1951).
11. Wilson, J. B.: *J. Assoc. Offic. Agr. Chemists*, **33**, 995 (1950).
12. Winkler, W. O.: *J. Assoc. Offic. Agr. Chemists*, **34**, 506 (1951).

CHAPTER XV

High-Molecular-Weight Organic Electrolytes

1. DETERMINATION OF THE DEGREE OF SUBSTITUTION OF CELLULOSE XANTHATE

An ion exchange method for the determination of the degree of substitution (D.S.) of cellulose xanthate solutions (viscose) has been devised by Samuelson and Gärtner (5). The method is based on the possibility of separating low-molecular-weight from high-molecular-weight anions by anion exchangers. The anion exchanger must be of the strongly basic type, as the reaction takes place in alkaline solution.

The sulfur-containing by-products present in viscose (trithiocarbonate and sulfide) are quantitatively retained in a column filled with a resin in the free-base form, whereas the cellulose xanthate passes the column. In the purified cellulose xanthate solution obtained the degree of substitution can be easily determined in a reproducible manner according to the zincate method. A high flow rate (coarse particles) and cooling are necessary in order to prevent decomposition of the cellulose xanthate during the experiment. The method can be applied to viscoses containing sulfite. The procedure is simple and rapid, the time required for the determination being about 2 hr. Several analyses can be performed simultaneously.

A comparison between the ion exchange method and the methods devised by Fink, Stahn, and Matthes, as well as by Barthélemy and Williams, showed rather good agreement. However, the ion exchange method gave better reproducibility and higher accuracy.

Procedure: About 3 g technical viscose is used in each experiment. The viscose is diluted with 250 ml ice-cooled distilled water and kept cool during the subsequent percolation through the ion exchange column (Fig. 27). If highest accuracy is required, the column should also be cooled during the experiments. This is especially necessary at very high degrees of substitution of the cellulose xanthate. Afterwards the column is washed with 100 ml water at the same flow rate as during the sorption step (5–8 ml per min).

The combined filtrate and washing water is collected in a 500-ml Erlenmeyer flask containing 10 ml of a sodium zincate solution, prepared according to Barthélemy and Williams. The mixture is boiled for 30 min and the flask then ice-cooled. After cooling, the contents of the flask are washed into a 600-ml beaker containing a cold solution of 50 ml of 1 M sulfuric acid and 30 ml of 0.1 N iodine. Immediately thereafter the mixture is transferred quantitatively back to the Erlenmeyer flask. After 20 min the iodine not consumed is titrated with a 0.1 N solution of sodium thiosulfate with starch as indicator. The cellulose content in the viscose is determined according to Jentgen on a separate sample. The D. S. is calculated according to the following formula:

$$D.S. = \frac{0.0405 \cdot (ml\ I_2 \cdot n_I - ml\ Na_2S_2O_3 \cdot n_t)}{grams\ cellulose\ in\ the\ viscose\ sample}$$

where n_I and n_t are the normalities of the iodine and thiosulfate solutions, respectively.

Column: 9×150 mm; Dowex 1 or Amberlite IRA-400 [OH$^-$; 0.4–0.8 mm].

After use the columns are emptied and the resin from several columns is collected in a beaker and treated with 4 N hydrochloric acid. The resin is then collected in a funnel, regenerated with 1.5 N sodium hydroxide, and finally washed with water. This procedure is less time consuming than separate regeneration of each column, the total time used for these operations being about 2 hr. The treatment with hydrochloric acid is made in a beaker and not directly in the columns because the gas evolved would cause channeling in the columns.

2. PURIFICATION OF DIRECT COTTON DYES

A method for the purification of direct cotton dyes, which may be of interest also from an analytical point of view, has been devised by Richardson (4). The method is based on the fact that the large organic anions of a dye with an average diameter of 30 Å or larger are prevented from entering the resin phase.

In the purification of a dye which is soluble in acid solution it is convenient first to exchange the cations for hydrogen ions by means of a sulfonic acid resin. In a subsequent step contaminating anions, inorganic as well as several organic ones, are removed by passing the solution through a column containing an anion exchanger in the free-base form. The resin may be of either weakly or strongly basic type.

With dyes yielding water-insoluble sulfonic acids and with acid-labile dyes reverse deionization may be used, i.e. direct passage of the solution of the crude dye through a strongly basic resin in the hydroxyl form. The hydroxyl ions are then removed by treatment with a carboxylic acid resin.

3. SOLUBLE PECTIN AND PECTIC ACID

Williams and Johnson (7) observed that pectin could be quantitatively determined by electrodeposition, provided the electrolyte concentration of the solution was low. The electrolytes were removed by passing the solution first through a sulfonic acid resin in the hydrogen cycle and afterwards through an anion exchanger of weakly basic type (free-base form). No pectin was lost during the process. The fact that pectic acid is not retained by the anion exchanger may be explained by the large dimensions of the anion.

The method has been used successfully for the analysis of fruit extracts, and it is stated that less time and attention are required than with older methods.

De-ashing of pectin solutions by means of ion exchange has also been studied by Lampitt, Money, Judge, and Urie (3).

Experiments which demonstrate the quantitative separation of galacturonic acid from polygalacturonic acid (pectic acid) by means of anion exchangers have been reported by Deuel, Solms, and Anyas-Weisz (2).

A detailed investigation on characterization of pectins has been published by Anyas-Weisz, Solms, and Deuel (1). Low-molecular-weight electrolytes are removed quantitatively from solutions containing pectins and pectates by percolation through columns of sulfonic acid resin in the hydrogen form and anion exchangers in the free-base form. According to these authors, the anion exchanger may be of either weakly or strongly basic type. The deionization may be performed in two steps or as a mixed-bed operation.

The effluent from the resin columns (or a mixed-bed column) is used for a determination of the free carboxyl groups (x) by titration with alkali against bromothymol blue or phenolphthalein.

In order to estimate the total number of carboxyl groups (p) the ester groups are saponified by addition of excess sodium hydroxide to a separate sample. After 2 hr at room temperature the low-molecular-weight ions are removed by the ion exchange method and the carboxyl groups determined as before. The methoxyl groups (y) can be calculated by the difference between these two titrations: $y = p - x$. The application of ion exchangers may also be useful in connection with the determination of the acetyl groups in pectins. Formulae are given for the recalculation of the titration data into weight of pectin and degree of esterification.

Before the analysis of the water-insoluble calcium pectate it is recommended that the solid substance be shaken in a water suspension with excess sodium resin to obtain a solution containing the sodium salt.

The method has been applied for the determination and characterization of pectins in a number of different preparations, e.g. apple juice, grape juice, and extracts from sugar-beets. An attempt to estimate galacturonic acid in sugar-beet juices has been made by Willenberg (6).

BIBLIOGRAPHY

1. Anyas-Weisz, L., Solms, J., and Deuel, H.: *Mitt. Lebensm. Hyg.*, **42**, 91 (1951).
2. Deuel, H., Solms, J., and Anyas-Weisz, L.: *Helv. Chim. Acta*, **33**, 2171 (1950).
3. Lampitt, L. H., Money, R. W., Judge, B. E., and Urie, A.: *J. Soc. Chem. Ind.*, **66**, 121 (1947).
4. Richardson, R. W.: *Nature*, **164**, 916 (1949); *J. Chem. Soc.*, **1951**, 910.
5. Samuelson, O., and Gärtner, F.: *Acta Chem. Scand.*, **5**, 596 (1951).
6. Willenberg, W.: *Zucker*, **4**, 159 (1951).
7. Williams, K. T., and Johnson, C. M.: *Ind. Eng. Chem.*, Anal. Ed., **16**, 23 (1944).

CHAPTER XVI

Aldehydes and Ketones

1. GENERAL CONSIDERATIONS

Aldehydes and ketones form, with bisulfite, addition compounds which are salts of strong acids. These are now generally considered to be α-oxysulfonic acids:

$$RCHO + HSO_3^- \rightleftharpoons RCHOHSO_3^-$$
$$R_2CO + HSO_3^- \rightleftharpoons R_2COHSO_3^-$$

As can be seen from the reaction formulae, a splitting of the α-oxysulfonic acids takes place on adding acid or alkali. The equilibrium constant for the reaction is different for different carbonyl compounds. The most stable is the formaldehyde-bisulfite compound. The stability diminishes according to the series: formaldehyde>acetaldehyde>benzaldehyde>furfural>acetone.

Samuelson and Westlin (5) showed that α-oxysulfonic acids corresponding to low-molecular-weight carbonyl compounds which occur in sulfite waste liquor can be taken up by an anion exchanger and then eluted from it by sodium bicarbonate solution. According to a patent of Samuelson, the carbonyl compounds are removed from alcohol either after adding bisulfite ions to the solution or by passing the alcohol solution through an anion exchanger in the bisulfite form.

The application of this principle in analytical chemistry has been investigated in a number of papers.

2. THE SORPTION STEP

Gabrielson and Samuelson (1) showed that different aldehydes and ketones can be quantitatively retained on passing the aldehyde solution through the bed of an anion exchanger in the bisulfite form. These authors used resins of strongly basic type. The break-through curves have the same shape as in experiments with inorganic acids, showing that the reaction occurs at high velocity. The break-through curve for a 0.2% solution of furfural is presented in Fig. 41.

The following aldehydes were easily taken up quantitatively from water solutions or mixtures of alcohol and water: acetaldehyde, furfural, benz-

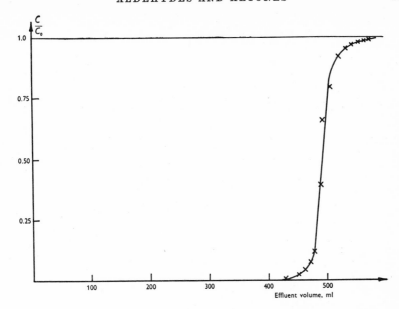

FIG. 41. Exchange isoplane (break-through curve) for a solution of 0.2% furfural
in water.
Column: 9.8 × 140 mm; Amberlite IRA–400 [HSO_3^-; 0.12–0.43 mm].
Flow rate: 2 ml/min.
Influent conc.: C_0.
Effluent conc.: C.   [from (1)]

aldehyde, salicylaldehyde, vanillin, crotonic aldehyde, and glyoxal. With
formaldehyde a quantitative retention could also be effected, but in order
to remove the last traces it was found necessary to use a larger resin
bed and a lower flow rate (0.7 ml sqcm^{-1} min^{-1}). These difficulties may
seem surprising because the formaldehyde bisulfite has a greater stability
than any of the other bisulfite compounds. The explanation seems to lie
in the polymerization of formaldehyde (1).

Among the ketones, acetone and methyl ethyl ketone have been studied
by Gabrielson and Samuelson (1). A quantitative uptake can be obtained,
but a larger amount of resin is required than for the aldehydes. This difference is explained by the lower stability of the corresponding α-oxysulfonic acids.

Recently Sjöström (8) has extended the investigations to include also
other types of ketones. The aromatic (saturated) ketones acetophenone and benzophenone as well as camphor are known not to form any
α-oxysulfonic acids. Experiments performed with these ketones dissolved

in 95% ethanol showed that the ketones pass quantitatively into the effluent.

Among unsaturated α–β ketones mesityl oxide and benzalacetophenone have been studied. These compounds are known to add bisulfite very easily to the double bond. Mesityl oxide is retained quantitatively from water solution, and benzalacetophenone was taken up quantitatively from a solution in 95% ethanol at extremely low flow rate. These experiments show that compounds containing a C=C double bond which is highly reactive against bisulfite can be taken up by an anion exchanger in the bisulfite form.

3. THE WASHING STEP

In the washing step there exists an important difference in behavior between the retained α-oxysulfonic acids and other strong acids, the former being to a greater or lesser extent decomposed and consequently displaced down the column. Therefore the resin cannot be washed with unlimited amounts of water without any leakage. The movement of the carbonyl band is dependent upon the stability of the corresponding α-oxysulfonic acids. In cases where the stability is low, e.g. with acetone, even a quantitative displacement may be effected by washing with water. By using a proper amount of water and a sufficient excess of resin, it is, however, possible to displace the solution left in the column after the sorption step without any leakage of carbonyl compounds (1).

4. THE ELUTION STEP

As already mentioned, carbonyl compounds which form unstable α-oxysulfonic acids may be eluted simply by washing with water. The amount of water required for a complete elution may be considerably reduced by washing at elevated temperature, as the decomposition of the retained complex increases with increased temperature. Acetone and methyl ethyl ketone may be easily eluted by washing with water at 60–75°C. Elution of aldehydes by means of hot water is, for practical purposes, impossible (1).

Aldehydes may be quantitatively eluted by washing with alkaline or neutral electrolyte solutions, an example being reproduced in Fig. 42 (1, 3). Acid solutions cannot be used, as they would cause evolution of SO_2 and consequently a channeling of the column. Samuelson and Sande (6) showed that a chromatographic separation of aldehydes can be obtained by elution with sodium carbonate buffers.

Mesityl oxide cannot be displaced by washing with hot water but is easily eluted by 1 N sodium chloride solution (8).

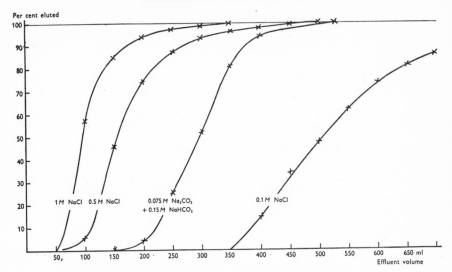

FIG. 42.   Integral elution curves for furfural (total amount 0.84 g).
Column: 9.8 × 550 mm; Amberlite IRA–400 [HSO_3^-; 0.12– 0.30 mm].
Flow rate: 2 ml/min.
Elutriants: 0.1 M NaCl.
0.5 M NaCl.
1 M NaCl.
0.075 M Na_2CO_3 + 0.15 M $NaHCO_3$.   [from (3)]

5. DETERMINATION OF ALCOHOL IN THE PRESENCE OF ALDEHYDES AND KETONES

Gabrielson and Samuelson (1, 2) applied anion exchangers in the bisulfite form to remove aldehydes and ketones from solutions containing alcohol in order to facilitate the determination of the alcohol. The operation is performed as a column process, and the alcohol is determined either directly in the effluent, after the water originally present in the column has been displaced, or by passing a certain amount of the solution through the column and subsequently washing with water. The former technique is to be preferred in determinations where the alcohol concentration is extremely low. The alcohol is determined pycnometrically. If it is desired to determine methyl alcohol and ethyl alcohol the pycnometric determination is conveniently supplemented by a colorimetric determination of methyl alcohol according to the chromotropic acid method. This method has been utilized to determine ethyl and methyl alcohol in condensates from the evaporation of sulfite waste liquor (7).

The following working conditions may serve as an example. Solutions containing 6.1 g methyl ethyl ketone per liter and varying amounts of alcohol were passed through the column: 9.8×550 mm; Amberlite IRA-400 [HSO_3^-; 0.12–0.30 mm], at the flow rate 2–2.5 ml sqcm^{-1} min^{-1}. Because of the great filter resistance of the resin, pressure was used in order to facilitate the passage of the solution through the column (Fig. 27). The first 70 ml of the effluent was discarded, and then a volume suitable for pycnometric alcohol determination was taken. Some results are reproduced in Table 20. It may be pointed out that, if only carbonyl compounds which form more stable α-oxysulfonic acids (e.g. aldehydes) are present, the resin bed may be shortened considerably (1). Figure 41 may serve as a guidance for the choice of column length.

TABLE 20

Added, g per liter		Found, g per liter
Methyl Ethyl Ketone	Ethanol	Ethanol
6.1	5.2	5.2
6.1	20.6	20.5
6.1	50.6	50.8

6. SEPARATION OF ALDEHYDES FROM KETONES

Certain ketones may be eluted quantitatively from the resin by means of hot water under conditions where aldehydes are moved only to a limited extent in the column. This fact has been utilized by Gabrielson and Samuelson (3) for a quantitative separation of aldehydes from acetone and methyl ethyl ketone. It must be noted that both ketones and aldehydes are retained and that this separation — according to the terminology adopted in this book — must be considered a chromatographic separation by stepwise elution. The rates of movement down the column are so different that the relative amounts of the compounds and small changes in working conditions have no significant influence upon the separation.

The mixture is taken up in a column containing an anion exchanger in the bisulfite form. Under the conditions used by Gabrielson and Samuelson it was found that 8 meq acetone or methyl ethyl ketone could be quantitatively removed from the column (cf. below) by means of 300 ml water at 75°C, whereas 10 meq furfural or acetaldehyde which had simultaneously been taken up by the resin could not be detected in the effluent even when the washing was continued until 2200 ml effluent had been collected. After the ketones have been desorbed by means of hot water, the aldehydes are eluted with 1 N sodium chloride and determined separately according to standard methods, e.g. colorimetrically. Excellent results were obtained, as demonstrated by the data given in Table 21. The method has been applied to the determination of acetone in sulfite waste liquor and sulfite alcohol.

TABLE 21

Added		Found	
g Acetone	g Furfural	g Acetone	g Furfural
0.300	0.844	0.299	0.840
0.500	1.01	0.495	1.03
0.700	0.506	0.708	0.500

Procedure:
Column: 9.8×550 mm; Amberlite IRA-400 [HSO_3^-; 0.12–0.30 mm].
Flow rate: 2.5 ml sqcm^{-1} min^{-1}.
Elution of ketones: 300–400 ml water at 75°C.
Elution of aldehydes: 200 ml 1 N sodium chloride at room temperature.

7. SEPARATION OF CARBONYL COMPOUNDS FROM ACETAL

Acetal [$CH_3CH(OC_2H_5)_2$] is decomposed on passing the water solution through an anion exchanger in the bisulfite form, the aldehyde being retained by the resin. If instead the acetal is dissolved in conc. ethanol, the acetal passes quantitatively into the effluent. This fact may be utilized for a separation of aldehydes and ketones from acetal, the separation being performed in ethanol solution by means of an anion exchanger in the bisulfite form (4).

BIBLIOGRAPHY

1. Gabrielson, G., and Samuelson, O.: *Svensk Kem. Tid.*, **62**, 214 (1950).
2. Gabrielson, G., and Samuelson, O.: *Acta Chem. Scand.*, in press.
3. Gabrielson, G., and Samuelson, O.: *Svensk Kem. Tid.*, in press.
4. Gabrielson, G., and Samuelson, O.: unpublished.
5. Samuelson, O., and Westlin, A.: *Svensk Kem. Tid.*, **59**, 244 (1947).
6. Samuelson, O., and Sande, K.-Å.: unpublished.
7. Samuelson, O., Ahlén, L., and Gabrielson, G.: to be published.
8. Sjöström, E.: *Svensk Kem. Tid.*, in press.

CHAPTER XVII

Sugars and Polyhydric Alcohols

1. SUGARS

Sugars are not retained by cation exchange resins. It must be observed, however, that an inversion may occur when the hydrogen cycle is operated. At elevated temperature this reaction goes quickly, but at room temperature the rate is so low that the cations may be exchanged for hydrogen ions without any detectable inversion, provided the time of contact is not extremely long (3).

Anion exchangers of weakly basic type do not take up sugars, whereas a considerable uptake can be achieved by means of anion exchangers of strongly basic type in the free-base form (cf. Chapter XVIII). In the presence of bisulfite or borate certain sugars may be taken up as complex ions by means of anion exchange resins. These observations will probably be of great importance in carbohydrate analysis.

A. *Determination of Reducing Sugars in Plant Extracts*

In the determination of reducing sugars in distillery slops, molasses, vegetables, and several other products considerable errors may occur because of the presence of non-sugar reducing substances. A number of purification methods have been suggested to remove the interfering impurities by means of precipitation and adsorption.

Work reported by several authors on the use of ion exchange resins for the purification of beet juices and cane juices for technical purposes suggested the idea of utilizing ion exchangers for removing non-sugars before the determination of reducing sugars, e.g. by reduction of cupric salts. Satisfactory results have been reported by Serbia (16), as well as by Williams *et al.* (18, 19). All the non-fermentable reducing substances as measured by the copper method were shown to be removed from several types of vegetable extracts. The ion exchange method was simple and accurate.

The purification was performed either as a common two-step column process (18) or in a batch procedure with mixed resins (16, 18). The batch method is simpler, but it was reported that not all resins were effective for the removal of the interfering substances. Certain resins which could be used in column operation were unsatisfactory in batch operation (19).

Batch procedure (19):

A plant extract in water is filtered through a mat of Celite Analytical Filter-Aid and diluted with water to obtain a concentration of 0.4 mg reducing sugar per ml of solution. To a 50-ml aliquot of the plant extract are added 2.0 g each of cation and anion exchange resins, and the mixture is shaken for a period of 2 hr. After filtration reducing sugars are determined according to common procedures.

Cation exchanger: Hydrogen form of sulfonic acid resin, e.g. Duolite C3.
Anion exchanger: Free-base form of weakly basic resin, e.g. Duolite A4.

The observation (cf. section 1C) that monosaccharides, which have the ability to add bisulfite, may be easily taken up from an ethanol solution (e.g. 95% ethanol) by an anion exchanger in the bisulfite form has also been used as a simple method for the determination of reducing sugars in solutions containing interfering substances. After the sorption step the column is washed with ethanol to remove the solution left in the column. Finally the sugars are displaced from the column by means of water and determined in the effluent according to common methods. This method has been applied to the determination of reducing sugars in sulfite waste liquor. In order to prevent a precipitation on addition of ethanol it is recommended that the calcium ions present in the original liquor be exchanged for sodium ions before the experiment (15).

B. *Miscellaneous Applications*

Partridge and Westall applied the two-step deionization, a weakly basic resin being used in the second step, for the removal of cations and contaminating acids from extracts of biological materials in their procedure for the qualitative analysis of sugars by paper chromatography (12). A similar procedure was adopted by Putnam *et al.* in connection with the preparation of radioactive (C^{14}) sugars from plants exposed to an atmosphere of radioactive carbon dioxide (14) and by Wolfrom and Wood (20) for the removal of sodium sulfate from solutions containing aldoses and glycitol [cf. also (1)]. MacLeod (8) used this method for the separation of the sugars which are present in an uncombined state in the barley corn. Care has to be taken to wash the anion exchanger completely free from the sodium hydroxide used in regeneration since at a high pH epimerization of sugars occurs.

Ion exchangers have also been employed to facilitate the identification and determination of sugars in sulfite waste liquor (Chapter XVIII).

Sundman, Saarnio, and Gustafsson (17) used an anion exchange resin of weakly basic type for deacidification of wood hydrolyzates in connection with a paper chromatographic investigation of the composition of wood. The sulfuric acid was retained in an anion exchange column instead of neutralizing with barium carbonate as is customary. Glucose, mannose, and xylose were shown to be unaffected and passed the column quantitatively.

C. Separation of Monosaccharides

Borate ions react with sugars to produce anionic sugar-borate complexes. Khym and Zill (7) reported that fructose, glucose, mannose, and galactose dissolved in weak sodium borate solutions were quantitatively retained by a column with an anion exchange resin of strongly basic type (free-base form). By elution with sodium borate solutions it was possible to effect a separation of the monosaccharides from each other. Preliminary experiments showed that a partial separation could be achieved between fructose, galactose, and glucose.

As discussed in Chapter XVI carbonyl compounds which have the ability to form α-oxysulfonic acids on addition of bisulfite can be taken up by an anion exchanger in the bisulfite form. In a preliminary communication Samuelson and Sjöström (15) report that xylose and mannose can be quantitatively retained from water solutions by an anion exchanger in the bisulfite form. A rather large excess of resin is required to complete the uptake, which is in agreement with the fact that the stability of the corresponding α-oxysulfonic acids is rather low. Fructose, which is known not to form any stable addition compound with bisulfite, passes quantitatively into the effluent and can in this manner be separated from xylose and mannose. Glucose is taken up less well than xylose and mannose, which is explained by the lower stability of the addition compound. On washing with water the retained sugars are eluted. When instead of water ethanol is used as a solvent the uptake increases considerably and excellent separations can be achieved in the elution step. The separation of various monosaccharides from each other has also been investigated. Conditions have been worked out which permit the separation of certain monosaccharides by stepwise elution with ethanol solutions of progressively decreasing concentration. Some results are presented in Fig. 43. This work is still in active progress.

2. SUGAR DERIVATIVES

McCready and Hassid (10) isolated and purified glucose-1-phosphate with the aid of ion exchange resins. The ester was prepared by phospho-

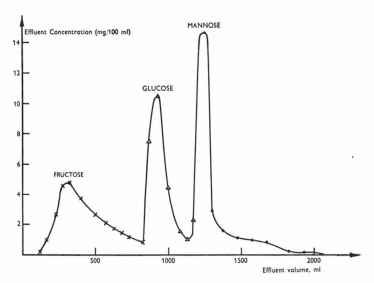

FIG. 43.   Chromatographic separation of monosaccharides by stepwise elution.
Column: 9 × 150 mm; Amberlite IRA–400 [HSO₃⁻; <0.12 mm].
Flow rate: 0.7 ml/min.
Elutriants: × 99.5% ethanol (by weight).
△ 95.0% ethanol.
● water.   [from (15)]

rolysis of starch in the presence of phosphate buffer. After precipitation of
inorganic phosphate the reaction mixture was first passed through a column of a sulfonic acid resin (H⁺ form). The effluent was run over an anion
exchanger of weakly basic type which retained the ester, whereas the soluble
impurities, including dextrins and proteins, passed through. The glucose-
1-phosphate was eluted with alkali.

Scott and Cohen (11) studied the separation of gluconic acid and 2-
ketogluconic acid from ribose by means of an anion exchanger in the
chloride form (strongly basic type). The acids were found to be quantitatively retained in the column, whereas ribose was recovered to 96% in the
effluent. By treating the column with 0.01 N hydrochloric acid a quantitative elution was effected. A partial separation of the two acids was achieved
in the elution step. Isbell (6) applied an anion exchanger in connection
with the determination of the molecular weight in polysaccharides by means
of an end group method. The carbonyl groups of polysaccharides are converted to carboxyl groups by the cyanhydrin method with $NaC^{14}N$. The
radioactive carboxyl derivative is taken up by an anion exchange resin,

separating it from the unreacted polysaccharide. After elution the radio-activity is measured, thus giving a measure of the carbonyl content (end groups) of the reacting polysaccharide.

3. GLYCEROL REMOVAL FROM AQUEOUS SOLUTIONS BY ANION EXCHANGE

It is well known that negatively charged complexes are formed between glycerol and boric acid and also with tetraborate. Zager and Doody (21) found that such complexes could be retained by means of anion exchangers of strongly basic type. The most satisfactory results (98% uptake) were reported for experiments in which a dilute water solution of glycerol was percolated through an anion exchange column previously treated with sodium tetraborate. The maximum amount of glycerol taken up was 0.167g per gram of resin (Amberlite IRA–400). The results seem to be of great interest from an analytical point of view.

Calvin (4) used the chromatographic elution from an anion exchange resin (Dowex 1) to identify and characterize samples of radioactive barium 3-phosphoglycerate prepared by photosynthesis. A similar method was employed by Fager and Rosenberg (5) to isolate phosphoglyceric acid from plant extracts.

4. DETERMINATION OF INOSITOL IN ANIMAL TISSUES

Platt and Glock (13) utilized a mixed bed of a cation exchanger and an anion exchanger in order to remove substances which interfere with the determination of inositol (hexahydroxy-cyclohexane) in solutions obtained by extraction of animal tissues. The cation exchanger of sulfonated-coal type was in the hydrogen form, and the anion exchanger of weakly basic type in the free-base form. Creatine and creatinine were recognized among the substances removed by the column.

BIBLIOGRAPHY

1. Aronoff, S., and Vernon, L.: *Arch. Biochem.*, **28**, 424 (1950).
2. Benson, A., and Calvin, M.: *Science*, **105**, 648 (1947).
3. Bodamer, G., and Kunin, R.: *Ind. Eng. Chem.*, **43**, 1082 (1951).
4. Calvin, M.: *J. Chem. Education*, **26**, 639 (1949).
5. Fager, E. W., and Rosenberg, J. L.: *Science*, **112**, 617 (1950).
6. Isbell, H. S.: *Science*, **113**, 532 (1951).
7. Khym, J. X., and Zill, L. P.: *J. Am. Chem. Soc.*, **73**, 2399 (1951).
8. MacLeod, A. M.: *J. Inst. Brewing*, **57**, 163 (1951).

9. Mariani, E.: *Ann. chim. applicata*, **39**, 283 (1949).
10. McCready, R. M., and Hassid, W. Z.: *J. Am. Chem. Soc.*, **66**, 560 (1944).
11. McNair Scott, D. B., and Cohen, S. S.: *Nature*, **111**, 543 (1950); *J. Biol. Chem.*, **188**, 509 (1951).
12. Partridge, S. M., and Westall, R. G.: *Biochem. J.*, **42**, 238 (1948).
13. Platt, B. S., and Glock, G. E.: *Biochem. J.*, **36**, XVIII (1942); **37**, 709 (1943).
14. Putnam, E. W., Hassid, W. Z., Krotkow, G., and Barker, H. A.: *J. Biol. Chem.*, **173**, 785 (1948).
15. Samuelson, O., and Sjöström, E.: to be published.
16. Serbia, G. R.: *Sugar*, **42**, No. 6, 26 (1947).
17. Sundman, J., Saarnio, J., and Gustafsson, K.: *Pappers- Trävarutid. Finland*, **31**, 467 (1949); **33**, 115 (1951).
18. Williams, K. T., Potter, E. F., Bevenue, A., and Scurzi, W. R.: *J. Assoc. Offic. Agr. Chemists*, **32**, 698 (1949).
19. Williams, K. T., Bevenue, A., and Washauer, B.: *J. Assoc. Offic. Agr. Chemists*, **33**, 986 (1950).
20. Wolfrom, M. L., and Wood, H. B.: *J. Am. Chem. Soc.*, **73**, 2933 (1951).
21. Zager, S. E., and Doody, T. C.: *Ind. Eng. Chem.*, **43**, 1570 (1951).

CHAPTER XVIII

Sulfite Waste Liquor

1. APPLICATION OF CATION EXCHANGERS

The procedure whereby the calcium ions in sulfite waste liquor are exchanged for hydrogen ions by means of sulfonic acid resins has been patented by Norsk Hydro. Erdtman adopted this method as the first step before fractionation of ligninsulfonic acid by precipitation with organic bases (1). Samuelson investigated the potentiometric titration curves of the liberated acids in sulfite waste liquor and different fractions prepared from sulfite waste liquor (9).

An interesting method for the determination of strong acids in sulfite waste liquor has been devised by Yorston (16). The cations are first exchanged for hydrogen ions. After addition of a large excess of glacial acetic acid (45 ml per 2.5 ml of liquor + 2.5 ml wash water) the solution is titrated conductometrically with 0.1 N potassium acetate in 90% acetic acid. This method has been applied to the determination of sulfonic acid groups in isolated barium salts of ligninsulfonic acids (10).

Removal of the metallic cations (iron and calcium) from sulfite waste liquor facilitates the colorimetric determination of silica and phosphoric acid in the liquor as already described in Chapter IX.

A conductometric method for the determination of sulfate by precipitation with barium chloride has been published by Peniston, Felicetta, and McCarthy (7). The method was found to be extremely rapid and superior to some earlier-known methods. However, Samuelson and Öhgren (12) found that the result was dependent upon the titration velocity, and as more accurate methods are available the procedure is not recommended if highest accuracy is desired.

According to Freudenberg, Lautsch, and Piazolo (4) it is not possible to de-ash sulfite waste liquor completely by cation exchange. Samuelson and Djurfeldt (11) found that the effluent from the cation exchange column after evaporation and burning gave a slight amount of ash, but that the residue consisted of silica and phosphoric acid, whereas the removal of cations was quantitative if proper conditions were chosen (see also Chapter IX: 1Dc and IX: 1E).

Erdtman, Lindgren, and Pettersson (2) utilized a cation exchanger in connection with the hydroxyl estimation in barium ligninsulfonate by acetylation. This salt could not be properly acetylated because of its insolubility in the acetylation mixture. This difficulty could be overcome by transforming the barium ligninsulfonate to the pyridinium salt by dissolving the barium salt in water and exchanging for hydrogen ions. After neutralization with pyridine the solution was evaporated and the pyridinium salt dried before acetylation.

2. APPLICATION OF ANION EXCHANGERS OF WEAKLY BASIC TYPE

Anion exchangers are useful tools for analysis of sulfite waste liquor. Samuelson (9) showed that anion exchangers of commercial type (e.g. Wofatit M in the free-base form), i.e. strongly cross-linked resins, could be used for the uptake of the low-molecular-weight acids from sulfite waste liquor. The non-electrolytes and the high-molecular-weight ligninsulfonic acids were not retained in the column. The retained acids may be eluted with sodium hydroxide, sodium carbonate, or ammonia. This makes possible a separation of the liquor into two fractions, which in many analyses may facilitate the procedure. In the experiments it is advisable first to exchange the cations in the original liquor for hydrogen ions by passing the liquor through a sulfonic acid resin in the hydrogen form. It was shown that among the acids retained by the anion exchanger were sulfonic acids, carboxylic acids, and inorganic acids. The methoxyl content was very low, indicating that only a slight amount of ligninsulfonic acid was retained. It was concluded that part of the sulfonic acids were sugarsulfonic acids.

Samuelson and Westlin (13) applied this method to investigations on the loosely bound SO_2 in sulfite waste liquor. They found that the greatest part of this SO_2 was retained by the resin, indicating that the greatest fraction is bound to low-molecular-weight compounds and only a minor part to the high polymer ligninsulfonic acid.

Stockman and Hägglund (15) removed the low-molecular-weight acids from sulfite waste liquor by anion exchange in order to facilitate determination of various sugars. The effluent from the anion exchanger was neutralized with barium carbonate, and the barium ligninsulfonate precipitated with alcohol, before determination of the sugars.

The sugar fraction may also be isolated by a combination of ion exchange and dialysis. The waste liquor may first be dialyzed, and the dialyzate passed through a sulfonic acid resin in the hydrogen form and subsequently through the free-base form of an anion exchanger of weakly basic type to remove cations and low-molecular-weight acids (6).

A prerequisite for the separation of high polymer ligninsulfonic acid from the low-molecular-weight acids is that the network skeleton of the ion exchanger be narrow. Lautsch (5) synthesized anion exchangers with wider network structure and observed that these preparations had the ability of retaining considerable amounts of ligninsulfonic acid. The capacity for ligninsulfonic acid calculated per unit weight of the exchanger increased when the amount of cross-linkages was lowered. At the same time the swelling increased. By using anion exchangers with varying network structures a fractionation of the ligninsulfonic acid could be obtained.

3. APPLICATION OF ANION EXCHANGERS OF STRONGLY BASIC TYPE

Whereas the sugars in sulfite waste liquor pass through the column when an anion exchanger of the weakly basic type is employed, Yorston (17) observed that when using a resin with strong basic groups (Amberlite IRA-400 in the OH⁻ form) as much as 40% of the copper-reducing substances had disappeared. The explanation was that part of the sugars were retained in the column. It was found that the sugars could be extracted by saturating the resin with carbon dioxide and washing with water. The stronger acids retained in the column were not eluted in this operation.

For practical investigations on the sugars in sulfite waste liquor the recommended procedure is first to exchange the metal cations for hydrogen ions, next to remove the low-molecular-weight acids by an anion exchanger of the weakly basic type, and finally to pass the solution through a column containing the sugar-adsorbing exchanger. Before the last step the pH should be adjusted by adding ammonia (cf. Chapter XVII: 1 A).

4. DETERMINATION OF THIOSULFATE AND POLYTHIONATE

Samuelson and Westlin (14) observed that ligninsulfonic acid interfered with the determination of tetrathionate in sulfite waste liquor. It was also observed that tetrathionate could be removed from ligninsulfonic acid by passing the solution through an anion exchanger, the ligninsulfonic acid not being retained. Regestad and Samuelson (8) have shown that the uptake of thiosulfate and polythionate from sulfite waste liquor by an anion exchanger and subsequent elution may be used for an accurate estimation of these compounds.

Most interesting is the observation that thiosulfate may be easily eluted by means of strong sodium chloride solution, whereas tetrathionate is unaffected. Tetrathionate may be displaced first after the resin has been treated with a sulfite solution which transforms tetrathionate into thiosulfate and trithionate according to the reaction:

$$S_4O_6{}^{2-}+SO_3{}^{2-}\rightarrow S_3O_6{}^{2-}+S_2O_3{}^{2-}$$

Procedure (thiosulfate and tetrathionate): Before the analysis the liquor is neutralized with $MgCO_3$ to about pH 7. Twenty milliliters of the liquor is run through an anion exchanger in the chloride form: 12.5×80 mm; Amberlite IRA–400 [Cl^-; 0.12–0.38 mm], at the flow rate 1.5 ml sqcm^{-1} min^{-1}. After washing with 20 ml water, elution is performed by means of 75 ml 4 N sodium chloride solution. Five milliliters formaldehyde solution (37–40%) and 20 ml acetic acid (10%) are added, and thiosulfate is determined by titrating rapidly with 0.03 N iodine with starch as indicator.

In order to determine tetrathionate the column is subsequently washed with 5 ml water and 30 ml 0.3 M Na_2SO_3. Afterwards the thiosulfate formed is eluted and determined as above, with the variation that the twofold amount of formaldehyde is added. The values are corrected for blank tests run under similar conditions.

BIBLIOGRAPHY

1. Erdtman, H.: *Svensk Papperstidn.*, **45**, 322 (1942).
2. Erdtman, H., Lindgren, B. O., and Pettersson, T.: *Acta Chem. Scand.*, **4**, 228 (1950).
3. Ernsberger, F. M., and France, W. G.: *J. Phys. & Colloid Chem.*, **52**, 267 (1948).
4. Freudenberg, K., Lautsch, W., and Piazolo, G.: *Cellulosechemie*, **22**, 97 (1944).
5. Lautsch, W.: *Angew. Chem.*, **57**, 149 (1944).
6. Mulvang, P. K., Agar, H. D., Peniston, Q. P., and McCarthy, J. L.: *J. Am. Chem. Soc.*, **73**, 1255 (1951).
7. Peniston, Q. P., Felicetta, V. F., and McCarthy, J. L.: *Anal. Chem.*, **19**, 332 (1947).
8. Regestad, S. O., and Samuelson, O.: to be published.
9. Samuelson, O.: *Svensk Papperstidn.*, **46**, 583 (1943).
10. Samuelson, O.: *Svensk Kem. Tid.*, **60**, 128 (1948).
11. Samuelson, O., and Djurfeldt, R.: unpublished.
12. Samuelson, O., and Öhgren, T.: unpublished.
13. Samuelson, O., and Westlin, A.: *Svensk Kem. Tid.*, **59**, 244 (1947).
14. Samuelson, O., and Westlin, A.: *Svensk Papperstidn.*, **51**, 179 (1948).
15. Stockman, L., and Hägglund, E.: *Svensk Papperstidn.*, **51**, 269 (1948).
16. Yorston, F. H.: *Pulp Paper Mag. Can.*, **48**, No. 12, 74 (1947).
17. Yorston, F. H.: *Pulp Paper Mag. Can.*, **50**, No. 12, 108 (1949).

CHAPTER XIX

Alkaloids

Alkaloids may be taken up by cation exchangers, synthetic zeolites (11, 18, 21) as well as organic cation exchangers. This ability of organic cation exchangers has been utilized for the recovery of alkaloids from plant extracts, e.g. cinchona alkaloids from cinchona bark (1, 3) and scopolamine from *Datura* plants (17). The method has been used on a commercial scale for a number of years. Results have also been reported on the uptake of alkaloids from *Atropa belladonna* (19, 20) and on removal of nicotine from tobacco drier gases (9). Only a few analytical methods for determination of alkaloids by means of ion exchange separations have been published thus far.

1. SYNTHETIC ZEOLITES

A. *Determination of Morphine in Urine*

A synthetic zeolite (Permutit) has been used by Oberst (14) to free morphine from substances which interfere with its colorimetric determination in urine.

Morphine is extracted from urine by the procedure of Pierce and Plant. The extract is evaporated to dryness and dissolved in water. Morphine is taken up from the water solution by means of Permutit and thus purified from interfering substances. After washing, saturated sodium carbonate is added to liberate the alkaloid in the presence of Folin-Denis phenol reagent. The blue color is read colorimetrically.

2. CATION EXCHANGE RESINS

In investigations by Applezweig it has been shown that several alkaloids can be removed by a cation exchanger of sulfonic acid type (sulfonated coal) (1, 2, 3). The exchanger is preferably used in the hydrogen form. A considerable adsorption may also take place if the cation exchanger is saturated with sodium or calcium; this adsorption may at least partly be ascribed to van der Waals' forces (9). In general this type of adsorption is less pronounced on sulfonated resins, and therefore resinous exchangers are to be preferred for analytical separations. A comparison of the behavior of different organic cation exchangers has been published by Mukherjee *et al.* (12, 13).

The displacement of the alkaloids from the resin is preferably performed by liberating the free base by means of alkali. Because of the limited solubility of most alkaloids in water or aqueous alkali, a non-aqueous solvent, such as ethyl alcohol, acetone, or chloroform, is used for the removal of the liberated alkaloid base from the column (17). The regeneration may be performed either in two steps, with an alkaline water solution followed by treatment with a solvent, or in one step, e.g. by using a solution of ammonia in alcohol. Consistent recoveries of 97% and more have been reported.

Cation exchangers of carboxylic type (Amberlite IRC-50) have been used by several investigators. Winters and Kunin (22) report a quantitative retention of nicotine when the resin is used in the hydrogen form. Complete uptake of quinine from quinine sulfate solution has been achieved when the resin is used in the sodium form, whereas nicotine (the free base) was found to pass quantitatively into the effluent. Substances present in the form of salts are taken up more readily if the resin is in the sodium form, whereas compounds existing as free bases are retained more easily if the resin is in the free-acid form. The carboxylic type of resin seems to offer great possibilities for the analytical separation of alkaloids.

Huyck (5) found that Amberlite IRC-50 in the hydrogen form could be used for extraction of ephedrine from an alcoholic solution. Elution could be easily obtained by means of 0.1 N hydrochloric acid.

A kinetical study on the uptake of quinine has been reported by Saunders and Srivastava (15).

According to Kunin (10), a carboxylic exchanger may be used for the separation of the more weakly basic alkaloids (strychnine and caffeine) from the more basic ones such as quinine, brucine, and nicotine. No details on procedure are given.

3. ANION EXCHANGE RESINS

Several authors have used alumina to liberate the bases from alkaloidal salts. The free bases may be estimated by titration in the effluent obtained after washing with alcohol. Jindra (6, 7) applied an anion exchange resin of weakly basic type to effect this separation.

The alkaloidal salt dissolved in a solvent — ordinarily ethyl alcohol — in which the salt and the free base are readily soluble is passed through the resin column, and, after washing with alcohol at 50°C, the free base is determined by potentiometric titration with standard acid. The pretreatment of the resin (e.g. Amberlite IR-4B) is performed with sodium carbonate solution. After washing with a large amount of water until the washings give no reaction with phenolphthalein, the water is displaced by the solvent used.

Satisfactory results have been obtained for a number of alkaloids. Reportedly the method is effective also in the presence of alkali and ammonium salts. However, it must be pointed out that a principal condition for a selective liberation of the alkaloid bases is that the anion exchanger contain basic groups of proper strength. An anion exchanger of quaternary ammonium type not only liberates the alkaloids but also converts alkali, ammonium, and amine salts quantitatively into the corresponding bases (or carbonates), so that the analysis will give the total amount of ions in the sample. For anion exchangers of weakly basic type errors may occur because of incomplete conversion of alkaloids which are strong or fairly strong bases, e.g. ephedrine and cotarine.

The anion exchange method has been applied to the determination of alkaloids in a number of drugs and galenicals. In one paper (8), where detailed information is given, it is prescribed that the alkaloids first be extracted from the solution to be analyzed with ether or some other solvent. After evaporation of the solvent, the alkaloid is dissolved in acid and the solution passed through the anion exchanger as described above.

BIBLIOGRAPHY

1. Applezweig, N.: *J. Am. Chem. Soc.*, **66**, 1990 (1944).
2. Applezweig, N.: *Ann. N. Y. Acad. Sci.*, **49**, 295 (1948).
3. Applezweig, N., and Ronzone, S.: *Ind. Eng. Chem.*, **38**, 576 (1946).
4. Griessbach, R.: *Austausch-Adsorbentien in der Lebensmittelindustrie*, Leipzig, 1949, p. 54.
5. Huyck, L. C.: *Am. J. Pharm.*, **122**, 228 (1950).
6. Jindra, A.: *J. Pharm. Pharmacol.*, **1**, 87 (1949).
7. Jindra, A., and Pohorsky, J.: *J. Pharm. Pharmacol.*, **2**, 361 (1950).
8. Jindra, A., and Pohorsky, J.: *J. Pharm. Pharmacol.*, **3**, 344 (1951); *Časopis Českého Lékárnictva*, **63**, 57 (1950).
9. Kingsbury, A. W., Mindler, A. B., and Gilwood, M. E.: *Chem. Eng. Progress*, **44**, 497 (1948).
10. Kunin, R.: *Anal. Chem.*, **21**, 87 (1949).
11. McIntosh, B. J., Kelsey, F. E., and Geiling, E. M. K.: *J. Am. Pharm. Assoc.*, **39**, 512 (1950).
12. Mukherjee, S., and Gupta, M. L. S.: *J. Proc. Inst. Chemists (India)*, **21**, 83 (1949).
13. Mukherjee, S., Gupta, M. L. S., and Bhattacharyya, R. N.: *J. Indian Chem. Soc.*, **27**, 156 (1950).
14. Oberst, F. W.: *J. Lab. Clin. Med.*, **24**, 318 (1938).
15. Saunders, L., and Srivastava, R.: *J. Chem. Soc.*, **1950**, 2915.
16. Sullivan, M. J., and Martin, G. J.: *Am. J. Pharm.*, **122**, 48 (1950).

17. Sussman, S., Mindler, A. B., and Wood, W.: *Chem. Inds.*, **57**, 455 (1945).
18. Ungerer, E.: *Kolloid-Z.*, **36**, 228 (1925).
19. Votá, A. S. P., and Yufera, E. P.: *Anales real soc. españ. fís. y quím.*, **44B**, 621 (1948)
20. Votá, A. S. P., and Yufera, E. P.: *Farmacognosia*, **10**, 81 (1950).
21. Whitehorn, J. C.: *J. Biol. Chem.*, **56**, 751 (1923).
22. Winters, J. C., and Kunin, R.: *Ind. Eng. Chem.*, **41**, 460 (1949).

CHAPTER XX

Amino Acids

1. GENERAL CONSIDERATIONS

An important application of ion exchange is in the preparation, purification, and analysis of amino acids. Under given conditions, certain amino acids may be retained in an ion exchange column, whereas others pass into the effluent. As the amino acids are amphoteric and exhibit isoelectric points which vary over a considerable pH interval, it is possible to obtain group separations by choosing ion exchangers having functional groups which will be active only towards amino acids having an isoelectric point within a certain pH interval. By taking advantage of the differences in charge at different pH values, separations into the following main groups can be achieved:

Basic amino acids: arginine, citrulline, histidine, hydroxylysine, lysine, ornithine.

Neutral amino acids: alanine, cysteine, cystine, glycine, isoleucine, leucine, methionine, proline, serine, threonine, valine.

Dicarboxylic amino acids: aspartic acid, glutamic acid.

Before the separation by means of ion exchangers, the aromatic amino acids (phenylalanine, tryptophane, and tyrosine) are conveniently removed by selective adsorption on active charcoal (65, 72).

The amino acids within a certain main group may afterwards be separated by means of ion exchange chromatography. Direct separations of complex mixtures have also been achieved in this way.

Furthermore, ion exchangers have been used for the separation of amino acids from interfering ions or non-electrolytes. This separation may be performed either by the uptake of the amino acids on an ion exchanger and subsequent elution or by removing ions by means of ion exchange under such conditions that the amino acids are not taken up.

A number of authors have used synthetic zeolites. This work is of chiefly historical interest, as the separations may be more easily performed by means of organic ion exchangers. Improved types of ion exchange resins recently available may facilitate the separations in comparison to those performed about ten years ago. No generally accepted standard procedure has as yet been established, and therefore it may be suitable to refer also to the earlier papers in some detail. However, among the methods hitherto published those which are based upon the chromatographic principle are by far the most important.

2. SYNTHETIC ZEOLITES

One of the earliest applications of ion exchange to laboratory problems was that of Whitehorn (77), who, in 1923, studied the uptake of different organic cations and amino acids. The basic amino acids histidine and lysine were found to be quantitatively retained in a column containing a synthetic zeolite (Permutit) in the sodium form, whereas several neutral amino acids passed into the effluent. This procedure has been utilized for the selective uptake of basic amino acids. Archibald (3), investigating the occurrence of glutamine in liver extracts, found that it could be freed from arginine by this method. Ninety per cent of the glutamine, but no arginine, was found in the effluent. After washing with water, the rest of the glutamine, contaminated with 25% of the arginine, was recovered. By elution with 25 ml 3% sodium chloride solution, the residual arginine was removed from the column.

According to Cristol and Foucade (26), ornithine, lysine, arginine, and histidine may be almost quantitatively removed by means of Permutit. Based on this principle, investigations were performed on the amino acid composition of human serum.

Dubnoff and Borsook (35) determined glycocyamine in biological fluids and tissue extracts. Since arginine interferes with the glycocyamine reaction, it was removed by means of sodium zeolite. Glycocyamine is not retained and is determined colorimetrically in the effluent. In a subsequent paper Dubnoff (34) describes the elution of arginine with a 3% sodium chloride solution and colorimetric estimation in the effluent.

According to Sims (67), it is difficult to obtain reproducible results when working with synthetic zeolites. However, by using the sodium form of a resinous cation exchanger of the sulfonic acid type, reliable values can be obtained. Arginine as well as glycocyamine is retained from salt-free solutions, but only arginine is taken up from a 0.3% sodium chloride solution. Glycocyamine is determined by the Sakaguchi reaction. The method may be used for microdetermination of glycocyamine and arginine in urine.

Some early experiments on ion exchange chromatography of amino acids by means of synthetic zeolites were published by Felix and Lang (38), by Sadikov and Lindkvist-Ruisakova (64), as well as by Kapeller-Adler and Stern (45).

3. ION EXCHANGE RESINS

The possibility of separating amino acids by means of ion exchange resins was mentioned by Griessbach (41), but it was not until 1942 that Freudenberg, Walch, and Molter (40) and Block (7, 8) independently showed that amino acids could be separated from other substances (e.g. sugars) and that a group separation of the amino acids could be performed. Englis and Fiess (37) studied the break-through curves for amino acids and observed that the type of curve was the same as for common cations.

A. *Cation Exchangers of Sulfonic Acid Type*

From a theoretical point of view, it is evident that the retention of different amino acids is dependent on the pH in the resin phase, because of the fact that the pH determines the charge of the amino acids. Only amino acids which have an isoelectric pH higher than the pH in the resin phase can be retained. As pointed out in Chapter II: 1, a sulfonic acid resin in the hydrogen form behaves as a strong, rather concentrated acid. Because of the extremely low pH in the resin phase all amino acids which come in contact with the resin will be positively charged and consequently taken up by the resin. This explains why all amino acids, e.g. even dicarboxylic amino acids, may be quantitatively retained in a column filled with sulfonic acid resin in the free-acid form (40, 18, 19, 65, 42). Consequently the amino acids may be separated from uncharged substances, e.g. sugars, by passing the solution through a cation exchanger of this type (48). If the acid groups of the cation exchanger are neutralized, e.g. by means of pyridine, ammonia, or alkali, the neutral amino acids, as well as histidine and the dicarboxylic amino acids, are not taken up from neutral or alkaline solution, because they are present largely as dipolar ions with net charge of zero or as anions. This statement is consistent with experimental results (20) according to which only basic amino acids are retained when the acid groups of the resin have been neutralized and the operation is performed in neutral medium. In acid medium also other amino acids are retained. As an example, there is a significant uptake of neutral amino acids from buffer solutions of pH 4.25 when the resin is substantially in the sodium form (69). The discrepancies in the results obtained by different authors (37, 42) may be explained by varying pH in the resin phase. Elution of the amino acids may be performed by means of alkaline, neutral, or acid solutions.

Histidine has a lower isoelectric point than arginine and lysine and is therefore in neutral medium retained less than the latter amino acids.

When the pH of the solution is lowered by addition of a proper amount of acid, the uptake of histidine is facilitated (20).

The buffering capacity of sulfonic acid resins is very small in the vicinity of the neutral point (Chapter II:2A). The pH in the resin phase is dependent upon the pretreatment of the resin and the composition of the solution. Small variations in the working conditions, as well as the type of resin, may therefore have an influence upon the separation. This type of cation exchanger therefore does not seem to be suitable for direct separation, for analytical purposes, of amino acids into groups by means of the simple ion exchange technique, but works very well when chromatographic techniques are employed.

B. Cation Exchangers of Carboxylic Acid Type

The carboxylic acid type of cation exchanger has the advantage over the sulfonic acid type that the buffering capacity is considerable within the pH interval suitable for the separation of amino acids (cf. Chapter II:3). The pH in the resin phase may be kept rather constant within this interval. This is an important advantage compared to the application of sulfonic acid resins, as far as group separations of amino acids are concerned.

The usefulness of cation exchangers of weakly acid type for separations of amino acids was recognized by Wieland (79), who found that the basic amino acids are selectively taken up from protein hydrolyzates by means of cation exchangers of this type (Wofatit C) (62).

Wieland's method was improved by Tiselius, Drake, and Hagdahl (72) in their investigations on group separation of amino acids by means of different adsorbents. These authors removed the aromatic amino acids by selective uptake in a column containing active charcoal and subsequently the basic amino acids in a second column containing Wofatit C. The uptake of the basic amino acids was performed in 5% acetic acid. Part of the neutral and acid amino acids are "retarded" in this column, but they may be washed out by passing 20% acetic acid through the column, the basic amino acids being unaffected. The basic amino acids are eluted by means of 1 N hydrochloric acid. The solution to be analyzed may have a content of hydrochloric acid not exceeding 0.01 N. At higher concentrations, the uptake of histidine is not complete.

According to Wieland (79) it is possible to use a carboxylic acid exchanger (Wofatit C) in the potassium form for a mutual separation of the basic amino acids. Of these, histidine shows the lowest isoelectric pH (7.6); the corresponding pH values for lysine and arginine are 9.7 and 10.8. Consequently it should be possible to take up lysine and arginine quantitatively in a column, whereas histidine should pass into the effluent, provided a proper pH exists in the resin phase. Wieland found that such a quantitative separation could be achieved. Schramm and Primosigh (65) were not able to confirm this result and stated that Wieland's analytical methods were less sensitive. If the potassium hydroxide used for neutralization of the resin was removed quantitatively by washing, histidine was observed to be retained. At incomplete washing, i.e. higher pH, histidine could be quantitatively removed with water, but in this case part of the other amino acids also appeared in the effluent.

In this connection it may be mentioned that clupeine (a strongly basic protamine of rather high molecular weight, built up to about two-thirds from arginine) is not taken up by tightly cross-linked cation exchange resins (carboxylic acid type), whereas arginine is quantitatively retained (62). However, resins with a low degree of cross-linking may be used also for the quantitative uptake of clupeine (31).

Winters and Kunin (81) investigated another ion exchanger of carboxylic acid type (Amberlite IRC-50). The resin was buffered at various pH values before use. The treatment involved first converting the resin to the sodium form by means of 4% sodium hydroxide, followed by treatment with the buffer solution at low flow rate. Then the residual solution was displaced from the column with distilled water [cf. (48)].

The authors report that buffering at pH 4.7 is suitable to achieve retention of all the basic amino acids. Lysine and arginine are retained if the exchanger is buffered to pH 7, whereas the other amino acids should be unaffected [cf. (71)].

The regeneration of the column may be easily performed by means of 0.1 N hydrochloric acid.

Sheehan and Bolhofer (66) isolated lysine and hydroxylysine from gelatin hydrolyzates by means of Amberlite IRC-50. Hydrochloric acid and the dicarboxylic amino acids were removed by passing the hydrolyzate through an anion exchanger of weakly basic type. After removal of arginine by precipitation with flavianic acid and the excess of reagent by a second column of anion exchanger, the pH of the solution was adjusted to 6.5–7. The solution was passed through a column of Amberlite IRC-50 buffered at pH 7. Lysine and hydroxylysine were retained and subsequently eluted with hydrochloric acid. Finally, these were separated chromatographically on alumina.

C. *Anion Exchangers of Weakly Basic Type*

Freudenberg, Walch, and Molter (40) suggested that an anion exchanger of weakly basic type (Wofatit M) in the free-base form can be used for the uptake of dicarboxylic amino acids, e.g. aspartic acid, from a mixture of amino acids. Later investigations have shown that a quantitative uptake of the dicarboxylic amino acids can be achieved, whereas the neutral amino acids are only slightly retained (37, 20, 15, 11, 57, 21). The amino acids taken up by the resin may be removed by regeneration with hydrochloric acid (e.g. 1 N) or sodium carbonate solution (2%).

For a quantitative separation of the dicarboxylic acids from the neutral amino acids, the resin is preferably used in the chloride form. As shown by Tiselius, Drake, and Hagdahl (72), this separation is conveniently performed as a column operation.

Cannan (18) used Amberlite IR-4 for the uptake of dicarboxylic amino acids from protein hydrolyzates by stirring the solution with the free-base form of the resin until the pH of the solution increased to 6–7. In order to complete the uptake, the solution obtained after separating the resin was acidified and treated with a new portion of resin. The elution of glutamic acid and aspartic acid was performed by extracting the resin with a moderate excess of hydrochloric acid. Analyses of protein hydrolyzates were performed with satisfactory results. A simplified titrimetric method for the determination of the dicarboxylic acids, isolated according to Cannan's method, has been devised by Kibrick (46). This and similar methods have also been used for preparative purposes, e.g. by Doherty and Popenoe (32).

Turba, Richter, and Kuchar (73) utilized an anion exchanger (Wofatit M) pretreated with 0.2 N acetic acid for selective retention of tryptophan from a mixture of neutral amino acids.

As an example of the practical applications of anion exchange resins it may be mentioned that Boulanger and Biserte (12) succeeded in separating α-aminoadipic acid from urine by passing the sample through an anion exchange resin of weakly basic type. By means of paper chromatography the amino acid was identified in the eluate obtained by treating the resin with 0.1 N acetic acid.

D. *Anion Exchangers of Strongly Basic Type*

According to Winters and Kunin (81), anion exchangers of the strongly basic type in the free-base form have the ability of retaining quantitatively all amino acids except arginine. The authors suggested the application of Amberlite IRA-400 for the separation of lysine and arginine by selective uptake of the lysine in a column in the free-base form. A buffer solution of pH 4.0 (0.1 N sodium acetate-acetic acid) proved to be an efficient eluting agent.

4. GROUP SEPARATION SCHEMES

From the above discussion it is obvious that more or less satisfactory separations of amino acids into groups may be achieved. From an analytical point of view, the most satisfactory results seem to be those reported by Tiselius, Drake, and Hagdahl (72) [cf. (61)].

The amino acid solution in 10 ml 5% acetic acid is forced through three columns coupled together in series.

I. Active charcoal, pretreated with dilute acetic acid.

II. Cation exchanger of carboxylic acid type (Wofatit C) conditioned in 10–15 cycles with N HCl-water, 0.5 N NaOH-water-N HCl, etc., and finally treated with 20% acetic acid.

III. Cation exchanger of sulfonic acid type (Wofatit KS), conditioned as above.

After washing with 50 ml 5% acetic acid, the top filter is removed and the remaining filters are washed with 20% acetic acid.

The top filter, which contains only aromatic amino acids, is eluted slowly with 30 ml 5% phenol in 20% acetic acid. From the second filter the basic amino acids are removed by means of 500 ml N HCl, and from the last filter neutral and dicarboxylic amino acids are eluted with 750 ml N HCl.

The eluate containing the neutral and dicarboxylic amino acids is evaporated to dryness. The acids, dissolved in 10 ml water, are passed through an anion exchange column (IV) containing Amberlite IR-4 in the chloride form. In order to displace the neutral amino acids, the column is washed with 100 ml water. The dicarboxylic acids which are retained can then be eluted with 250 ml N HCl.

If cysteine and cystine are present, hydrogen sulfide should be added to all solutions in which cystine can be precipitated or oxidized to cysteic acid. This is especially important for the first procedure, in which active charcoal is used as an adsorbent [cf. Schramm and Primosigh (65)].

Ion exchangers have been utilized by Sperber (68) in connection with group separations of the amino acids in protein hydrolyzates by means of ionophoresis. By adding an anion exchanger (Amberlite IR-4) to the central compartment of a three-cell apparatus, the pH changes in ionophoresis can be overcome. This will largely prevent other amino acids than the basic ones from migrating to the cathode. The dicarboxylic acids will be taken up by the resin. Ordinarily, two runs are sufficient to complete the separation into acid, neutral, and basic amino acids.

5. CHROMATOGRAPHIC SEPARATION OF AMINO ACIDS BY MEANS OF CATION EXCHANGERS

The displacement development has been applied with success to the separation of amino acids by means of cation exchangers of sulfonic acid type. Several interesting papers have been published by Partridge et al. (51–60).

The method developed is of particular value for preparative work, but the results are also of interest from an analytical point of view.

The mechanisms of these separations have been discussed in detail by Davies (29). They depend upon (a) the extent of ionization of the individual amino acids in their passage through the column, (b) the charges carried by the ions present, and (c) the van der Waals' forces between the ion exchanger and the solutes present. If the influence of these van der Waals' forces could be neglected, the monoamino acids would be expected to emerge in an order depending upon the dissociation constant (k_1) for the reaction

$$A^+ \rightleftharpoons A^{\pm} + H^+$$

Partridge's experimental results support this theory.

Methionine is more strongly retained than could be expected from the k_1 value. This is probably due to a strong contribution from the van der Waals' forces. As the temperature increases, the influence of these forces would be expected to diminish. Experiments performed by Partridge and Brimley (59) confirm that the position in the order of displacement at higher temperature approaches more closely the position expected from the dissociation constant.

For the fractionation of protein hydrolyzates, it is advisable first to remove the aromatic amino acids by adsorption on charcoal, the reason being that these amino acids are held by the resin by non-ionic forces, which have a deleterious effect upon the ion exchange separation. The remaining mixture of amino acids is taken up in a column of a sulfonic acid resin in the hydrogen form. The amino acids are afterwards displaced by means of a base such as ammonia or sodium hydroxide, which has a higher affinity for the resin than any of the components to be separated. Ammonia is to be preferred because it is easily removed by evaporation of the effluent. The developer is introduced onto the top of the column, and, as it displaces the components downwards, they separate into discrete bands.

The position of the band and the shape of the front may be determined by continuous measurement of electrical conductivity and pH of the effluent (5), but with a complex mixture such as a protein hydrolyzate this method is not sensitive enough. In this case the recommended procedure is to divide the solution flowing from the column into a large number of fractions and to analyze each fraction by means of paper chromatography (51).

In a typical experiment (53) Partridge separated the amino acids in a protein hydrolyzate (64 g egg albumin) on a column containing 400 g Zeo-

Karb 215 (sulfonated resin of phenolic type). The development was performed by means of 0.15 N ammonia. The effluent was collected in 64 fractions, each of 90 ml. Seven discrete bands were obtained: (I) aspartic acid; (II) glutamic acid, serine, and threonine; (III) glycine and alanine; (IV) valine and proline; (V) leucine, isoleucine, methionine, and cystine; (VI) histidine and glucosamine; (VII) lysine.

Further separation of the components within a certain band may be secured by readsorption and elution with a suitable elutriant. For instance, the separation of glucosamine and histidine (band VI) may be achieved by readsorption on Zeo-Karb 215 and elution by means of 0.05 N sodium chloride, which removes glucosamine. Histidine is afterwards displaced by means of ammonia (54).

In cases where the band contains dicarboxylic as well as neutral amino acids (band II) a further separation may be achieved by retaining the dicarboxylic type on an anion exchanger (53) (cf. section 7).

Partridge, Brimley, and Pepper (58) observed that sulfonated resins of phenolic type have certain disadvantages due to the presence of phenolic groups which react very slowly. This feature of the resins is a serious disadvantage as far as working at high pH is concerned and prevents their effective use for separations involving lysine and arginine. In order to avoid this difficulty sulfonated polystyrene resins are recommended for a separation of the basic amino acids.

The rate of exchange is dependent upon the degree of cross-linking (Chapter IV), and it proved necessary to use a lightly cross-linked resin in order to achieve an effective separation of lysine and arginine. In this case the ion exchanger suffers large volume changes with changes in composition of the solution (Chapter II:1). These changes may cause channeling at the passage of solutions through the resin layer. In order to avoid serious disturbances caused by channeling, two columns are used, the second being smaller than the first (cf. Chapter VII:2C).

A technique similar to that of Partridge et al. has been used by Westall (75, 76) for isolation of different amino acids from beet root, and by Hulme (43) for preliminary fractionation of the amino acids present in the protein of apple fruit [cf. also (17)].

Moore and Stein point out that for analytical purposes the elution technique possesses higher resolving power than the displacement development employed by Partridge and coworkers.

In a preliminary communication, the authors (69) report the successful separation of almost all common amino acids by means of stepwise elution.

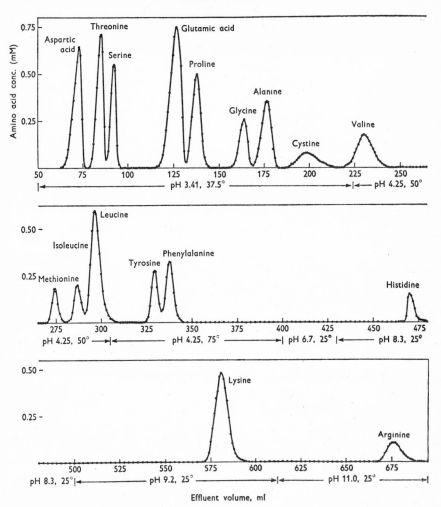

Fig. 44.   Separation of amino acids (6 mg) from a synthetic mixture simulating the
composition of a protein hydrolyzate.
Column: 9 × 1 000 mm; Dowex 50 [Na+; 0.03–0.06 mm].
Elution with buffers of the pH and temperature indicated as elutriants.
[from (70)]

The resin (Dowex 50) was employed in the hydrogen form with subsequent
elution by means of hydrochloric acid at increasing concentrations (1 N
to 4 N). Even better results were obtained when the resin was used in the
sodium form, elution being effected by sodium citrate buffers of progres-

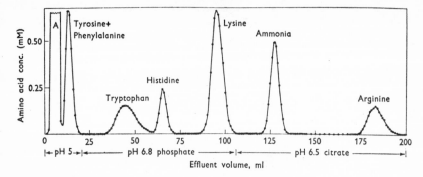

FIG. 45. Separation of the basic amino acids (6 mg) on a column of Dowex 50; 9 × 150 mm. The column was operated in the sodium form at 25° with the buffers indicated. The large peak, A, comprises all the amino acids emerging before tyrosine in Fig. 44.   [from (70)]

sively increasing pH (70). Improved separations could be achieved by increasing the temperature during the course of elution.

Three to six milligrams of the amino acid mixture is taken up on a 9 × 1000 mm column. With a buffer of pH 3.4, aspartic acid, threonine, serine, glutamic acid, proline, glycine, alanine, cystine, and valine emerge quantitatively as discrete peaks in the order given. When the pH is increased to 4.25, the following amino acids are eluted as separate bands: methionine, isoleucine, leucine, tyrosine, and phenylalanine. Histidine appears at pH 8.3, lysine at pH 9.2, and arginine at pH 11 (Fig. 44).

A large number of 1-ml fractions are taken by means of a fraction collector and analyzed by the photometric ninhydrin method. The analysis of a protein hydrolyzate requires 4–5 days. Integration of the elution curves has given quantitative recoveries (100 ± 3% on the average) except for the basic amino acids. These acids may be estimated quantitatively in a separate experiment with the aid of a smaller column (9 × 150 mm) with buffers in the pH range 5–6.8 (Fig. 45).

The procedure has been applied to blood plasma dialyzates and urine. The performance of the ion exchange column is not altered by the presence of the inorganic salts, and the fractionation may be made directly without preliminary salt removal. The important method of Moore and Stein was later applied by other authors (74, 39, 28, 36).

6. CHROMATOGRAPHIC SEPARATION OF DICARBOXYLIC AMINO ACIDS BY MEANS OF ANION EXCHANGERS OF WEAKLY BASIC TYPE

Drake (33) demonstrated that a quantitative separation of aspartic and glutamic acid could be achieved by chromatographic elution from an anion exchange resin of weakly basic type. The resin (Amberlite IR-4B) was pretreated with N hydrochloric acid and water.

About 3 mg of each of the amino acids were retained in a column containing 630 mm³ of the resin. Glutamic acid was eluted with 0.05% acetic acid until a spot test of the eluate with ninhydrin was negative. Afterwards, aspartic acid was removed by passing N hydrochloric acid through the column. The spot tests were taken automatically by means of a special apparatus.

Partridge and Brimley (57) found that the separation was unsatisfactory when the free-base form of the resin was used.

Consden, Gordon, and Martin (24) separated glutamic acid and aspartic acid in wool hydrolyzate by a similar method. These amino acids were first separated from the neutral and basic acids by retention on a column at pH 3–4, eluted in a small volume with N hydrochloric acid, placed on a column already brought to pH 2.5 by washing with 0.003 N hydrochloric acid, and eluted with the same solution. If cysteic acid was present, it was eluted by means of N hydrochloric acid after the elution of glutamic acid and aspartic acid.

7. CHROMATOGRAPHIC SEPARATION OF AMINO ACIDS BY MEANS OF ANION EXCHANGERS OF STRONGLY BASIC TYPE

Davies, Hughes, and Partridge (30) found that amino acids could be effectively separated by means of displacement chromatography after retention on a column of anion exchanger of strongly basic type. By using the resin in the free-base form, it was possible to separate glutamic acid from leucine, and leucine from methionine.

In earlier investigations by Partridge et al. (57) it had been shown that leucine and methionine could not be effectively separated by means of cation exchange resins, one reason being their closely similar dissociation constants (leucine $pk_1 = 2.36$; methionine $pk_1 = 2.28$) for the reaction

$$A^+ \rightleftharpoons A^\pm + H^+$$

For the reaction

$$A^{\pm} \rightleftharpoons A^- + H^+$$

the differences in the pk values (pk_2) are greater (leucine $pk_2 = 9.60$; methionine $pk_2 = 9.21$). This explains why the separation on a resin of strongly basic type is relatively simple (30).

In another publication of Partridge and Brimley (60) it was shown that mixtures of the following pairs of amino acids could be separated by displacement with 0.1 N hydrochloric acid: glycine-alanine, valine-proline, methionine-leucine. A mixture of serine and threonine did not separate.

The order of displacement from strongly basic resins is largely determined by the order of pk_2: (I) arginine; (II) lysine; (III) proline; (IV) alanine; (V) valine, leucine, glycine; (VI) threonine, serine; (VII) histidine; (VIII) methionine; (IX) phenylalanine.

Also in this case, certain amino acids appear in mixed bands, but by performing the separation in two steps it should be possible to achieve a complete separation. The primary separation would be carried out using a sulfonic acid resin, and the mixed bands so obtained would be separated by means of an anion exchanger of strongly basic type.

The fractionation on anion exchange columns has been used by Crumpler et al. (27) in investigations on the composition of human urine.

BIBLIOGRAPHY

1. Albanese, A. A., and Frankston, J. E.: *J. Biol. Chem.*, **159**, 185 (1945).
2. Archibald, R. M.: *J. Biol. Chem.*, **156**, 121 (1944).
3. Archibald, R. M.: *J. Biol. Chem.*, **159**, 693 (1945).
4. Barry, T. H.: *Food*, **1949**, p. 68.
5. Bendall, J. R., Partridge, S. M., and Westall, R. G.: *Nature*, **160**, 374 (1947).
6. Biserte, G., and Boulanger, P.: *Bull. soc. chim. biol.*, **32**, 601 (1950).
7. Block, R. J.: *Proc. Soc. Exptl. Biol. Med.*, **51**, 252 (1942).
8. Block, R. J.: *Arch. Biochem.*, **11**, 235 (1946).
9. Block, R. J.: *Federation Proc.*, **5**, 123 (1946).
10. Block, R. J.: *Chem. Revs.*, **38**, 501 (1946).
11. Block, R. J., and Bolling, D.: *The Amino Acid Composition of Proteins and Foods*, Springfield, Illinois, 1947, p. 292.
12. Boulanger, P., and Biserte, G.: *Compt. rend.*, **232**, 1451 (1951).
13. Bradford, V. H., and Pucher, G. W.: *J. Biol. Chem.*, **83**, 1 (1929).
14. Brenner, M., and Burckhardt, C. H.: *Helv. Chim. Acta*, **34**, 1070 (1951).
15. Buc, S. R., Ford, J. H., and Wise, E. C.: *J. Am. Chem. Soc.*, **67**, 92 (1945).
16. Campbell, P. N.: *Biochem. J.*, **48**, XIX (1951).
17. Campbell, P. N., Work, T. S., and Mellanby, E.: *Biochem. J.*, **48**, 106 (1951).
18. Cannan, R. K.: *J. Biol. Chem.*, **152**, 401 (1944).
19. Cannan, R. K.: *Ann. N. Y. Acad. Sci.*, **47**, 135 (1946).

20. Cleaver, C. S., Hardy, R. A., and Cassidy, H. G.: *J. Am. Chem. Soc.*, **67**, 1343 (1945).

21. Cleaver, C. S., and Cassidy, H. G.: *J. Am. Chem. Soc.*, **72**, 1147 (1950).

22. Consden, R., and Gordon, A. H.: *Biochem. J. Proc.*, **43**, X (1948).

23. Consden, R., and Gordon, A. H.: *Biochem. J.*, **46**, 8 (1950).

24. Consden, R., Gordon, A. H., and Martin, A. J. P.: *Biochem. J.*, **42**, 443 (1948).

25. Consden, R., Gordon, A. H., and Martin, A. J. P.: *Biochem. J.*, **44**, 548 (1949).

26. Cristol, P., and Foucade, J.: *Compt. rend. soc. biol.*, **131**, 414 (1939).

27. Crumpler, H. R., Dent, C. E., Harris, H., and Westall, R. G.: *Nature*, **167**, 307 (1951).

28. Cutinelli, G., Ehrensvärd, G., Reio, L., Saluste, E., and Stjernholm, R.: *Acta Chem. Scand.*, **5**, 353 (1951).

29. Davies, C. W.: *Biochem. J.*, **45**, 38 (1949).

30. Davies, C. W., Hughes, R. B., and Partridge, S. M.: *J. Chem. Soc.*, **1950**, 2285.

31. Deuel, H., Solms, J., and Anyas-Weisz, L.: *Helv. Chim. Acta*, **33**, 2171 (1950).

32. Doherty, D. G., and Popenoe, E. A.: *J. Biol. Chem.*, **189**, 447 (1951).

33. Drake, B.: *Nature*, **160**, 602 (1947).

34. Dubnoff, J. W.: *J. Biol. Chem.*, **141**, 711 (1941).

35. Dubnoff, J. W., and Borsook, H.: *J. Biol. Chem.*, **138**, 381 (1941).

36. Ehrensvärd, G., Reio, L., Saluste, E., and Stjernholm, R.: *J. Biol. Chem.*, **189**, 93 (1951).

37. Englis, D. T., and Fiess, H. A.: *Ind. Eng. Chem.*, **36**, 604 (1944).

38. Felix, K., and Lang, A.: *Z. physiol. Chem.*, **182**, 125 (1929).

39. Fling, M., and Horowitz, N. H.: *J. Biol. Chem.*, **190**, 277 (1951).

40. Freudenberg, K., Walch, H., and Molter, H.: *Naturwissenschaften*, **30**, 87 (1942).

41. Griessbach, R.: *Angew. Chem. Beihefte*, No. **31** (1939).

42. Hems, B. A., Page, J. E., and Waller, J. G.: *J. Soc. Chem. Ind.* (*London*), **67**, 77 (1948).

43. Hulme, A. C.: *J. Sci. Food Agr.*, **2**, 160 (1951).

44. Jones, T. S. G.: *Disc. Faraday Soc.*, **1949**, No. 7, 285.

45. Kapeller-Adler, R., and Stern, E.: *Biochem. Z.*, **235**, 390 (1931).

46. Kibrick, A.: *J. Biol. Chem.*, **152**, 411 (1944).

47. Kunin, R.: *Anal. Chem.*, **21**, 87 (1949).

48. Levy, L., and Coon, M. J.: *J. Biol. Chem.*, **192**, 807 (1951).

49. MacLeod, A. M.: *J. Inst. Brewing*, **57**, 163 (1951).

50. Muntz, J. A.: *J. Biol. Chem.*, **182**, 489 (1950).

51. Partridge, S. M.: *Disc. Faraday Soc.*, **1949**, No. 7, 296.

52. Partridge, S. M.: *Nature*, **163**, 236 (1949).

53. Partridge, S. M.: *Biochem. J.*, **44**, 521 (1949).

54. Partridge, S. M.: *Biochem. J.*, **45**, 459 (1949).

55. Partridge, S. M.: *Chemistry & Industry*, **1950**, 383.

56. Partridge, S. M., and Westall, R. G.: *Biochem. J.*, **44**, 418 (1949).

57. Partridge, S. M., and Brimley, R. C.: *Biochem. J.*, **44**, 513 (1949).

58. Partridge, S. M., Brimley, R. C., and Pepper, K. W.: *Biochem. J.*, **46**, 334 (1950).

59. Partridge, S. M., and Brimley, R. C.: *Biochem. J.*, **48**, 313 (1951).

60. Partridge, S. M., and Brimley, R. C.: *Biochem. J.*, **49**, 153 (1951).

61. Rauen, H. M.: *Angew. Chem.*, **60A**, 250 (1948).
62. Rauen, H. M., and Felix, K.: *Z. physiol. Chem.*, **283**, 139 (1948).
63. Roberts, M., and Adam, H. M.: *Brit. J. Pharmacol.*, **5**, 526 (1950).
64. Sadikov, V. S., and Lindkvist-Ruisakova, E. V.: *Compt. rend. acad. sci. U. R. S. S.*, N. S., **1**, 575 (1934).
65. Schramm, G., and Primosigh, J.: *Z. physiol. Chem.*, **282**, 271 (1947).
66. Sheehan, J. C., and Bolhofer, W. A.: *J. Am. Chem. Soc.*, **72**, 2466 (1950).
67. Sims, E. A. H.: *J. Biol. Chem.*, **158**, 239 (1945).
68. Sperber, E.: *J. Biol. Chem.*, **166**, 75 (1946).
69. Stein, Wm. H., and Moore, S.: *Cold Spring Harbor Symposia Quant. Biol.*, **14**, 179 (1949).
70. Stein, Wm. H., and Moore, S.: Abstr. of Papers, Am. Chem. Soc. 118th Meeting, 1950, p. 10M; *J. Biol. Chem.*, **192**, 663 (1951).
71. Suzuki, T., Hagiwara, F., and Kubota, M.: *Japan J. Pharm. & Chem.*, **23**, 191 (1951).
72. Tiselius, A., Drake, B., and Hagdahl, L.: *Experientia*, **3**, 21 (1947).
73. Turba, F., Richter, M., and Kuchar, F.: *Naturwissenschaften*, **31**, 508 (1943).
74. Velick, S. F., and Udenfriend, S.: *J. Biol. Chem.*, **191**, 233 (1951).
75. Westall, R. G.: *Nature*, **165**, 717 (1950).
76. Westall, R. G.: *J. Sci. Food Agr.*, **1**, 191 (1950).
77. Whitehorn, J. C.: *J. Biol. Chem.*, **56**, 751 (1923).
78. Wieland, Th.: *Die Chemie*, **56**, 213 (1943).
79. Wieland, Th.: *Ber.*, **77**, 539 (1944).
80. Wieland, Th.: *Fortschr. chem. Forsch.*, **1**, 211 (1949).
81. Winters, J. C., and Kunin, R.: *Ind. Eng. Chem.*, **41**, 460 (1949).

CHAPTER XXI

Nucleotides, Nucleosides, and Purine and Pyrimidine Bases

1. GENERAL CONSIDERATIONS

The nucleoproteins, which are combinations of nucleic acids and proteins, are important constituents of cells. The nucleic acids are large molecules (mol. wt. 10^4–10^6) which can be degraded into nucleotides. The nucleotides contain a purine or pyrimidine base, a carbohydrate, and an acid group (phosphate) in simple proportions. Because of their ampholytic character, the nucleotides may be retained by cation exchangers in the hydrogen form, as well as by anion exchangers, but are much more strongly retained by the latter. Cation exchangers in the salt form may be used, e.g., for converting the barium salt to the sodium salt (24, 2).

By prolonged hydrolysis, nucleosides are formed. These are compounds of a purine or a pyrimidine base and a sugar, i.e., dephosphorylated nucleotides. Cation and anion exchangers have been used for the separation of nucleosides as well as of the purine and pyrimidine bases derived from them.

2. NUCLEOTIDES

The technique for the separation of nucleotides is in principle the same as for the separation of amino acids as described in Chapter XX:5. The most interesting work in this field has been that of Cohn and Carter (6, 7, 11, 4), who have effected quantitative separations of nucleotides, nucleosides, and purine and pyrimidine bases by means of a column of anion exchange resin of the strongly basic type. The resin is used in the chloride or formate form, and separation of the ribonucleotides from each other is achieved by a stepwise alteration of pH by means of dilute acids and buffers. The differences in pk from compound to compound seem to be decisive for the separation. At pH 2.7, the following order is obtained: cytidylic, adenylic, uridylic, and guanylic acids. Desoxynucleotides were isolated with the same technique by Cohn (9) and later by other workers (16, 27, 32).

This application of the ion exchange technique to the analysis of nucleic acid digests by Cohn has led to improved methods of preparation and analysis of the nucleotides, nucleosides, and bases, as well as to the discovery of many new nucleotides, including two new sets of isomers (7, 8, 13, 20),

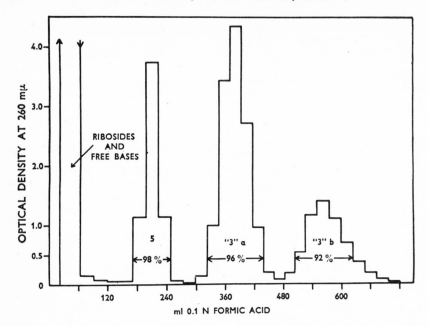

FIG. 46.   Separation of adenosine-5′-phosphate and two adenylic acids (now believed
to be 2′ and 3′ phosphates of adenosine) of yeast nucleic acid (alkali-hydro-
lyzed) by chromatographic elution.
Column: 10×140 mm; Dowex 1 [H^+; 0.03–0.06 mm].
Elutriant: 0.1 N formic acid.
Flow rate: 0.5 ml/min.
Test materials: Commercial adenylic acids, about 20 mg total.   [from (12)]

(Fig. 46). This work is still in active progress, and the technique has been
adopted by many workers in the field of nucleic acids (33, 30, 31).

Cohn and Carter (12) have applied the technique to the separation of
adenosine polyphosphates. The method has been used by Kornberg and
Pricer (18) in their investigation of the structure of phosphopyridine nu-
cleotide.

In his first publication Cohn (5) demonstrated that the separation of ribonucleotides may also be performed by means of cation exchange resins of strongly acid
type. According to Cohn (private communication), this separation is far inferior to
the anion exchange method previously described [cf. (19)]. It may also be mentioned that Montreuil and Boulanger (22) have separated cytidylic and adenylic
acids from guanylic and uridylic acids by retaining the former acids in a cation
exchange column. Reportedly, the guanylic and uridylic acids pass into the effluent.

3. NUCLEOSIDES

Harris and Thomas (15) devised an ion exchange method for the isolation of uridine from yeast ribosenucleic acid. Cytidine and adenosine were found to be retained quantitatively by means of a H^+-saturated cation exchanger (sulfonic acid type), whereas uridine, which does not have a free amino group as do the others, passed into the effluent. A recovery of 98.5% has been reported.

Cytidine and adenosine may be subsequently eluted by means of a water solution containing 2% pyridine. Elmore (14), who performed similar experiments, used 0.1 N ammonia for the elution of cytidine.

A method for the preparation of desoxyribosides after enzymatic hydrolysis of thymonucleic acid in which use is made of a cation exchanger of sulfonic acid type has been devised by Reichard and Estborn (25). A separation of the different desoxyribonucleosides is achieved by stepwise elution in acid and alkaline solutions.

Schmidt *et al.* used an anion exchanger in the free-base form for the removal of anionic compounds from solutions containing nucleosides, the latter not being retained (26).

4. PURINE AND PYRIMIDINE BASES

Smith and Wender (28) have used a cation exchanger of sulfonic acid type for the separation of xanthine and guanine. The solution to be analyzed is acidified to pH 1 by means of hydrochloric acid and passed through a column filled with the sodium form of the resin. Both bases are taken up, but on subsequent elution by means of a buffer solution of pH 9 xanthine is desorbed quantitatively, whereas no guanine could be detected in the effluent.

Soodak, Pircio, and Cerecedo (29) used a cation exchanger for the separation of the two pyrimidine bases cytosine and uracil before a colorimetric determination. The hydrogen form of a sulfonic acid resin is reported to retain cytosine, which has a free amino group, quantitatively, whereas only a minor amount of uracil, which does not contain such a group, is taken up. By means of a synthetic zeolite (Decalso) a quantitative separation can be achieved.

The chromatographic technique has been successfully adopted by Cohn (5) for the separation of uracil, cytosine, guanine, and adenine from each other. When a sulfonic acid resin in the hydrogen form was used, uracil (uncharged in acid solution) was found to pass immediately into the effluent, whereas cytosine, guanine, and adenine appeared in separate bands on elution with 2 N hydrochloric acid. Thymine and uracil, which are both non-ionized in acid, cannot be separated according to this method. However, it was shown that all purine and pyrimidine bases can be separated by means of stepwise elution from a column containing an anion exchanger of strongly basic type. Cohn's cation exchange technique has since been employed by Abrams (1).

BIBLIOGRAPHY

1. Abrams, R.: *Arch. Biochem.*, **30**, 44 (1951).
2. Calaby, J. H.: *Arch. Biochem. Biophys.*, **31**, 294 (1951).
3. Carter, C. E.: *J. Am. Chem. Soc.*, **73**, 1537 (1951).
4. Carter, C. E., and Cohn, W. E.: *J. Am. Chem. Soc.*, **72**, 2604 (1950).
5. Cohn, W. E.: *Science*, **109**, 377 (1949).
6. Cohn, W. E.: *J. Am. Chem. Soc.*, **71**, 2275 (1949).
7. Cohn, W. E.: *J. Am. Chem. Soc.*, **72**, 1471 (1950).
8. Cohn, W. E.: *J. Am. Chem. Soc.*, **72**, 2811 (1950).
9. Cohn, W. E.: *J. Am. Chem. Soc.*, **73**, 1539 (1951).
10. Cohn, W. E.: *J. Cellular Comp. Physiol.*, **38**, Suppl. 1, 21 (1951).
11. Cohn, W. E., and Carter, C. E.: *J. Am. Chem. Soc.*, **72**, 2606 (1950).
12. Cohn, W. E., and Carter, C. E.: *J. Am. Chem. Soc.*, **72**, 4273 (1950).
13. Cohn, W. E., and Volkin, E.: *Nature*, **167**, 483 (1951).
14. Elmore, D. T.: *Nature*, **161**, 931 (1948).
15. Harris, R. J., and Thomas, J. F.: *Nature*, **161**, 931 (1948); *J. Chem. Soc.*, **1948**, 1936.
16. Hurst, R. O., Little, J. A., and Butler, G. C.: *J. Biol. Chem.*, **188**, 705 (1951).
17. Kerr, S. E., Seraidarian, K., and Brown, G. B.: *J. Biol. Chem.*, **188**, 207 (1951).
18. Kornberg, A., and Pricer, W. E.: *J. Biol. Chem.*, **186**, 557 (1950); **191**, 535 (1951).
19. LePage, G. A., and Heidelberger, C.: *J. Biol. Chem.*, **188**, 593 (1951).
20. Loring, H. S., Luthy, N. G., Bortner, H. W., and Levy, L. W.: *J. Am. Chem. Soc.*, **72**, 2811 (1950).
21. Marrian, D. H., Spicer, V. L., Balis, M. E., and Brown, B. G.: *J. Biol. Chem.*, **189**, 583 (1951).
22. Montreuil, J., and Boulanger, P.: *Compt. rend.*, **231**, 247 (1950).
23. Neilands, J. B., and Åkeson, Å.: *J. Biol. Chem.*, **188**, 307 (1951).
24. Polis, B. D., and Meyerhof, O.: *J. Biol. Chem.*, **169**, 389 (1947).
25. Reichard, P., and Estborn, B.: *Acta Chem. Scand.*, **4**, 1047 (1950); *J. Biol. Chem.*, **188**, 839 (1951).
26. Schmidt, G., Cubiles, R., Zöllner, N., Hecht, L., Strickler, N., Seraidarian, K., Seraidarian, M., and Thannhauser, S. J.: *J. Biol. Chem.*, **192**, 715 (1951).
27. Sinsheimer, R. L., and Koerner, J. F.: *Science*, **114**, 42 (1951).
28. Smith, S., and Wender, S.: *J. Am. Chem. Soc.*, **70**, 3719 (1948).
29. Soodak, M., Pircio, A., and Cerecedo, L. R.: *J. Biol. Chem.*, **181**, 713 (1949).
30. Totter, J. R., Volkin, E., and Carter, C. E.: *J. Am. Chem. Soc.*, **73**, 1521 (1951)
31. Volkin, E., and Carter, C. E.: *J. Am. Chem. Soc.*, **73**, 1516 (1951).
32. Volkin, E., Khym, J. X., and Cohn, W. E.: *J. Am. Chem. Soc.*, **73**, 1533 (1951).
33. Weed, L. L., and Wilson, D. W.: *J. Biol. Chem.*, **189**, 435 (1951).

CHAPTER XXII

Vitamins

The most important analytical application of ion exchangers in the vitamin field is in the assay of some members of the vitamin B complex. For this reason special consideration will be given to these substances. As is well known, the factor originally designated as vitamin B has been shown to be a complex composed of at least ten individuals which are chemically well characterized. Vitamins B_1 (thiamine) and B_2 (riboflavin) are bases and may therefore under proper conditions be taken up by means of cation exchangers. Thiamine is a stronger base than riboflavin, and a separation of these vitamins from each other can also be achieved.

1. SYNTHETIC ZEOLITES

A. *Vitamin B_1 (thiamine)*

A synthetic zeolite (Decalso) was used in early investigations by Cerecedo and coworkers in order to take up thiamine from solutions obtained by extraction of rice polishings (4), yeast (5), or wheat germ (6).

A convenient method for the quantitative estimation of thiamine is based on the oxidation of the vitamin to thiochrome in alkaline medium. This compound is extracted with isobutyl alcohol and may be determined fluorometrically in ultraviolet light. In applying the fluorescence method to biological materials, it is necessary to remove as completely as possible fluorescing substances which interfere with the accurate determination of thiamine. As shown by Hennessy and Cerecedo (16, 15), contaminants are eliminated by the use of a column filled with a synthetic zeolite (Decalso). Thiamine is taken up, whereas the interfering substances pass through, and after washing with water the vitamin is removed by introducing a 25% potassium chloride solution, 0.1 N in hydrochloric acid, into the column (7, 9).

This procedure or modifications of it have been used by a great number of authors for the determination of thiamine in cereals (39, 10), urine (11, 25, 22, 30, 38, 26, 35), and blood (12). The procedure is of utmost importance in vitamin chemistry and is a standard method of vitamin assay. For detailed information on the procedure the reader is referred to the monograph published by the Association of Vitamin Chemists, Inc. (29).

Najjar and Ketron (32, 33) observed the presence in urine of N-methyl-nicotinamide, which is retained and eluted together with thiamine. This substance exhibits a greenish blue fluorescence which interferes with the fluorometric determination of thiamine. A procedure for eliminating these difficulties, as well as methods for determination of this nicotinic acid derivative in urine, has been proposed (19, 22).

Hochberg, Melnick, and Field (18, 27, 28) used a similar ion exchange procedure. In this case, however, thiamine was determined colorimetrically after its reaction with diazotized p-aminoacetophenone. In the analysis of urine a preliminary extraction of thiamine by means of benzyl alcohol was made in order to eliminate the influence of the salts which, according to these authors, prevent the complete uptake of thiamine.

B. Vitamin B_2 (riboflavin)

Riboflavin is retained to only a slight extent by a synthetic zeolite in the potassium form (8) and may therefore be determined in the effluent from the column. Fujiwara and Shimizu (13) found that a pyridine-treated zeolite has less affinity for riboflavin than the potassium zeolite and that riboflavin retained on the former type of exchanger is easily eluted by washing with water, without any leakage of thiamine.

C. Vitamin K_1

A synthetic zeolite has also been used for the isolation of vitamin K_1 (1). The retention of this substance seems to be due to a "physical adsorption."

2. CATION EXCHANGE RESINS

A. Vitamin B_1 (thiamine)

In a reviewing article Myers (31) reported that thiamine can be taken up quantitatively and reversibly by the sulfonated resin Amberlite IR-100. Details were presented in a paper by Herr (17). A quantitative retention was achieved when the resin was used in the free-acid form as well as in the sodium form. Difficulties were observed in removing the vitamin from the resin. With concentrated hydrochloric acid as regenerant it was possible to obtain an almost complete regeneration. Even with this regenerant a large volume was required to achieve elution of the vitamin.

Winters and Kunin (41) reported an almost quantitative uptake of thiamine by means of a cation exchanger of carboxylic acid type. The resin was used in the sodium form [cf. (37)].

B. *Vitamin B₂ (riboflavin)*

According to Herr, riboflavin is only slightly taken up by a sulfonic acid resin in the hydrogen form. However, the capacity of a cation exchange resin to retain riboflavin is sufficient to make possible an uptake for analytical purposes.

Fujiwara and Shimizu (13) and Nishio (34) devised a method for micro-determination of riboflavin by using a cation exchange resin (sulfonated phenolic type) for retention of the vitamin. The determination is based on a measurement of the fluorescence of the riboflavin solution. Part of the interfering substances (e.g. thiamine) have a stronger affinity than ribo-flavin for cation exchangers. These substances are removed by percolating the solution, adjusted to pH 4–5, through a column of synthetic zeolite pretreated with pyridine-acetic acid solution. The effluent from the column is passed through a second column containing the ion exchange resin (KH-9) in the pyridine form. Both columns are washed with water.

Riboflavin is retained in the resin column, which is afterwards washed with hot dilute acetic acid (0.2 ml glacial acetic acid to 100 ml water) in order to remove interfering substances. Riboflavin is then eluted with pyridine-acetic acid solution (pH 7). The fluorescence is measured after oxidation with permanganate and subsequent addition of hydrogen per-oxide until the color of permanganate disappears.

3. ANION EXCHANGE RESINS

A. *Vitamin C (ascorbic acid)*

The separation of ascorbic acid from non-acidic substances by means of anion exchange resins has been reported by several authors (14, 24). An application of analytical interest, namely, the isolation of ascorbic acid in urine, was described by Jackel, Mosbach, and King (20). The authors found that a quantitative uptake could be achieved with water solutions, but with samples of rat urine it was necessary first to remove the bulk of oxalic acid preservative by addition of lead acetate. Before the passage through an anion exchange column the excess lead ions were removed by means of a sulfonic acid resin in the hydrogen cycle or by addition of a slight excess of oxalic acid.

The uptake of ascorbic acid was effected by means of a weakly basic resin (Amberlite IR-4B) which was used in the free-base form. Regeneration was performed by means of 1 N hydrochloric acid, and the eluate used for isolation of ascorbic acid as 2,4-dinitrophenylosazone. The non-adsorption of glucose was established by adding C^{14}-labeled glucose before the ion exchange treatment.

B. *Vitamin B_6 (pyridoxine)*

In connection with the determination of vitamin B_6 (pyridoxine) Brown, Bina, and Thomas (2) used the anion exchanger Amberlite IR-4 for the removal of interfering substances. Pyridoxine was not taken up by the resin. On the other hand Shimizu and Shiba (40) found that the vitamin can be taken up by means of cation exchangers of carboxylic acid type. A method for the determination of vitamin B_6 in yeast is based upon this observation.

C. *Other B-Vitamins*

Kato and Shimizu (23) used a two-step ion exchange procedure to eliminate interferences of different fluorescent substances before the fluorometric determination of nicotinamide. Cationic impurities are retained by passing the extract solution through a cation exchange resin of the carboxylic type (sodium form). Before this operation the solution is brought to pH 5 to prevent the uptake of nicotinamide. Washing is performed with hot water. Anionic impurities are subsequently removed by means of an anion exchanger of strongly basic type in the free-base form.

A two-step deionization has also been applied by Jackson *et al.* for the isolation of vitamin $B_{12\,b}$ from neomycin fermentations (21).

The determination of pantothenic acid has been referred to in Chapter XXIV:4.

BIBLIOGRAPHY

1. Binkley, S. B., Mac-Corquodale, D. W., Thayer, S. A., and Doisy, E. A.: *J. Biol. Chem.*, **130**, 219 (1939).
2. Brown, E., Bina, A., and Thomas, J.: *J. Biol. Chem.*, **158**, 455 (1945).
3. Burns, J. J., and King, C. G.: *Science*, **111**, 257 (1950).
4. Cerecedo, L. R., and Hennessy, D. J.: *J. Am. Chem. Soc.*, **59**, 1617 (1937).
5. Cerecedo, L. R., and Kaszuba, F. J.: *J. Am. Chem. Soc.*, **59**, 1619 (1937).
6. Cerecedo, L. R., and Thornton, J. J.: *J. Am. Chem. Soc.*, **59**, 1621 (1937).
7. Conner, R. T., and Straub, G. J.: *Ind. Eng. Chem.*, Anal. Ed., **13**, 380 (1941).
8. Conner, R. T., and Straub, G. J.: *Ind. Eng. Chem.*, Anal. Ed., **13**, 385 (1941).
9. Daglish, C.: *Quart. J. Pharm. Pharmacol.*, **20**, 257 (1947).
10. Dawbarn, M. C.: *Australian J. Exptl. Biol. Med. Sci.*, **27**, 207 (1949).
11. Egaña, E., and Meiklejohn, A. P.: *J. Biol. Chem.*, **141**, 859 (1941).
12. Fujita, A., and Yamadori, M.: *Arch. Biochem.*, **28**, 94 (1950).
13. Fujiwara, M., and Shimizu, H.: *Anal. Chem.*, **21**, 1009 (1949); *Z. anal. Chem.*, **131**, 159 (1950).

14. Gore, H. C.: *Fruit Products J.*, **27**, 75 (1947).
15. Hennessy, D. J.: *Ind. Eng. Chem.*, Anal. Ed., **13**, 216 (1941).
16. Hennessy, D. J., and Cerecedo, L. R.: *J. Am. Chem. Soc.*, **61**, 179 (1939).
17. Herr, D. S.: *Ind. Eng. Chem.*, **37**, 631 (1945).
18. Hochberg, M., and Melnick, D.: *J. Biol. Chem.*, **156**, 53 (1944).
19. Hochberg, M., Melnick, D., and Oser, B. L.: *J. Biol. Chem.*, **158**, 265 (1945).
20. Jackel, S. S., Mosbach, E. H., and King, C. G.: *Arch. Biochem. Biophys.*, **31**, 442 (1951).
21. Jackson, W. G., Whitfield, G. B., DeVries, W. H., Nelson, H. A., and Evans, J. S.: *J. Am. Chem. Soc.*, **73**, 337 (1951).
22. Johnson, R. E., Sargent, F., Robinson, P. F., and Consolazio, F. C.: *Ind. Eng. Chem.*, Anal. Ed., **17**, 384 (1945).
23. Kato, M., and Shimizu, H.: *Science*, **114**, 12 (1951).
24. Klose, A. A., Stark, J. B., Purvis, G. G., Peat, J., and Fevold, H. L.: *Ind. Eng. Chem.*, **42**, 387 (1950).
25. Mason, H. L., and Williams, R. D.: *J. Biol. Chem.*, **146**, 589 (1942).
26. Mawson, E. H., and Thompson, S. Y.: *Biochem. J.*, **43**, 3 (1948).
27. Melnick, D., and Field, Jr., H.: *J. Biol. Chem.*, **127**, 515 (1939).
28. Melnick, D., and Field, Jr., H.: *J. Biol. Chem.*, **130**, 97 (1939).
29. *Methods of Vitamin Assay*, New York, 1951, p. 111.
30. Michelsen, O., Condiff, H., and Keys, A.: *J. Biol. Chem.*, **160**, 361 (1945).
31. Myers, F. J.: *Ind. Eng. Chem.*, **35**, 858 (1943).
32. Najjar, V. A.: *Bull. Johns Hopkins Hosp.*, **74**, 392 (1944).
33. Najjar, V. A., and Ketron, K. C.: *J. Biol. Chem.*, **152**, 579 (1944).
34. Nishio, M.: *J. Japan. Biochem. Soc.*, **21**, 147 (1949).
35. Nose, Y., and Tashiro, T.: *J. Japan. Biochem. Soc.*, **21**, 130 (1949).
36. Oda, R., Shimizu, H., and Yamanaka, Y.: *Repts. Inst. Chem. Research, Kyoto Univ.*, **16**, 42 (1947).
37. Oda, R., Shimizu, H., and Nakayama, Y.: *Chem. High Polymers*, **5**, 142 (1948).
38. Papageorge, E., and Lamar, M. V.: *Arch. Biochem.*, **14**, 310 (1947).
39. Ridyard, H. N.: *Nature*, **157**, 301 (1946).
40. Shimizu, H., and Shiba, H.: *J. Chem. Soc. Japan [Pure Chem. Sect.]*, **72**, 442 (1951); *J. Japan. Chem.*, **5**, 55 (1951).
41. Winters, J. C., and Kunin, R.: *Ind. Eng. Chem.*, **41**, 460 (1949).

CHAPTER XXIII

Antibiotics

1. PENICILLIN

Penicillin, which is a substance of considerable molecular dimensions, contains amino groups as well as carboxyl groups, and it might be expected that cation exchangers and anion exchangers could be used for the uptake of penicillin provided the degree of cross-linking of the resin is not so high that penetration of the molecule into the resin is prevented.

A most interesting study of the influence of the degree of cross-linking on the capacity of an anion exchange resin for penicillin has been published by Kunin and Myers (8). It was observed that with a high degree of cross-linking, i.e. with a resin of commercial type, the free-base form of the strongly basic resin had only a slight sorption capacity for penicillin, whereas the total exchange capacity of a porous resin could be used for the uptake of penicillin. The results are summarized in Table 21.

TABLE 21

Relative Degree of Cross-linking	Swelling Dry-Wet %	Total Exchange Capacity meq/g	Penicillin Capacity meq/g
1	540	3.2	3.2
2	225	3.1	2.6
3	180	3.1	2.3
4	160	2.9	1.8
8	125	2.6	0.1

Working under conditions where no considerable retention takes place may be utilized for the purification of penicillin. Cruz-Coke, Gonzalez, and Hulsen (1) report that a filtrate which retains all the penicillin activity is obtained by filtering crude penicillin first through a cation exchanger of sulfonic acid type at pH 6–7 and then through an anion exchange resin of weakly basic type. Toxic materials are removed by this treatment.

2. STREPTOMYCIN AND STREPTOTHRICIN

The ion exchange technique is used in the standard procedure for the determination of streptomycin in fermentation broths. Because of its basic nature streptomycin may be retained by means of cation exchangers. According to Doery, Mason, and Weiss (3), cation exchange resins of carboxylic type are most useful for this purpose [cf. (12)]. The interfering substances present are eliminated by taking up streptomycin on a column with the sodium-saturated resin, whereas the contaminants pass into the effluent. Streptomycin is easily eluted by means of dilute hydrochloric acid and determined quantitatively by the maltol assay method (3). A batch procedure for the determination of streptomycin and mannosidostreptomycin has also been published (13).

The retention of streptothricin by means of synthetic zeolites and cation exchangers of strongly acid type has been reported (7).

The free dihydrostreptomycin base has been prepared by passing a solution containing the sulfate over a strongly basic anion exchange resin in the hydroxyl form (10).

3. OTHER ANTIBIOTICS

A synthetic zeolite (Decalso) has been used by Saltzman (11) in connection with the determination of aureomycin in blood and urine. Aureomycin is retained by the zeolite from dilute solution. Elution is performed at elevated temperature by means of a 5% sodium carbonate solution, and aureomycin is determined fluorometrically in the eluate.

Jones has adopted a cation exchange resin of sulfonic acid type to remove alanine from a culture medium containing the antibiotic polymyxin (5). A cation exchanger of carboxylic acid type has been used for the isolation of neamine from an acid hydrolyzate of neomycin (9). This procedure has also been employed to isolate a new antibiotic which has been assigned the name netropsin (4).

In this connection it may be mentioned that ion exchange procedures have been reported also for the purification of lavendulin and actinorubin (6).

Dalgliesh et al. (2) used Partridge's technique for the chromatographic separation of amino acids (Chapter XX) to study the amino acid content of the antibiotic actinomycin. Five amino acids were identified after acid hydrolysis of the antibiotic.

BIBLIOGRAPHY

1. Cruz-Coke, E., Gonzalez, F., and Hulsen, W.: Science, 101, 340 (1945).
2. Dalgliesh, C. E., Johnson, A. W., Todd, A. R., and Vining, L. C.: J. Chem. Soc., 1950, 2946.
3. Doery, H. M., Mason, E. C., and Weiss, D. E.: Anal. Chem., 22, 1038 (1950).

4. Finlay, A. C., Hochstein, F. A., Sobin, B. A., and Murphy, F. X.: *J. Am. Chem. Soc.*, **73**, 341 (1951).
5. Jones, T. S. G.: *Biochem. J. Proc.*, **42**, XXXV (1948).
6. Junowics-Kocholaty, R., and Kocholaty, W.: *J. Biol. Chem.*, **168**, 757 (1947).
7. Kocholaty, W., and Junowics-Kocholaty, R.: *Arch. Biochem.*, **15**, 55 (1947).
8. Kunin, R., and Myers, R. J.: *Disc. Faraday Soc.*, **1949**, No. 7, 114.
9. Leach, B. E., and Teeters, C. M.: *J. Am. Chem. Soc.*, **73**, 2794 (1951).
10. Rhodehamel, Jr., H. W., McCormick, S. L., and Kern, S. F.: *Science*, **111**, 233 (1950).
11. Saltzman, A.: *J. Lab. Clin. Med.*, **35**, 123 (1950).
12. Schenck, J. R., Shaw, J. L., and Hargie, M. P.: Abstr. of Papers, Am. Chem. Soc. 113th Meeting, 1948, p. 8C.
13. St. John, C. V., Flick, D. E., and Tepe, J. B.: *Anal. Chem.*, **23**, 1289 (1951).

CHAPTER XXIV

Other Biochemical and Biological Applications

1. AMINES

The uptake of several amines by means of synthetic zeolites was established by Whitehorn (49). Hitherto, only a few analytical procedures for the isolation of amines by means of ion exchange have been published.

The uptake of histamine from blood and other biological fluids by means of synthetic zeolites (38) and cotton acid succinate (27) has been reported. The most favorable results seem to have been obtained in experiments with a carboxylic acid resin, with which a complete elution may easily be effected by means of dilute acid. This method has been used by Lubschez (24), as well as by Bergström and Hansson (3).

Adrenaline may also be taken up by synthetic zeolites (49). Bergström, v. Euler, and Hamberg (2) isolated l-nor-adrenaline from cattle adrenals by means of a cation exchanger of carboxylic acid type. The same procedure has been applied by Bergström and Hansson (3) to the purification of adrenaline and by v. Euler and Hellner (12) to the determination of nor-adrenaline, adrenaline, and hydroxytyramine in urine.

Jindra and Šipoš (19) determined sulfamides by hydrolysis of the amides to sulfanilic acid and an amine. The hydrolytic products were separated on Amberlite IR-100, and the sulfanilic acid was determined by potentiometric titration.

2. PEPTIDES

Consden et al. (7, 8, 9) used an anion exchanger (Amberlite IR-4 adjusted to pH 3–4) to remove acidic amino acids and peptides from solutions obtained by partial acid hydrolysis of wool. The non-acidic fraction was oxidized with bromine water, and the cysteic acid and acidic cysteic acid peptides formed were then quantitatively retained in another anion exchange column. Elution of the amino acids and peptides was performed with 1 N hydrochloric acid. By means of ionophoresis, the acidic peptides were separated into groups with similar mobilities.

The uptake of di- and tripeptides by means of sulfonic acid resins in the H^+ form was studied by Brenner and Burckhardt (4). For the products under investigation an uptake of 94–100% was achieved. Elution could be performed by means of 1 N hydrochloric acid. Experiments with anion exchangers showed only a low retention of most peptides. The authors point out that the conditions are, in principle, the same as those for the uptake of amino acids.

Other applications of the ion exchange technique in this field are the purification of the pressor substance hypertensin (angiotonin) (10) and the antibiotic polymyxin (Chapter XXIII: 3).

3. PROTEINS

A fractional precipitation of blood plasma proteins may be achieved by lowering the ion concentration of the solution. This may be accomplished by dilution or by dialysis. A convenient manner of performing a fractional precipitation is to remove the salt stepwise by means of ion exchange. This principle has been used by Reid and Jones (36, 37). Special precautions must be taken to prevent denaturation of the proteins, which occurs if the pH value of the blood serum is not kept close to neutral. The authors recommend a batch procedure with stepwise addition of a mixture of a sulfonic acid resin in the free-acid form and the free-base form of a strongly basic resin (37). When the salt concentration required for precipitation of the first fraction (γ-globulin) is reached, the solution is strained off from the resin and centrifuged to separate the γ-globulin. Upon the progressive removal of salt, β- and α-globulins are precipitated. Studies of the precipitation of proteins in blood by means of ion exchangers have also been published by Hill, Haberman, and Guy (16). In this connection it may be mentioned that a cation exchanger has been used in electrophoresis experiments with proteins (40). A sulfonic acid resin placed in one arm of the U-tube was found not to alter the charge distribution of the protein components. The uptake of clupeine by means of a lightly cross-linked resin has been mentioned in Chapter XX.

A most interesting application of the ion exchange technique in protein chemistry has been devised by Warner and Weber (48). These authors found that iron could be removed from conalbumin by adding citrate and subsequently passing the solution through an anion exchange resin in the chloride form. The uptake of the iron citrate complex was found to be complete.

4. ENZYMES

A few applications of ion exchange resins for the isolation of enzymes have been published. McColloch and Kertesz (26) reported the complete removal of pectin-methylesterase from commercial pectinases by retention on a cation exchanger of sulfonic acid type. The resin was used in the free-acid form. Pectinpolygalacturonase was not retained by the resin.

Gilbert and Swallow (15) found that several enzymes could be freed from ions by passing the solution through columns of cation and anion exchange resins without significant loss. (The H+ form of a sulfonic acid resin and the free-base form of a weakly basic resin were used.) The authors point out that the non-adsorption and recovery of the enzyme in a soluble form are no proof that minor changes have not occurred. It was observed that urease and α- and β-amylase were inactivated irreversibly, but that pepsin, which is particularly stable to acid, passed unchanged through the columns. Therefore the usual arrangement for dialysis was adopted, except that mixed resins were used for removing salts passing through the cellophane membrane. If special precautions were taken, this method could be used for removing ions from enzyme solutions without denaturation.

Cation exchangers of carboxylic acid type have proved useful for the uptake of enzymes of relatively low molecular weight. This feature of the resins has been utilized to purify and fractionate enzymes by a chromatographic technique. In order to obtain satisfactory results the use of a small particle size of the resin (about 0.05 mm) is recommended.

Paléus and Neilands (33) purified cytochrome c, using a resin of carboxylic type (Amberlite IRC-50). The resin was pretreated with an ammonia-ammonium acetate solution at pH 9. Cytochrome c lodged at the top of the column, and a gold-colored impurity, protein in nature, passed into the effluent. On elution with a buffer at pH 10.8 the cytochrome separated into different fractions, which moved down the column.

A similar procedure has been used by Hirs, Stein, and Moore (17) for the purification of ribonuclease and lysozyme. The latter enzyme resolved in two well-separated symmetrical peaks [cf. (46)].

On the other hand, certain enzymes are reported to pass a cation exchanger of weakly acid type without being retained to a significant extent. According to Talboys (45), resins of this type are suitable for removing impurities from solutions containing bacterial pectinase, the latter not being retained. A similar application has been reported by Muntz and Hurwitz (31).

Ion exchange resins have proved to be valuable tools in research on coenzyme A (Co A) and degradation products of the coenzyme (6, 41, 5, 20). Co A can be taken up efficiently from liver extracts by anion exchange resins in the chloride form. This observation has been utilized by Novelli and

Schmetz (32) to improve the determination of pantothenic acid in tissues.

An anion exchanger of weakly basic type has been used to replace sulfate by acetate in connection with fractional precipitation of the α-amylase of human saliva (28). Some early experiments on the purification of urease by means of a synthetic zeolite have been described by Folin and Youngburg (14).

Joselow and Dawson (20) separated ionic copper from solutions of ascorbic acid oxidase by means of a cation exchanger of sulfonic acid type (Na+). The separation could be achieved without damage to the activity of the enzyme. The authors reported that the bond between the copper and protein in the enzyme is non-dissociable.

5. VIRUSES

An application of great medical interest is the purification of viruses. Muller (30) removed nitrogenous impurities from suspensions of several neurotropic viruses by treatment with a cation exchanger of sulfonic acid type, the viruses not being retained. Morgan (29) employed a cation exchange resin to remove an inhibitor for the mumps virus hemolysin occurring in allantoic fluid of embryonated eggs infected with mumps virus.

Anion exchange resins of strongly basic type have also been utilized, e.g. for isolation of viruses from feces. In this way an uptake of poliomyelitis virus has been obtained, the bulk of extraneous material being removed in the filtrate. By means of 10% Na_2HPO_4 solution, the virus may be eluted as a clear colorless solution which retains the original infectivity (23).

6. BLOOD

It has been recognized for a long time that calcium is involved in the coagulation of blood. Precipitation with oxalates or fluorides or addition of citrate or heparin prevents coagulation. By exchanging the calcium ions for sodium ions by means of a cation exchange resin, coagulation may be conveniently inhibited. The treated blood may be used for hematological, serological, and biochemical investigations (43, 44, 35, 11, 42, 22). Heparin is reported not to interfere with the removal of calcium, whereas addition of citrate prevents the uptake of calcium because of complex formation (18).

Markus (25) applied a cation exchange resin to remove substances which interfere with the colorimetric determination of lactic acid in blood and other body fluids. The steps in the method are: (a) deproteinization, (b) desugaration, (c) cation exchange, and (d) colorimetric determination (*p*-hydroxydiphenyl). A column filled with the free-acid form of a sulfonic acid resin is used in the ion exchange step. All cations, including Cu^{2+}, and the last traces of amino acids are removed. Lactic acid is determined in an aliquot of the effluent. (As mentioned in Chapter II:2B, lactic acid may be adsorbed by cation exchange resins. This source of error may be eliminated by washing the resin after the sorption step.)

In regard to total base in blood see Chapter VIII:1P.

It may also be mentioned that Bennett and Niemann (1) have applied the deionization principle in connection with the isolation of blood group A-specific substance from hog gastric mucin.

7. URINE

As reported in Chapter I, the determination of ammonia in urine according to Folin and Bell (13) was the first application of an ion exchange separation in analytical chemistry. In this procedure 1 ml urine is diluted with 5 ml water and added to 2 g sodium zeolite (Permutit) slurried in 5 ml water. Ammonia is taken up by the zeolite. After being shaken for 5 min, the solution is removed by decantation, and after washing the zeolite with water ammonia is liberated by addition of sodium hydroxide. An aliquot of the solution is subjected to the Nessler determination.

The separation of ammonia from urine has also been performed by means of cation exchange resins (50). This procedure has also been used to isolate magnesium.

Urea is not taken up by the zeolite, a fact which has been utilized by Youngburg (51) in a method for its quantitative determination [cf. also (34)].

Other applications of ion exchangers in urine analysis are the determinations of morphine (Chapter XIX:1A), vitamins (Chapter XXII:1A), and radioactive tracers (Chapter XIII:1F).

8. GASTRIC ACIDITY

As mentioned in Chapter III:3, the ion exchange equilibrium in a system containing a cation exchanger of carboxylic acid type is extremely sensitive towards changes in the *p*H value of the solution. This property of the resin has been utilized by Segal, Miller, and Morton (39) for the determination of gastric acidity without subjecting the individual to intubation.

An indicator resin was prepared by allowing the acid form of a carboxylic resin to take up the quinine base from 20 mg of quinine hydrochloride per 1 g resin.

In vivo experiments were performed by administering the indicator resin orally in 2-g doses with 50 ml of 7% alcohol, as gastric stimulant. The time of appearance of quinine in the urine was estimated and gave a measure of the gastric acidity.

BIBLIOGRAPHY

1. Bennett, E. L., and Niemann, C.: *J. Biol. Chem.*, **176**, 969 (1948).
2. Bergström, S., v. Euler, U. S., and Hamberg, U.: *Acta Chem. Scand.*, **3**, 305 (1949).
3. Bergström, S., and Hansson, G.: *Acta Physiol. Scand.*, **22**, 87 (1951).
4. Brenner, M., and Burckhardt, C. H.: *Helv. Chim. Acta*, **34**, 1070 (1951).
5. Chantrenne, H.: *J. Biol. Chem.*, **189**, 227 (1951).
6. Chantrenne, H., and Lipmann, F.: *J. Biol. Chem.*, **187**, 757 (1951).
7. Consden, R., and Gordon, A. H.: *Biochem. J. Proc.*, **43**, X (1948).
8. Consden, R., and Gordon, A. H.: *Biochem. J.*, **46**, 8 (1950).
9. Consden, R., Gordon, A. H., and Martin, A. J. P.: *Biochem. J.*, **44**, 548 (1949).
10. Cruz-Coke, E., Gonzalez, F., and Hulsen, W.: *Science*, **101**, 340 (1945).
11. De Nicola, P., and Rosti, P.: *Boll. ist. sieroterap. milan.*, **27**, 180 (1948).
12. v. Euler, U. S., and Hellner, S.: *Acta Physiol. Scand.*, **22**, 161 (1951).
13. Folin, O., and Bell, R. D.: *J. Biol. Chem.*, **29**, 329 (1917).
14. Folin, O., and Youngburg, G. E.: *J. Biol. Chem.*, **38**, 111 (1919).
15. Gilbert, G. A., and Swallow, A. J.: *Biochem. J.*, **47**, 502 (1950).
16. Hill, J. M., Haberman, S., and Guy, R.: *Am. J. Clin. Path.*, **19**, 134 (1949).
17. Hirs, C. H. W., Stein, W. H., and Moore, S.: *J. Am. Chem. Soc.*, **73**, 1893 (1951).
18. Hussey, C. V., Quick, A. J., Stefanini, M., Consolazio, C. F., and Sargent, F.: *J. Biol. Chem.*, **184**, 105 (1950).
19. Jindra, A., and Šipoš, F.: *Chem. Listy*, **44**, 235 (1950); *Časopisu Českého Lékárnictva*, **63**, 211 (1950).
20. Joselow, M., and Dawson, C. R.: *J. Biol. Chem.*, **191**, 1 (1951).
21. King, T. E., and Strong, F. M.: *Science*, **112**, 562 (1950); *J. Biol. Chem.*, **189**, 315 (1951).
22. Klement, R.: *Naturwissenschaften*, **37**, 211 (1950).
23. Lo Grippo, G. A.: *Proc. Soc. Exptl. Biol. Med.*, **74**, 208 (1950).
24. Lubschez, R.: *J. Biol. Chem.*, **183**, 731 (1950).
25. Markus, R. L.: *Arch. Biochem.*, **29**, 159 (1950).
26. McColloch, R. J., and Kertesz, Z. I.: *J. Biol. Chem.*, **160**, 149 (1945).
27. McIntire, F. C., Roth, L. W., and Shaw, J. L.: *J. Biol. Chem.*, **170**, 537 (1947).
28. Meyer, K. H., Fischer, Ed. H., Bernfeld, P., and Staub, A.: *Experientia*, **3**, 455 (1947).
29. Morgan, H. R.: *Proc. Soc. Exptl. Biol. Med.*, **77**, 276 (1951).
30. Muller, R. H.: *Proc. Soc. Exptl. Biol. Med.*, **73**, 239 (1950).
31. Muntz, J. A., and Hurwitz, J.: *Arch. Biochem. Biophys.*, **32**, 137, (1951).
32. Novelli, G. D., and Schmetz, F. J.: *J. Biol. Chem.*, **192**, 181 (1951).
33. Paléus, S., and Neilands, J. B.: *Acta Chem. Scand.*, **4**, 1024 (1950).
34. Pohorecka-Lelesz, B.: *Bull. soc. chim. biol.*, **8**, 178 (1926).
35. Quick, A. J.: *Am. J. Physiol.*, **148**, 211 (1947).
36. Reid, A. F., and Jones, F.: *Am. J. Clin. Path.*, **19**, 10 (1949).

37. Reid, A. F., and Jones, F.: *Ind. Eng. Chem.*, **43**, 1074 (1951).
38. Roberts, M., and Adam, H. M.: *Brit. J. Pharmacol.*, **5**, 526 (1950).
39. Segal, H. L., Miller, L. L., and Morton, J. J.: *Proc. Soc. Exptl. Biol. Med.*, **74**, 218 (1950).
40. Sober, H. A., Kegeles, G., and Gutter, F. J.: *Science*, **110**, 564 (1949).
41. Stadtman, E. R., Novelli, G. D., and Lipmann, F.: *J. Biol. Chem.*, **191**, 365 (1951).
42. Stefanini, M.: *Proc. Soc. Exptl. Biol. Med.*, **67**, 22 (1948).
43. Steinberg, A.: *Proc. Soc. Exptl. Biol. Med.*, **56**, 124 (1944).
44. Sweet, W. J., and Sweeney, O. R.: *Proc. Iowa Acad. Sci.*, **51**, 299 (1944).
45. Talboys, P. W.: *Nature*, **166**, 1077 (1950).
46. Tallan, H. H., and Stein, W. H.: *J. Am. Chem. Soc.*, **73**, 2976 (1951).
47. Turner, R. A., Pierce, J. G., and du Vigneaud, V.: *J. Biol. Chem.*, **191**, 21 (1951).
48. Warner, R. C., and Weber, I.: *J. Biol. Chem.*, **191**, 173 (1951).
49. Whitehorn, J. C.: *J. Biol. Chem.*, **56**, 751 (1923).
50. Yoshino, Y.: *J. Chem. Soc. Japan*, Pure Chem. Sect., **72**, 457 (1951).
51. Youngburg, G. E.: *J. Biol. Chem.*, **45**, 391 (1921).

CHAPTER XXV

Investigations of Complex Salt Solutions

1. GENERAL CONSIDERATIONS

The organic ion exchangers offer great possibilities for the study of the composition and stability of complex salt solutions. The investigations can be carried out either by an equilibrium method, e.g. the shaking of a solution with an ion exchanger until equilibrium is reached, or under non-equilibrium conditions. The equilibrium method is without doubt the more important. This method can be used for determining the composition and degree of dissociation of the complexes.

Cation exchangers are most useful for investigations of anionic and uncharged complexes. Strong as well as weak complexes may be studied by the equilibrium method. The application of cation exchangers for quantitative studies of cationic complexes is subject to serious limitations and is more complicated, but recent investigations show that cation exchange equilibrium can be utilized also for solutions containing complexes of positive net charge. In special cases where only the latter type of complexes is present it is simpler to use anion exchangers of strongly basic type.

The non-equilibrium method can be used only for strong complexes and gives chiefly information as to the composition of the complex, in most cases only of a qualitative kind. However, in certain stable complex systems (e.g. basic chromium salts), for which the interpretation of the results from the equilibrium method, as well as from usual physicochemical methods, would be extremely difficult, the non-equilibrium method has proved to be of great value. The procedure is simple and may be performed either as a column operation or in a batch system.

2. THE CATION EXCHANGE EQUILIBRIA IN A CATION EXCHANGER

A. *Anionic and Uncharged Complexes*

Investigation of the ion exchange equilibrium on cation exchange resins of sulfonic acid type may, as shown by Samuelson (26, 27), be used as a simple and rapid method for the determination of the complex equilibrium in a solution containing anionic complexes and uncharged complexes. The method results in a determination of the free central group in the solution.

The system is assumed to contain the cations A and B, with valences p and q, respectively, and the anions R and S. The only complexes existing are assumed to be of the type BS_n. The Donnan theory leads to the equation

$$\left(\frac{a_{A_w}}{a_{A_r}}\right)^{\frac{1}{p}} = \left(\frac{a_{B_w}}{a_{B_r}}\right)^{\frac{1}{q}}$$

where a_{A_w}, a_{B_w} = ion activities in the solution

a_{A_r}, a_{B_r} = ion activities in the resin phase.

If A and B have the same valence, the ratio between ion activities in the resin phase can be replaced with the ratio between the mole fractions (n) in the special case where the concentration in the resin phase is extremely low. The mole-fraction ratio is determined by analysis of the ion exchanger after filtration and displacement of the solution with water. In this ideal case the ion exchange equilibrium is not displaced on washing. From the Donnan equation the following is obtained:

$$a_{B_w} = a_{A_w} \cdot \frac{n_{B_r}}{n_{A_r}}$$

from which the dissociation of the complex can be calculated if the total amount of the ingoing components is known.

In normal cases, however, the procedure must involve the determination of the exchange equilibrium in the absence of the complex-forming agent (calibration series) as well as in the presence of this agent. In the first series the amount of A is suitably kept constant, together with the amount of ion exchanger and solution volume. The amount of B is varied. This experimental series gives the relation between the concentration of B in the outer solution and the amount of B in the ion exchanger in complex-free solution. In the next experimental series the amount of A, the amount of ion exchanger, and the volume are the same as in the first series. The amount of B is suitably kept constant while the ratio S/R is varied. The amount of B in the ion exchanger is determined; and, by using the relation, found in the first series, between the ion concentration in the ion exchanger and the outer solution, the concentration of non-complex-bound B ions in the outer solution is calculated.

A calculation of the complexity of the system B-S is possible only on the supposition that A and S do not give any complexes. Otherwise only a relative estimation can be obtained. Apart from ion A a number of other ions can also be present in the system if the amounts are the same in both experimental series, and no complexes are formed.

If cations of different valence occur in the system, an error results because of the displacement of the equilibrium of the ion exchanger on dilution. This means that a displacement of the equilibrium takes place on washing the ion exchanger. If the amount of outer solution is large in comparison with the volume remaining in the ion exchanger after filtration, the influence of this factor is small. Moreover, the errors in both the experimental series will be about the same, so that a compensation is obtained. There then arises also another source of error which must be guarded against if great accuracy is desired. The ion exchange equilibrium is in this case dependent upon the volume of the resin phase (inside solution). This can be different because of varying swelling, even if the ion activities for the cations in the outer solution are the same. However, in normal procedures this source of error is not significant.

Washing difficulties can of course be avoided by analyzing the outer solution after equilibrium has been reached and calculating the ion amounts in the ion exchanger by difference through a comparison with the ion amounts introduced into the system. However, for strong complexes, it becomes a matter of great difficulty to carry out the determination accurately enough in this way. Irrespective of whether the analysis is done directly on the ion exchanger or the determination is made by difference, a series of calibration experiments must be carried out. The results of these can be either collated graphically or used to calculate empirical exchange constants.

Samuelson (27) applied the method to investigations of the complexity of ferric polymetaphosphate solutions. The method was later used by Djurfeldt and Samuelson (5) for investigations of copper, zinc, and manganese polymetaphosphate.

Schubert et al. (29–37) showed that the procedure is simplified when one of the components of the complex is present on the tracer level. The uptake of a tracer cation B^{+q} has been found to be directly proportional to the concentration of the tracer in the outside solution, provided the weight of the resin and volume of solution are constant. The proportionality factor is called the distribution coefficient (K_d). This simple relation makes possible simplification of the calculations (cf. Chapter III:2C).

The distribution coefficient K_d^0 in the absence of the complex-forming agent is determined by calibration experiments. Moreover, the distribution coefficient (K_d) is determined under identical conditions except for the presence of the complex-forming agent.

The dissociation constant K_c of the complex BS_n follows from the mass action law:

$$K_c = \frac{C_B \cdot C_S^n}{C_{BS_n}}$$

Schubert, Russell, and Myers (35) derived the following relation between these quantities:

$$K_c = \frac{C_S^n}{(K_d^0/K_d) - 1}$$

As shown from the equation a straight line should be obtained by plotting $[(K_d^0/K_d) - 1]$ against the concentration C_S on a log-log plot. The validity of this equation has been demonstrated in several papers by Schubert *et al.*

It is not necessary to measure K_d^0 directly, as it is possible to derive it from values of K_d by graphical or analytical methods. Schubert (30) recommends a plot of $1/K_d$ against C_S^n and extrapolation of the resulting straight line for proper n values to zero concentration of S, as indicated by the relation:

$$\frac{1}{K_d} = \frac{C_S^n}{K_d^0 \cdot K_c} + \frac{1}{K_d^0}$$

The investigations of Schubert *et al.* deal with solutions of strontium citrate and strontium tartrate (33), barium citrate (34), complexes of calcium with citric acid, tricarballylic acid (36), and tartaric acid (30). Subsequently the ion exchange technique utilizing radiotracers has been employed for the study of complex ions formed between calcium and strontium and aspartic, succinic, and malic acids, butylamine, ethanolamine, and formaldehyde (32). The effect of temperature and ionic strength on the stability of the strontium citrate complex has also been investigated by Schubert (32). Schubert and Lindenbaum (37) have performed quantitative measurements of the stability of the complex ions formed between tracer amounts of calcium and strontium and twenty-five different organic acids under approximately physiological conditions. The complex ions formed were of the 1:1 type. Equations necessary to calculate the complex constant under conditions where two complex-forming ligands are present and where the complex ion itself is taken up by the resin are given. The investigations of radium complexes with a number of organic acids deserve special attention (35). With this method, where only tracer amounts are necessary for the experiments, such investigations can be made without endangering the health of the observer and without too considerable cost. These advantages could be of great importance in other systems. Some data on rare earth citrate complexes were presented in a paper by Tompkins and Mayer (41). Radioactive tracers were also used in that work [cf. also (3)].

B. *Cationic Complexes*

In most investigations it has been assumed that the uptake of complex cations by the exchanger may be neglected. The results have been interpreted either as complex formation or in terms of activity coefficients.

Vanselow (42) suggested that cation exchangers can be used for the determination of the ratio between the activities of two cations in mixed electrolytes by an equilibrium method, and applied the procedure to barium-cadmium exchange on bentonite. The method is based on the assumption that the activity coefficients in the inside solution of the ion exchanger are unaffected when the composition of the outside solution varies. However, this assumption is not generally valid. On the contrary, the activity coefficients in the ion exchanger vary considerably as the relative amounts of the two cations are changed. Therefore the method may be adopted only in special cases where this condition is fulfilled.

If, however, one of the ions is present in tracer amounts, the cation exchange equilibria may be used for calculating a relative activity coefficient of the tracer cation in the outside solution. Connick and Mayer (4) applied this principle in investigations on the relative activity coefficients of cerous salts.

The ion exchange equilibrium between cerous and hydrogen ions, e.g. in chloride solution, may be written as

$$\frac{X_{Ce^{3+}}}{X_{H^+}^3} \cdot \frac{C_{H^+}^3}{C_{Ce^{3+}}} \cdot \frac{\gamma_{H^+}^3}{\gamma_{Ce^{3+}}} = K_a \tag{1}$$

where C denotes concentration in the solution, γ is the activity coefficient of the species indicated, and X is the equivalent fraction of the ions in the ion exchanger. K_a may be considered a constant provided the variations in the equivalent fraction in the resin phase are small. This condition is fulfilled for solutions containing a small concentration of the cerous ion and a relatively large concentration of the acid. Another condition which should also be fulfilled is that the swelling of the resin (i.e. the volume of the resin phase) be the same in all experiments. As the swelling is influenced by the concentration of the outside solution (25), the equation may not be valid if the acid concentration is varied over a wider range.

Multiplying numerator and denominator of eq. 1 by $\gamma_{Cl^-}^3$ gives

$$\left[\frac{X_{Ce^{3+}}}{X_{H^+}^3} \cdot \frac{C_{H^+}^3}{C_{Ce^{3+}}}\right] \cdot \gamma_{\pm HCl}^6 = K_a \cdot \gamma_{\pm CeCl_3}^4 \tag{2}$$

The quantity within brackets $[Q]$ is measured directly from the ion exchange experiments, and $\gamma_{\pm HCl}$ may be equal to that for solutions containing only hydrochloric acid, as the cerous ions are present only in tracer amounts.

$$\gamma_{\pm CeCl_3} = k_{H^+}[Q \cdot \gamma_{\pm HCl}^6]^{1/4}; \quad k_{H^+} = \frac{1}{K_a^{1/4}}$$

The ratio $\gamma_{\pm CeCl_3}/k_{H^+}$ can therefore be calculated from the available data and may be used as a relative measure for the activity coefficient of the cerous salt.

In cases where it is possible to measure the ion exchange equilibrium at different concentrations of the bulk electrolyte, absolute values of the activity coefficients of the tracer electrolyte can be obtained. This principle has been used by Schubert (35) for the determination of the activity coefficients of barium nitrate in tracer amounts at varying concentrations of uranyl nitrate. The data obtained for the quantity Q are extrapolated to zero concentration, and $\gamma_{\pm Ba(NO_3)_2}$ is calculated from the equation

$$\gamma_{\pm Ba(NO_3)_2} = \left(\frac{Q}{Q_{extrapol.}}\right)^{1/3} \cdot \gamma_{\pm UO_2(NO_3)_2}$$

$[Q_{extrapol.} = K_a$ (eq. 4 d, Chapter III).]

The method can be applied only if the exchangeable ions are of the same valence.

Connick and Mayer found that the relative activity coefficients of cerous chloride and nitrate were considerably lower than those for cerous perchlorate and interpreted their results in terms of complex ion formation. An attempt was made to correct for the amount of $CeCl^{2+}$ and $CeNO_3^{2+}$ in the resin. The correction is rather uncertain, and furthermore the possibility exists of some variation in K_a due to changes in swelling, as the concentration in the outside solution was varied over a wide range.

Sulfate ions were also shown to form fairly strong complexes with cerous ions. These experiments were performed at almost constant ionic strength with varying concentrations of sodium sulfate and sodium perchlorate. This method is preferable not only because large activity-coefficient corrections are avoided but also because no significant change in swelling will occur under these conditions.

Disregarding the uptake of $CeSO_4^+$ by the resin, values of the complex constant

$$C_1 = C_{CeSO_4^+}/(C_{Ce^{3+}} \cdot C_{SO_4^{2-}})$$

may be calculated from the equation

$$C_1 = \left(\frac{Q_{NaClO_4}}{Q} - 1\right)\frac{1}{C_{SO_4^{2-}}}$$

Mayer and Schwartz (23) made similar investigations on the association of cerous ions with iodide, bromide, and fluoride ions.

Fronaeus (6) developed an interesting method for the calculation of the complexity constants in systems containing the cation B^{2+} and the ligand S^-. This author considered the uptake not only of the central ion B^{2+} but also of the first complex BS^+. In order to make a calculation possible the experiments should be performed under conditions where the molar concentration of $(B^{2+} + BS^+)$ in the resin phase is low and constant in all experiments. The deduction of the equations, which is in line with the calculation methods used in modern complex chemistry, is rather complicated and would require too much space in this book. Readers interested in these questions must therefore be referred to the original paper (in English).

The method was applied to solutions containing cupric acetate. The solution was kept at unit ionic strength by addition of sodium perchlorate, the total concentration of copper in all experiments being low compared with the sodium-ion concentration. From a series of equilibrium experiments, the complexity constants of the complexes $CuAc^+$, $CuAc_2$, and $CuAc_3^-$ were computed. Excellent agreement with potentiometric determinations was achieved.

3. THE EQUILIBRIUM DISTRIBUTION OF ANIONIC LIGANDS BETWEEN A CATION EXCHANGER AND A SOLUTION CONTAINING COMPLEX IONS HAVING POSITIVE CHARGE

Günther-Schulze published in 1922 two papers on complex formation in salt solutions by cation exchange (21). Solutions containing different complex copper salts or chloride solutions of different divalent ions were shaken with a certain amount of a synthetic zeolite (Permutit), and from the change in concentration of the solution conclusions were drawn as to the existence of different complex cations. If, for instance, a solution of copper chloride was treated with potassium zeolite, a considerable decrease in chloride concentration was observed which was ascribed to the uptake of complex copper cations. Experiments by Samuelson (28), using an organic cation exchanger, showed that no such effects could be observed, and that Günther-Schulze's results were probably due to a precipitation of basic salts.

A synthetic zeolite was also used by Gustavson (8) in early investigations on the complexity of chromium salts. However, as later pointed out by, among others, Gustavson himself (9), some of the data are of questionable value because of the instability of the zeolite. However, data inexplainable at the time of investigation, e.g. regarding the behavior of extremely basic chromic chlorides, were confirmed and satisfactorily explained by the ion exchange method 25 years later.

Günther-Schulze calculated the composition of the complex cations directly from the changes in composition of the outside solution. As pointed out by Samuelson (28), it is not permissible to calculate the dissociation of the complex in the outside solution directly from the distribution of the anion between the ion exchanger and the outside solution because of the fact that the anion concentrations in the resin phase and in the outside solution differ considerably. The interpretation of the results is therefore extremely difficult.

Let us assume that a solution containing the ions Me^{2+}, A^-, and the cationic complex MeA^+ is in equilibrium with a cation exchanger. According to the Donnan theory, the following equation is valid:

$$\frac{\sqrt{a_{Me_w^{2+}}}}{\sqrt{a_{Me_r^{2+}}}} = \frac{a_{MeA_w^+}}{a_{MeA_r^+}} = \frac{a_{Cl_r^-}}{a_{Cl_w^-}}$$

With high concentration in the outer solution, the concentrations in the outer solution and in the resin phase approach one another, but in all cases in a cation exchanger the cation concentration is greater and the anion concentration lower in the resin phase than in the outer solution. In both inorganic and organic cation exchangers of technical type the resin phase (inside solution) is of particularly high concentration. This means that one must take into account the fact that the complex equilibrium is to a large extent displaced in the resin phase compared to the outer solution. As is clear

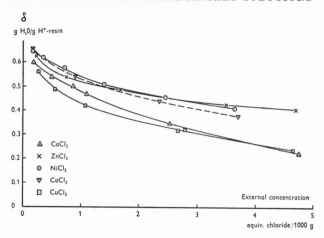

FIG. 47.   Determination of the apparent water adsorption (δ) from different chloride
solutions.   [from (28)]

from the Donnan equation and the complex equilibrium, this implies that
in the resin phase there exists a smaller fraction of complex cations than
in the outer solution. The higher the concentration in the resin phase and
the lower the concentration in the outside solution the greater is the influence of this factor.

As pointed out by Samuelson (28), this explains why weak complexes,
as in chloride solutions of zinc, nickel, cobalt, and copper, cannot be detected
in experiments with cation exchangers. In all the experiments a negative
adsorption of chloride was obtained; i.e. water was more easily taken up
than chloride ions. The negative adsorption was of the same order of magnitude as for calcium chloride solutions. (Fig. 47.)

The Donnan theory explains also that retained strong complexes containing anionic ligands, such as cationic chromium sulfate complexes, or
certain cobalt complexes, e.g. $[Co(NH_3)_4(NO_2)_2]^+$, and even the extremely
stable $[Co(NH_3)_5Cl]^{2+}$, are decomposed when the resin is kept in water (25).

4. THE COLUMN METHOD

In his fundamental paper on ion exchange resins Griessbach (7) related
some experiments on the uptake of copper complexes from ammoniacal
copper solutions by means of a column containing a cation exchange resin.
It was shown that at the break-through point for copper the composition
of the resin corresponded to a mole ratio $Cu:NH_3 = 1:4.2$. On continued
filtration the composition changed to $1:2.0$. The conclusion was drawn

that copper was, in the beginning, taken up as $Cu(NH_3)_4^{2+}$ but that the composition of the complex successively changed to $Cu(NH_3)_2^{2+}$.

In experiments on the separation of chromium and sulfate by means of cation exchange columns Samuelson (24) observed that the separation was incomplete except in the case of the violet hexaquochromium sulfate. For the green chromium sulfate solutions a certain amount of chromium passed into the effluent and part of the sulfate was retained. This was explained by the fact that not all the chromium occurs in cationic form and that, in addition, a part of the chromium occurs as complex sulfato-chromium cations. The amount of chromium in the effluent and the retained amount of sulfate were shown to be dependent upon flow rate and the volume of the resin bed, but even at extremely low flow rate and with large excess of resin the separation was far from complete.

A serious drawback of the column method when applied to investigations of complexes is that in most cases the equilibrium is considerably displaced during the passage of the solution through the column (26). In a cation exchange column certain cations may be taken up quantitatively even if in the original solution they were present as anionic complexes [cf. e.g. (26)].

Furthermore, many cations containing anionic ligands are more or less rapidly decomposed after being taken up in a resin. The time of filtration, as well as the time of washing, is therefore of importance. The process should be performed quickly in order to prevent as far as possible a shift in equilibrium.

As pointed out by Gustavson (19), the direct displacement of an anionic ligand in cationic complexes, such as the stable sulfato group in sulfato-hydroxy-chromium cations, by penetration of the functional group of the exchanger (SO_3^- and particularly COO^-) occurs at times upon prolonged interaction.

The column method is of interest only for investigation of stable complexes. Even for most rather strong complexes the method can give only an approximate picture of the complex formation in a solution.

Samuelson applied this method to solutions containing ferric polymetaphosphate and observed that different results were obtained when the ion exchanger was used in the hydrogen form and in the ammonium form (26). Despite all complications some interesting results could be obtained, and the extreme simplicity of the method would suggest that its use is justified in certain cases.

The most important application of the column method is in the analysis of chromium complexes and basic chrome tanning liquors. This field was studied at length in several papers by Gustavson (9–20) and later by Adams (1). Gustavson developed a simple method, based on this principle, for analysis of chrome tanning liquors.

Since part of the chromium complexes are irreversibly fixed by the exchanger and hence withdrawn from the system, and, furthermore, since several types of complexes with different sign and number of charges are present in solution together with neutral salts, the complexity of the system cannot be calculated in the ordinary manner.

In the analysis of basic chromic sulfates Gustavson observed that, when the solution was percolated through a cation exchange column, the amount of chromium taken up did not differ more than 2% of the total amount present on varying the content of cations from 1 to 4 meq. The total cation exchange capacity of the column was 30 meq. Variations of the flow rate within certain limits did not affect the results appreciably. According to Gustavson, this finding applied also to the amount of sulfate taken up by the cation exchanger, i.e. the observed acidity of the retained sulfato-chromic complexes.

In later papers Gustavson prefers the sodium form of the resin to the hydrogen form (15). The effluent from the cation exchanger will contain sodium ions and non-cationic chromium complexes. The acidity of these complexes is determined by titrating the boiling solution against phenolphthalein. The cationic chromium fraction and the acidity of the complex cations are also determined as the difference between the analysis of the original liquor and the effluent from the cation exchanger, or by analysis of the eluate after regeneration with 5 M hydrochloric acid.

Applying this method to basic chromium chloride solutions, Gustavson observed that in certain analyses chloride was retained in the column. The observed values for the acidity of the chloro-chromic cations were very greatly dependent upon the dimensions of the filter, the flow rate, and the particle size of the resin (14). Therefore, for these less stable complexes, the method can be considered only a qualitative test. Retention of chloride indicates the presence of positively charged chloro-chromic complexes, but even if the chloride quantitatively passes through the filter the absence of cationic chloride complexes is not proved, as it has been shown that even rather strong complexes may be completely decomposed on passage through a cation exchanger.

Many other applications were included in Gustavson's investigations, which have substantially added to our knowledge of the mechanism of the chrome tanning process.

Gustavson has also investigated the behavior of different complex chromium salts on filtration through a column containing an anion exchanger in the chloride form. The anionic fraction may be retained in the column. However, as pointed out by Adams (1) and Gustavson (14), different complications make the interpretation of the results difficult. The introduction of strongly basic anion exchangers offers better possibilities of investigating anionic chromium complexes, since retention of non-anionic chromium and formation of amine complexes with the resin are eliminated (18).

A modified column technique has been used by Leden (22) as a rapid method for detecting the presence of anionic complexes in salt solutions. For example, anion exchangers of strongly basic type transformed into the iodide form were found to retain cadmium on passing a cadmium iodide solution through the column. The cadmium ions were held so strongly that they could not be removed by washing with a moderate quantity of water. Similar experiments with cadmium perchlorate and sulfate and resins saturated with these anions showed that cadmium appeared in the effluent as soon as the water originally present in the column had been displaced. Experiments with chloride and acetate showed that a certain retardation was obtained, but on washing with water the cadmium ions were eluted. From the experiments it was concluded that iodide gives strong anionic complexes, and chloride and acetate weak complexes of negative charge, whereas no such complexes exist in solutions containing perchlorate or sulfate. This is in agreement with results obtained by other methods.

It may also be mentioned that anion exchangers have been used for preparative purposes to displace certain anionic ligands in complexes by others. For example, the displacement of chloro ligands from chloro-ethylenediamine-cobalt (III) salts by hydroxyl groups may be achieved simply by passing the solution through a column filled with the free-base form of a strongly basic resin (2).

5. BATCHWISE OPERATION UNDER NON-EQUILIBRIUM CONDITIONS

Batch operation under non-equilibrium conditions has been used by Gustavson (11, 18, 19) and Theis and Thorstensen (39, 38) for investigations of solutions containing basic chromic salts, e.g. chrome tanning liquors. According to Gustavson (18), the method has certain advantages over the column method.

A solution containing cationic, anionic, and non-ionic (uncharged or colloidal) chromium complexes is shaken with a cation exchange resin in large excess in order to make possible a quantitative uptake of chromium cations. The intention is not to reach the final complex equilibrium, and the time of reaction must be chosen so short that no appreciable shift in equilibrium between the complexes should occur. After the period of shaking the resin is filtered off and washed quickly with water.

Provided that no transformation of non-ionic or anionic complexes into cations has occurred, the amount of cationic chromium can be calculated by analyzing either the solution or the ion exchanger. If no shift in the complex equilibrium has taken place, it is also possible to determine the amount of the anionic ligand, e.g. sulfate in the cationic complex.

In a parallel experiment an anion exchanger of the strongly basic type may be utilized for determining the amount of anionic chromium (18). The resin is used in the salt form (e.g. as chloride). The non-ionic complexes are equal to the difference between total chromium and the sum of cationic and anionic chromium.

Gustavson recommends the following procedure for analysis of basic chromium sulfate solutions: For determination of cationic chromium, an amount of wetted cation exchanger of an exchange capacity of 5 meq (1 g Dowex 50, finely divided), employed as sodium salt, is shaken in a large test-tube with a solution of the chromium salt containing 1 meq cations for a short period, e.g. 10–15 min. The solution is sucked off, the exchanger washed quickly, and the combined filtrate analyzed. The anionic chromium is obtained in corresponding series with 2 g Amberlite IRA-400 in chloride form.

The sodium cycle is preferred to the hydrogen cycle in the exchange of chromium for three main reasons: (1) adsorption of non-cationic chromium is more pronounced in the acid form; (2) the acid set free in the exchange of the neutral salts, usually present, changes non-cationic chromium into the cationic form; and (3) the adsorption of weak acids by the cation exchanger may cause considerable errors in work with resins in the free-acid form (18, 40).

The results for the composition of the cationic complex, e.g. the values of the complex-bound sulfate ions of the cationic chromium sulfate complexes obtained by means of cation exchangers, are generally too low, as a decomposition of the complex seems to be unavoidable (19). In solutions where all chromium is present as cations, Gustavson (19) found that correct values could be obtained by experiments with anion exchangers of strongly basic type (Amberlite IRA-400). The solution is shaken with excess anion exchanger in the chloride form in order to exchange the free sulfate ions in the solution against chloride ions, leaving the sulfato groups of the chromium complexes intact. It is interesting to note that the values reported are independent of the time of reaction (30 min to 24 hr).

It must be pointed out that these procedures which have proved useful for the extremely stable complexes present in solutions containing basic chromic sulfates may not be suitable for solutions in which the complex equilibrium is shifted rapidly, e.g. those of basic chromium chlorides.

A special modification of the shaking method, useful for the study of the effect of neutral salts on the chromium fixation by sodium salts of cation exchangers, has been devised by Gustavson (11), operating systems with an excess of cations of the solution of chromic salt. A grading of the reactivity of various chromium complexes is obtained by variation of the ratio of amount of exchanger and cations of the solution. By operation with the carboxylic type of cation exchanger, partially transferred into the sodium form, various aspects of the function of the carboxyl ions of collagen in chrome fixation have been investigated. Interesting similarities exist between this type of exchanger and the hide protein (19).

BIBLIOGRAPHY

1. Adams, R. S.: *J. Am. Leather Chemists' Assoc.*, **41**, 552 (1946).
2. Basolo, F., and Steninger, D. H.: *J. Am. Chem. Soc.*, **72**, 5748 (1950).
3. Brown, W. E., and Rieman, W.: *J. Am. Chem. Soc.*, **74**, 1278 (1952).
4. Connick, R. E., and Mayer, S. W.: *J. Am. Chem. Soc.*, **73**, 1176 (1951).
5. Djurfeldt, R., and Samuelson, O.: to be published.
6. Fronaeus, S.: *Acta Chem. Scand.*, **5**, 859 (1951).
7. Griessbach, R.: *Angew. Chem. Beihefte*, **No. 31** (1939).
8. Gustavson, K. H.: *J. Am. Leather Chemists' Assoc.*, **19**, 446 (1924); *Ind. Eng. Chem.*, **17**, 577 (1925).
9. Gustavson, K. H.: *Svensk Kem. Tid.*, **56**, 14 (1944).
10. Gustavson, K. H.: *J. Intern. Soc. Leather Trades' Chemists*, **30**, 264 (1946).
11. Gustavson, K. H.: *Svensk Kem. Tid.*, **58**, 2 (1946).
12. Gustavson, K. H.: *Svensk Kem. Tid.*, **58**, 274 (1946).
13. Gustavson, K. H.: *Colloquiumsber. Inst. Gerbereichem. Techn. Hochschule Darmstadt*, **4**, 5 (1949).
14. Gustavson, K. H.: *J. Am. Leather Chemists' Assoc.*, **44**, 388 (1949).
15. Gustavson, K. H.: *J. Am. Leather Chemists' Assoc.*, **45**, 536 (1950).
16. Gustavson, K. H.: *J. Soc. Leather Trades' Chemists*, **34**, 259 (1950).
17. Gustavson, K. H.: *Svensk Kem. Tid.*, **62**, 165 (1950).
18. Gustavson, K. H.: *J. Soc. Leather Trades' Chemists*, **35**, 160 (1951).

19. Gustavson, K. H.: *Svensk Kem. Tid.*, **63**, 167 (1951).
20. Gustavson, K. H.: *J. Soc. Leather Trades' Chemists*, **35**, 270 (1951).
21. Günther-Schulze, A.: *Z. Elektrochem.*, **28**, 89, 387 (1922).
22. Leden, I.: *Svensk Kem. Tid.*, in press.
23. Mayer, S. W., and Schwartz, S. D.: *J. Am. Chem. Soc.*, **73**, 222 (1951).
24. Samuelson, O.: *Svensk Kem. Tid.*, **52**, 115 (1940).
25. Samuelson, O.: *Diss.*, Tekn. Högskolan, Stockholm, 1944.
26. Samuelson, O.: *Svensk Kem. Tid.*, **56**, 277 (1944).
27. Samuelson, O.: *Iva*, **17**, 9 (1946).
28. Samuelson, O.: *Iva*, **17**, 17 (1946).
29. Schubert, J.: *J. Phys. Colloid Chem.*, **52**, 340 (1948).
30. Schubert, J.: *Anal. Chem.*, **22**, 1365 (1950).
31. Schubert, J.: *J. Am. Chem. Soc.*, **73**, 4488 (1951).
32. Schubert, J.: *J. Phys. Chem.*, **56**, 113 (1952).
33. Schubert, J., and Richter, J. W.: *J. Phys. Colloid Chem.*, **52**, 350 (1948).
34. Schubert, J., and Richter, J. W.: *J. Am. Chem. Soc.*, **70**, 4259 (1948).
35. Schubert, J., Russell, E. R., and Myers, Jr., L. S.: *J. Biol. Chem.*, **185**, 387 (1950).
36. Schubert, J., and Lindenbaum, A.: *Nature*, **166**, 913 (1950).
37. Schubert, J., and Lindenbaum, A.: to be published.
38. Serfass, E. J., Theis, E. R., Thorstensen, T. C., and Agarwal, R. K.: *J. Am. Leather Chemists' Assoc.*, **43**, 132 (1948).
39. Theis, E. R., and Thorstensen, T. C.: *J. Intern. Soc. Leather Trades' Chemists*, **31**, 124 (1947).
40. Tolliday, J. D., Thompson, G. W. H., and Forman, G.: *J. Soc. Leather Trades' Chemists*, **32**, 291 (1948); *J. Am. Leather Chemists' Assoc.*, **45**, 378 (1950).
41. Tompkins, E. R., and Mayer, S. W.: *J. Am. Chem. Soc.* **69**, 2859 (1947).
42. Vanselow, A. P.: *J. Am. Chem. Soc.*, **54**, 1307 (1932).

CHAPTER XXVI

Purification and Recovery of Analytical Reagents

1. DEIONIZATION OF WATER

For certain laboratory purposes it is possible to use deionized water instead of distilled water (3, 7). The cost of the deionization may be lower than that of distillation if large volumes of water are concerned. The cheapest and also most effective method for the removal of electrolytes is the mixed-resin operation. The best results are achieved when the cation exchanger is of strongly acid type and the anion exchanger of strongly basic type. Only strongly basic resins are capable of removing silica. The specific resistance of the deionized water may be 10^7 ohms per cm, which is much higher than that of common distilled water (6, 8). However, it must be remembered that non-electrolytes and colloidal ions may be present in the water and that these are not removed in the deionization. This is the reason why a direct deionization of the water is of limited interest to the analytical chemist.

On the other hand, the quality of the distilled water frequently leaves a great deal to be desired. Common impurities are traces of ammonia, copper, lead, and zinc, as well as considerable amounts of carbon dioxide and sometimes also volatile organic acids.

For several analytical purposes the removal of such impurities from distilled water by means of ion exchange resins is of utmost importance. Liebig, Vanselow, and Chapman (7) showed that the copper content of a distilled water was reduced from 0.2 ppm to 0.0035 ppm after one passage through a sulfonic acid resin (column: 35×1200 mm; Amberlite IR-100 [H+]; flow rate 8 liters per hour). After five passages through the same column the copper content was less than 10^{-4} ppm. Data for the removal of other trace elements from distilled and tap water are also reported by these authors.

Sometimes it may be sufficient to remove only the cationic impurities by means of sulfonic acid resins in the hydrogen form. For instance, in the determination of trace elements the removal of objectionable traces of copper and other heavy metals from distilled water may be a great advantage. Another example is the determination of carboxyl groups in cellulose according to alkalimetric methods. In this procedure the cellulose sample is first treated with acid to substitute the cations bound to the cellulose by hydrogen ions. The acid must be washed out carefully, requiring a considerable quantity of water which must be free from cations to prevent an uptake by the cellulose. In many cases the usual distilled water does not meet the requirements, but satisfactory results are obtained if the distilled water is first passed over a cation exchange resin (10).

A similar application is for improving the quality of the distilled water used for the washing of ion exchange resins, e.g. when the ion exchange method is utilized for the determination of total salt concentration (Chapter VIII).

Another application of some interest to the analyst is the removal of radioactive tracers from laboratory waste water (1).

2. PURIFICATION OF ALCOHOL

For certain analyses, for instance when spectrophotometric methods are employed, it may be of importance that the alcohol used as a solvent be completely free from aldehydes. Even alcohol of c.p. grades does not always meet the requirements. A convenient way to remove the aldehydes is to percolate the alcohol through a column filled with an anion exchanger in the bisulfite form (9) (cf. Chapter XVI). A complete removal of the aldehydes may be achieved by this simple method, which has been used for analytical purposes in the author's laboratory.

3. GELATIN FOR NEPHELOMETRIC DETERMINATION OF SULFATE

Gelatin is advantageously used as a protective colloid in the determination of sulfate. However, it may be difficult to obtain gelatin which is free from sulfate. Under these circumstances it has been necessary to make a correction for blank test. This disadvantage is avoided by de-ashing the gelatin by means of the ion exchange technique. The method is known from an early patent by Holmes and has been applied for analytical purposes by Honda (4).

4. PREPARATION OF CARBONATE-FREE SODIUM HYDROXIDE

Davies and Nancollas (2) have devised an interesting method of preparing carbonate-free sodium hydroxide for volumetric work by means of an anion exchanger of strongly basic type. The preparation is based on the fact that the carbonate ions are preferentially taken up by the resin and therefore can be separated from hydroxyl ions according to the frontal analysis principle.

A 50-ml tube is filled to two-thirds of its volume with the resin (Amberlite IRA-400), which may initially be in the chloride form. This column will be suitable for preparing 1 liter of carbonate-free 0.1 N sodium hydroxide from a sodium hydroxide solution made up without special precautions. The alkali is passed through the column until the effluent is chloride-free, and the tube is then transferred to the stock bottle for carbonate-free sodium hydroxide.

The direct regeneration of the exhausted column by sodium hydroxide is difficult, and therefore Davies and Nancollas recommend the use of hydrochloric acid as regenerant.

5. RECOVERY OF ANALYTICAL REAGENTS

The application of ion exchange resins for the recovery of valuable reagents has been proposed by several authors. Sussman, Nachod, and Wood (11) used an anion exchanger (weakly basic) for the uptake of platinum as chloroplatinate ion. The regeneration of the resin was incomplete, but entire recovery of the precious metal was achieved by ashing the resin and dissolving the ash in aqua regia.

The recovery of silver from silver chromate and silver chloride as well as uranyl ions from uranyl solutions and precipitates obtained in sodium analysis has been mentioned by Kunin (5). The uptake is performed by means of a sulfonic acid resin in the hydrogen form.

BIBLIOGRAPHY

1. Ayres, J. A.: *Ind. Eng. Chem.*, **43**, 1526 (1951).
2. Davies, C. W., and Nancollas, G. H.: *Nature*, **165**, 237 (1950).
3. Harrisson, J. W. E., Myers, R. J., and Herr, D. S.: *J. Am. Pharm. Assoc.*, **32**, 121 (1943).
4. Honda, M.: *J. Chem. Soc. Japan*, **70**, 55 (1949).
5. Kunin, R.: *Anal. Chem.*, **21**, 87 (1949).
6. Kunin, R., and McGarvey, F. X.: *Ind. Eng. Chem.*, **43**, 734 (1951).
7. Liebig, G. F., Vanselow, A. P., and Chapman, H. D.: *Soil Sci.*, **55**, 371 (1943).
8. Reents, A. C., and Kahler, F. H.: *Ind. Eng. Chem.*, **43**, 730 (1951).
9. Samuelson, O. (to Mo och Domsjö AB): Swedish Pat. 125443 (1946).
10. Samuelson, O., and Hartler, N.: *Svensk Kem. Tid.*, **62**, 197 (1950).
11. Sussman, S., Nachod, F. C., and Wood, W.: *Ind. Eng. Chem.*, **37**, 618 (1945).

APPENDIX

Characteristics of some commercially available cation exchangers

Name	Type	Total Exchange Capacity		Manufacturer
		meq per g	meq per ml	
Amberlite IR–100	Sulfonated phenolic resin	1.7	0.6	Rohm and Haas
Amberlite IR–105	Sulfonated phenolic resin	2.7	1.0	Rohm and Haas
Amberlite IR–112	Porous sulfonic resin	4.5	1.4	Rohm and Haas
Duolite C–3	Sulfonated phenolic resin	3.2	1.0	Chemical Process
Lewatit KS	Sulfonated phenolic resin	3.0	1.2	Farbenfabriken Bayer
Lewatit PN	Sulfonated phenolic resin	1.9	0.9	Farbenfabriken Bayer
Wofatit K	Sulfonated phenolic resin	2.5	0.9	I. G. Farben. Wolfen
Wofatit KS	Sulfonated phenolic resin	2.5	0.9	I. G. Farben. Wolfen
Wofatit P	Sulfonated phenolic resin	1.4	0.5	I. G. Farben. Wolfen
Zeo–Rex	Sulfonated phenolic resin	2.7	0.9	Permutit
Zeo–Karb	Sulfonated coal	1.7	0.6	Permutit
Amberlite IR–120	Sulfonated hydrocarbon	4.2	2.0	Rohm and Haas
Dowex 50 (Nalcite HCR)	Sulfonated hydrocarbon	4.5	2.1	Dow Chemical
Permutit Q	Sulfonated hydrocarbon	4.9	2.3	Permutit
Amberlite IRC–50	Carboxylic	10.0	4.2	Rohm and Haas
Lewatit C	Carboxylic	5.0	1.6	Farbenfabriken Bayer
Permutit H–70	Carboxylic	8.2	3.7	Permutit
Wofatit C	Carboxylic	7.0	2.5	Farbenfabriken Bayer
Decalso	Synthetic zeolite	1.4	0.8	Permutit

Characteristics of some commercially available anion exchange resins

Name	Type	Total Exchange Capacity		Manufacturer
		meq per g	meq per ml	
Amberlite IR–4 B	Weakly basic	10.0	2.5	Rohm and Haas
Amberlite IR–45	Weakly basic	5.5	2.0	Rohm and Haas
De–Acidite	Weakly basic	7.0	1.9	Permutit
Dowex 3 (Nalcite WBR)	Weakly basic	6.0	2.7	Dow Chemical
Duolite A–2	Weakly basic	7.0	1.2	Chemical Process
Duolite A–3	Weakly basic	6.8	1.1	Chemical Process
Ionac A–300	Medium basic	6.0	1.9	Permutit
Lewatit M	Weakly basic	3.5	1.7	Farbenfabriken Bayer
Lewatit MI	Medium basic	10.2	2.7	Farbenfabriken Bayer
Permutit W	Weakly basic	4.5	1.3	Permutit
Wofatit M	Weakly basic	7.0	1.2	Farbenfabriken Bayer
Amberlite IRA–400	Strongly basic	3.0	1.1	Rohm and Haas
Amberlite IRA–410	Strongly basic	3.0	1.1	Rohm and Haas
Dowex 1 (Nalcite SBR)	Strongly basic	2.5	1.1	Dow Chemical
Dowex 2 (Nalcite SAR)	Strongly basic	2.5	1.1	Dow Chemical
Lewatit MII	Strongly basic	—	—	Farbenfabriken Bayer
Permutit S	Strongly basic	3.3	1.1	Permutit

The tables have been compiled from data furnished through the courtesy of several manufacturers (Bayer, Dow Chemical, Rohm and Haas, Permutit) as well as from data in the literature. The capacities are not comparable in all cases as different methods of determination have been applied. The capacity and general behavior of ion exchangers for analytical purposes are most conveniently studied by the break-through curves (cf. Chapter V: 3). The characterization of resins by means of potentiometric neutralization curves is helpful to estimate the degree of monofunctionality, etc. (Chapter II). The titration is preferably performed in the presence of a salt, e. g. 1 N NaCl.

Addresses:

The Chemical Process Co., 58 Sutter St., San Francisco, Calif.
The Dow Chemical Co., Midland, Mich.
The Permutit Co., 330 West 42nd St., New York 18, N.Y.
The Rohm and Haas Co., Philadelphia, Pa.
I. G. Farbenindustrie, Wolfen, Germany.
Farbenfabriken Bayer, Leverkusen-Bayerwerk, Germany.

Dow ion exchange resins with varying degrees of cross-linking

Mesh Size	Resin	Per Cent Cross-Linking (Divinyl Benzene)	Form	Meq per g	Meq per ml
20–50 mesh	Dowex 50 (Nalcite HCR)		Na$^+$	4.5	2.1
20–50 mesh	Dowex 1 (Nalcite SBR)		Cl$^-$	2.5	1.1
20–50 mesh	Dowex 2 (Nalcite SAR)		Cl$^-$	2.5	1.1
20–50 mesh	Dowex 3 (Nalcite WBR)		Base	6.0	2.7
Minus 50 mesh*	Dowex 50 or 50 W	1	H$^+$	5.2	0.4
Minus 50 mesh	Dowex 50 or 50 W	2	H$^+$	5.2	0.7
Minus 50 mesh	Dowex 50 or 50 W	4	H$^+$	5.2	1.1
Minus 50 mesh	Dowex 50 or 50 W	8	H$^+$	5.1	1.8
Minus 50 mesh	Dowex 50 or 50 W	12	H$^+$	5.0	2.3
Minus 50 mesh	Dowex 50 or 50 W	16	H$^+$	4.9	2.5
Minus 50 mesh	Dowex 1 or 2	1	Cl$^-$	3.5	0.5
Minus 50 mesh	Dowex 1 or 2	2	Cl$^-$	3.5	0.8
Minus 50 mesh	Dowex 1 or 2	4	Cl$^-$	3.5	1.2
Minus 50 mesh	Dowex 1 or 2	8	Cl$^-$	3.2	1.4
Minus 50 mesh	Dowex 1 or 2	10	Cl$^-$	3.2	1.5

* These resins are available in different mesh sizes. Dowex 50 W is a light-colored form of Dowex 50. All data given in this table were furnished by Dr. R. M. Wheaton, The Dow Chemical Co.

Standard Screens

Mesh Size	Opening, mm
10	2.00
20	0.85
30	0.50
40	0.36
50	0.29
60	0.25
70	0.21
80	0.17
100	0.14
120	0.125
150	0.105
170	0.088
200	0.074
250	0.062
280	0.052
325	0.044

AUTHOR INDEX

SUBJECT INDEX

A

Acetal, separation from carbonyl compounds, 195

Acetal synthesis, catalyzed by ion exchange, 18

Acetaldehyde, uptake, 190

Acetates, alkalimetric titration, 127

Acetic acid, adsorption by cation exchangers, 21

Acetone, in sulfite waste liquor and sulfite alcohol, 194
uptake, 190

Acetophenone, 191

Acetyl groups, determination in organic compounds, 129

Acid concentration, influence on break-through capacity, 60
influence on break-through curve, 58
influence on elution curve, 66

Acids, adsorption by cation exchangers, 21, 77

Actinomycin, amino acids in, 235

Actinorubin, purification, 235

Active groups in ion exchangers, 12

Activity coefficients, determination in mixed electrolytes, 248, 249
of cerous salts, 249

Adenine, 227

Adenosine, 227

Adenosine polyphosphates, separation, 226

Adenylic acid, 225

Adipic acid, adsorption by cation exchangers, 22

Adrenaline, in urine, 237
uptake and purification, 237

Adsorption, of acids, 90
of water, 91

Adsorption isotherms, 33

Alanine, 210, 218, 220, 222

Alcohol, in presence of aldehydes and ketones, 193
purification, 260

Alcoholysis, catalyzed by ion exchange, 18

Aldehyde bisulfite, 9, 190

Aldehydes, 190
chromatographic separation, 192
condensation products with weakly basic resins, 94
in alcohol, 260
separation from acetal, 195
separation from ketones, 194
separation from organic acids, 183
uptake, 93, 190

Alkali metals, chromatographic separation, 173
in apple juice, 168
in natural water, 166
in presence of complex cyanides, 139
in presence of different anions, 136
in presence of phosphate, 137
in presence of sulfate and phosphate, 155
separation, 110
separation from iron or cobalt, 140
separation from sulfate and phosphate, 136
separation from vanadate, chromate, molybdate, tungstate, phosphomolybdate, phosphotungstate, and silicotungstate, 76, 141
separation from various cations, 156

Alkaloids, 134, 206
acidimetric determination, 207
displacement, 206
uptake, 206

Aluminum, in phosphate rocks and commercial dicalcium phosphate, 146, 147

Aluminum, in presence of iron, 158